The Origin of Overweight

Yvonne Foss

* *LJB* * Lilian John Books

Editing by:
Andrea Kay www.yourstruleighediting.com
Andrew Colborne www.abbivale.co.uk
Index by:
Adam Pozner trinovaindexingservices.weebly.com
Cover by:
idobookcovers.com
Printed in the UK by:
Printondemand–worldwide www.printondemand-worldwide.com
Published by:
Lilian John Books www.lilianjohnbooks.com

Digital edition first published 2014
Print edition first published 2015

ISBN 978–0–9930042–1–6

Disclaimer

Every effort has been made to ensure that the information in this book is complete and accurate. Nevertheless, the book may contain errors or omissions. Advances in medical and scientific research mean that the information can become out of date soon after publication. The author and publisher cannot warrant that the information contained herein is in every respect accurate or complete. If you note any omissions or errors, please contact the publisher who will be pleased to make the necessary corrections in future editions.

The author is not engaged in providing professional advice in any field. The ideas and suggestions contained in this book are the opinion of the author and are not intended as a substitute for consulting a physician. Readers who are overweight or have medical problems should consult their own physician and not rely on the contents of this book. Readers should consult a physician or healthcare professional before beginning any new treatment or regime. The author and publisher shall not be liable or responsible for any injury, loss, expense or damage arising from any of the contents of this book.

Anecdotes are fictional and any resemblance to actual persons or situations is coincidental.

Every effort has been made to trace all copyright holders, but if any have been inadvertently overlooked please contact the publisher who will be pleased to rectify the error. Where websites are cited, the home page address is given to avoid long URLs (the prefix http:// has been omitted). Permissions for citing websites have been requested from the website owners but if any have been overlooked, please contact the publisher who will be pleased to rectify the error.

To

Alia Farenden-Smith, *née* Afzal

15.2.1968 – 16.7.2008

CONTENTS

A Tribute to Scientists vi
Acknowledgements vi

The Great Epidemic of the Global Age 1
Introduction: Shedding Sunlight on Overweight 7

PART I: VITAMIN D

Chapter 1: Helpful Radiation 20
Chapter 2: Vitamin D Poverty 50
Chapter 3: Atmospheric Obstruction 79
Chapter 4: The Sunlight Paradox 101

PART II: WEIGHT

Two Humans and Two Habitats 116
Chapter 5: Fatstat Facts 118
Chapter 6: Ice Age Endurance 142

PART III: UNDERSTANDING AND TACKLING OVERWEIGHT

Chapter 7: An Evolutionary Exploration 176
Chapter 8: Weightonomics 218
The End of the Great Epidemic of the Global Age 243
Chapter 9: The Reversal Strategy 244
Chapter 10: Crisps 273

APPENDIX

A Summary of Research Findings into Overweight and Vitamin D 307
NOTES, REFERENCES, AND FURTHER READING 313
Index 376

A Tribute to Scientists

Scientific research is exciting and rewarding, but it is never easy and at times it can be laborious and tedious. While scientists are working hard doing what they do – whether it is irradiating food, covering strips of paper with silver, cleaning their roof instruments of debris, or analysing data – I relish the joy and delight of using their painstaking work to support my ideas. At times in this book I have attempted a potted history, or made a passing mention, of some research but none of it does justice to the efforts of the individuals who do the research. To name every scientist whose work has been used in this book would require another book at least, and inevitably I have missed out the names of many people whose work contributed. In any case, my work is incomplete. There are thousands of publications, particularly about vitamin D, and I have cherry-picked the ones that appear to support my arguments. Another author would have chosen differently. To those people whose names have not been mentioned and to those who are mentioned too briefly, I apologise.

Acknowledgements

I would like to thank the teachers who inspired me, particularly Farzin Farzaneh, Joop Gäken and Kevin Ford. I would like to thank John M. Parker for information about the ultraviolet transmittance of glass, and Jan Myburgh for information about obese fish in Lake Loskop. For kindly sending me copies of their publications, I thank Peter Elwood, Ann Webb, Avner Offer, David B. Allison, Robert Browne, Steven Barrett, Franziska Großschädl, Elina Hypponen, Siân Robinson, Anthony D. Barnosky, Xiao Ou Shu, Arthur Mesas, Anthony Norman, Rae Goodman, Sebastiano Gattoni-Celli, Inmaculada González-Molero, Rebecca Kanter, Ian Givens, Carlos Ballaré, Carrie Earthman, and Gerhard Wiesenfeldt. For constructive comments during preparation of sections of the script I would like to thank Robert Heaney and Carrie Earthman. For reading sections of the script at different stages during the writing process I would like to thank Yvonne Lepper, Teresa Foss, and Lesley Anderson. For helpful suggestions during revision of the first draft I would like to thank Caroline Davidson and Victoria Kwee. I thank Simon Avery for the cover design, my editors Andrea Kay and Andrew Colborne for their scrupulous attention to detail, and Adam Pozner for his meticulous compilation of the index. I thank Ian Giddings for technical support and David Anderson for design suggestions. Lastly, I thank my family for their steadfast love and support. None of those mentioned above bear any responsibility for the published book.

The Great Epidemic of the Global Age

THE FIRST THING PEOPLE noticed was a gain in weight.

At first it was quite mild. People said it was just 'padding', 'a spare tyre', 'a beer belly', or their 'love handles' – it was just an extra store of energy and although it could be a little uncomfortable, it was nothing to worry about. Then it got worse and they called it obesity. It was noted that people who had gained weight often had medical conditions like high blood pressure and were more likely to develop diabetes and heart disease. As the epidemic progressed, the cases got more severe, and in some instances caused disability.

At first it was regarded as a problem only for those whose overweight was all too plain to see, until scans showed that even people who did not appear to be overweight had fat around their internal organs. Some people described this fat as 'toxic' because it was associated with ill health, but nobody explained why fat accumulating around internal organs should be associated with ill health if it was just an excess store of energy.

When it affected a few prosperous middle-aged individuals, people said it was the result of good living; it was a sign of prosperity, a mark of high status. When it spread to the less well off, people said it was the fault of the poor and uneducated who were unable or unwilling to look after themselves properly. Nobody noticed the contradiction.

The epidemic began in just a few countries. These countries were the wealthiest countries; they were modern, advanced, progressive, and in the forefront of developing new technologies and agricultural innovations. It was said that affluence in these countries made life too comfortable, allowing the inhabitants to become greedy and lazy. Then it spread to other countries complacent that their populations were fit and healthy. In the later stages of the epidemic, it spread to poor countries where some of the population became overweight while others were underweight because they had too little food. Nobody explained why it was more common among rich people in poor countries and poor people in rich countries.

As the epidemic progressed from the 1970s through the 1980s and 1990s and into the beginning of the twenty-first century, it spread from one country to another, affecting more and more individuals and increasing in its severity. By 2010 it affected a fifth of the world's total population. In most countries more than half the population was overweight. In some countries, two thirds of the population were affected. In a few countries almost all the people were overweight.

The severity of an epidemic was judged by its effect on mortality. Unlike previous epidemics, marked by high rates of acute illness and death within a short time of onset of the disease, in this one people lived with the condition for a long time without getting severely ill and dying, so at first it didn't seem so bad. The health of populations was assessed by two things: life expectancy and infant mortality. By both measures, the population remained healthy throughout the epidemic. Life expectancy was still high and infant mortality was still low. But because of advances in medical technology and pharmacology, these measures were outdated. Babies continued to be conceived, to be born and to survive because of medical intervention into conception, pregnancy, birth and the neonatal period. People who got sick were treated and cured, or at least kept alive. Terminal diseases were becoming chronic diseases. People were living longer, but often with chronic diseases such as arthritis and dementia. So while everyone congratulated themselves on being healthier than ever before, there were millions of people suffering from ill health and disabilities; healthcare was becoming increasingly expensive, and health services were finding it harder to cope with additional demands.

When the epidemic was first recognised, it was seen as an 'obesity' epidemic. The cause was not understood so the treatments were ineffective. It was regarded as a weight gain problem caused by a shift in energy balance, and the treatments assumed that it was purely a matter of getting the energy balance right. Early attempts to deal with the epidemic were confused by the question of whether weight gain itself was a medical problem or not. Some people said it was a medical condition, some said it was a disease and some said it wasn't a medical problem at all because it was an individual lifestyle choice or a social problem. Some people said the medical conditions associated with obesity should be treated but the weight gain should not. It was all rather confusing. They didn't understand at the time that overweight was a symptom of a bigger problem and the shift in energy balance was a consequence not a cause.

Pharmaceutical companies worked hard to develop drugs to treat overweight, but none of them was very effective because the root cause of weight gain was not understood. Physicians, with no specific tools at their disposal to help their overweight patients, said people should prevent themselves from gaining weight, and when they became overweight, they should cure themselves. With no help from the medical establishment, sufferers turned to private industry. Some people made a lot of money offering treatments that alleviated the symptoms temporarily but marketing them as cures. When the symptoms came back the clients came back for more treatment – a pattern that could go on all their lives. If clients complained that a treatment didn't work, they were blamed for not carrying out the treatment properly, but mostly they didn't complain because they blamed themselves. Surgery became available for the more severe cases and turned out to be an effective treatment, but some people said sufferers shouldn't have medical treatment because they shouldn't have let themselves get in that condition in the first place. Others said they were just worried about the cost of surgery for the millions of people who were overweight. As the debate continued, overweight became one of the few health conditions left untreated and allowed to worsen to its extremes.

At first weight gain was accepted as normal, but as it became more severe, it was blamed on those affected. Some of the people affected were the subject of prejudice and discrimination. They were bullied in the playground and shouted at in the street, and it was often suggested they were psychologically disturbed. Sometimes they were excluded from things purely because of their weight, and were blamed for the cost of health services and the welfare bill. Their condition was often plain for all to see. There was no need to carry a bell or wear distinctive clothing as the people with leprosy did in mediaeval times.

As the epidemic got worse, people started looking elsewhere to find someone to blame. Some people said it was the government's fault for giving the wrong advice about nutrition, and some governments said it was the fault of the food industry. When children were affected the parents were blamed, as if they had the skills to mould the size and shape of their children as a sculptor crafts a figure from clay. Nobody wondered why there was a lag between the rise in overweight in adults and children when they were supposedly caused by changes that occurred at the same time.

Policy-makers concentrated their efforts on food and nutrition but the results weren't helpful. Food became an obsession and nutritional advice was all about reducing nutrients. People were told to eat less sugar, fat and salt, as if these were no longer nutrients but had become poisons. Foods became divided into 'healthy' and 'unhealthy' on the basis of their fat, sugar and salt content, and sometimes purely on the basis of their energy content. Nutritionists forgot about making sure people were getting all the nutrients they needed and didn't notice the increasing malnutrition.

People liked to look for a villain (*fat, saturated fat, trans fats, sugar, cola, fast food, the food industry, schools, parents, the government, TV* or *celebrity chefs*) which they could attack with impunity, because it was easier than looking for the real reasons for obesity, which were less easy to understand and needed sensible, complex measures to deal with.

The problems of weight gain and ill health were seen as human problems, but then people noticed that animals were affected too. Pet cats and dogs, horses and zoo animals had the same problems of weight gain and associated conditions like diabetes. Fish in Lake Loskop, South Africa, were getting fat and dying, frogs in the Sierra Nevada, USA, were dying, and old trees were dying in the Central Highlands of Victoria, Australia. Ecologists noted the start of a mass extinction – only the sixth to occur in 540 million years. At the same time, the Arctic sea ice was melting, the snow line in the mountains was creeping upwards, the temperature was warming, and extreme weather was becoming more common.

People said the climate was changing and it was caused by the burning of fossil fuels. Others disagreed and thought the climate wasn't changing, or, even if it was, it had nothing to do with fossil fuel burning. Those who agreed thought something needed to be done but they were slow to respond. In the meantime, fossil fuel continued to be burned and the concentration of carbon dioxide in the atmosphere increased. There were some reports of pollution causing health problems but they didn't seem to be very important because people couldn't see the direct effects of the atmospheric changes on themselves. When people saw smog, fog, or haze they worried about respiratory diseases, but they didn't worry about the effects it would have on atmospheric ultraviolet-B levels. They had almost forgotten that ultraviolet-B was essential for humans and all other animals for making vitamin D.

When vitamin D was first discovered, at the beginning of the twentieth century, it was thought to be a bone vitamin, but by the end of the century it was realised that many different organs and systems in the body, including the immune system, required vitamin D to function properly. By that time, a technique for measuring vitamin D in the blood had become available, and as vitamin D levels were measured in more and more people, it was realised that vitamin D deficiency was widespread and severe, and all sorts of diseases and medical conditions were linked to vitamin D deficiency.

As vitamin D is made in the body when exposed to sunlight, it was thought to be a problem only for people living at high latitudes where there was not much sunlight in the winter. Then it was found that vitamin D deficiency was also very common at low latitudes – even in the sunniest places including Hawaii, Saudi Arabia and Australia. It gradually became evident that vitamin D deficiency was epidemic, just like obesity. Then it was noted that people who were overweight, and had obesity associated conditions, like high blood pressure and diabetes, were deficient in vitamin D. Experts tended to assume that overweight caused vitamin D deficiency because they thought they already knew the cause of overweight. In addition, because so many different factors affect vitamin D levels, the connection between vitamin D and weight was very complex and not obvious at first. Nobody wondered why vitamin D was the only vitamin that animals could make in the sunlight, or why sunlight was an absolute requirement for the synthesis of vitamin D.

The age of global ecology and biogeographics was still in its infancy. It was 150 years after Darwin published *The Origin of Species* but people still tended to think of humans as above and apart from all other living things and the rest of the universe, and still wondered whether humans were evolving or not. At first it didn't occur to anyone that weight gain could be the sign of a direct effect of climate change on the human body.

Introduction

Shedding sunlight on overweight

I HAD NO INKLING, when I started out, that by the time I came to put the finishing touches to this book, in the middle of the 'obesity epidemic', it would intersect with several of the issues of the day. It was at the end of a year of exceptional weather. I was in the south-east of England, where a long hot summer had followed a long cold winter and the coldest spring since 1962, and there was debate about the significance of this unusual weather for long-term climate change. On TV I watched a discussion about hydraulic fracturing, or fracking, a process used to extract fossil fuels from the ground. The proponent suggested that, without new sources of fossil fuels, we would run out of electricity. I noted the *argumentum in terrorem*. On a news website, I read that the deadly villain of the obesity epidemic is not fat, it is sugar, but I thought 'deadly villains' were the stuff of childhood – some of us left them behind in our comic books when we grew up. In a science journal I read of a debate about evidence that moderate overweight is not as unhealthy as is often stated. An esteemed clinician didn't want people to know about this study. He argued that telling people about it would lead to patients getting fatter but I wondered why he hadn't noticed that people have been desperately trying to control their weight for decades, and not just because their doctors tell them to do so. I checked my email and found a message from a friend who had attached a photograph taken from her lab window in Singapore showing smog so thick and putrid that she had to wear a mask even in her air-conditioned laboratory. In a newspaper, I read a hypercritical commentary about childhood obesity, so thick and putrid with ignorance and prejudice I had to stop reading halfway through. Elsewhere I read that humans have stopped evolving. Climate change, fossil fuels, the cause of overweight, advice to control weight, smog, childhood obesity, human evolution: all of these matters of contemporary observation, debate and discussion are linked together here in this book.

This book is about the origin of overweight. It is about the start of my weight gain and yours, and that of our parents and our children. It is about the rise in overweight in the population in recent decades and since the Industrial Revolution. It is about the biological advantage of overweight in animals. It is about a mechanism that evolved in the earliest of living things – a mechanism to respond to the sunlight.

This is not a weight loss book or a diet book. We have had the assistance of thousands of diet books and programmes using every rational approach to help us to lose weight, and while they can help to achieve weight loss for individuals sometimes, they are not a solution to the obesity epidemic. In spite of all their efforts at dieting and exercise, some people cannot lose weight, while others can lose weight but still remain overweight. At the same time, thin people become overweight for the first time, parents are horrified to see their children become overweight, and diabetes is becoming more common. If dieting or healthy eating worked consistently, we would not have the problem of a worldwide epidemic of obesity. We think the cause is simple (too much eating) and the solution is simple (eat less) but decades of experience – decades of failure – tell us otherwise. Dieting and exercise can treat the symptoms, but they do not cure because they do not remove the cause of overweight.

Overweight appears to be intractable because it is caught in a dark mire of blame, shame, prejudice and supposition. This book deals with overweight as part of a great epidemic of the global age, as an adaptation to a change in the environment, of which overweight is a visible sign. The first step in bringing this epidemic to an end is to understand the origin of overweight.

The origin of this book

In 2009 the journal *Medical Hypotheses* published an article in which I proposed a detailed hypothesis that vitamin D deficiency is the cause of overweight. I submitted the article in September 2008 and the article became available online in the following December. Since then it has been one of the most cited and downloaded articles in the journal. This book is essentially a description of that hypothesis with an emphasis on how it can help us to understand our real-life experience of overweight. I believe that in the long term we can use this new understanding to turn overweight from the common, chronic condition that it is today, into a rare, acute condition that can be treated easily, quickly and safely.

The idea that led to this book was serendipitous. My appreciation of vitamin D had begun when I was working as a postgraduate in Farzin Farzaneh's department at King's College School of Medicine and Dentistry in London. It was a science department in a Medical School, where we used scientific techniques to understand the mechanisms of disease. Our motivation was our natural curiosity and our deep interest in science, but we were always aware of the hope invested in us by patients and their loved ones – hope that our research would lead to improved care and treatments. I was assisting Ian Trayner with his research into leukaemia when I first became acquainted with vitamin D. We studied how the sugars on the surface of leukaemia cells changed as they developed from immature cells into white blood cells – a normal process that is disrupted in leukaemia. One of the agents we used to bring about this change was a hormone derived from vitamin D called calcitriol. Like most people, I had known vitamin D as a bone vitamin that we made in our skin in sunlight and that was about the sum of my knowledge of vitamin D. I was surprised when I realised vitamin D could actually alter gene expression and took part in the normal development of the cells of many types of tissue. A few years later illness struck me personally. It left me unable to work and my PhD studies in epigenetics had to be suspended. My scientific career was over and my new career as a patient began. Instead of *working* in medical research, I was now on the other side, having joined the ranks of those desperately hoping for a breakthrough in medical research.

My interest in overweight was a background curiosity for many years and my effort to explore the field did not begin until, to help me understand my own illness, I became interested in the role of vitamin D in the immune system. When I came to update my knowledge about vitamin D, a brief exploration of the academic literature revealed that vitamin D experts agreed there was an epidemic of vitamin D deficiency. This puzzled me at first because, although it made sense in that we were spending less time outdoors and therefore getting less sunlight, if vitamin D deficiency was as widespread as was suggested, there should be some obvious manifestation of it. Where was the epidemic of disease? It wasn't long before I found it, because at the time there was intense media interest in the increase in overweight, the word 'fat' appearing frequently in newspaper headlines and in the titles of TV programmes, euphemisms cast aside to allow for institutional derision. Could vitamin D deficiency be the cause of overweight?

Everyone knew overweight was caused by eating too much, eating the wrong foods, and not doing enough exercise. And everyone knew vitamin D deficiency caused bone diseases like rickets. The idea that vitamin D deficiency could cause overweight seemed unlikely, but what was a novel idea at the time I started working on my article, has now become part of the mainstream thinking. There is a huge amount of research going on into both overweight and, separately, vitamin D deficiency. In recent years the two have been coming together and there is a growing interest in the connection. You can find a summary of the research studies into overweight and vitamin D deficiency in the Appendix. Please be aware, however, that any such summary becomes out of date soon after the writing is complete, because new studies are being released on a regular basis.

In this book, I propose that vitamin D deficiency is the cause of overweight. I explore the origin of vitamin D and the advantage of overweight with a biological perspective. I argue that if we first deal with vitamin D deficiency, then dealing with overweight will follow easily, but first we need to understand the link between them. To understand the link, we need to go beyond the canonical views of vitamin D as a bone vitamin we obtain easily from everyday exposure to sunlight, and overweight as a simple question of energy balance.

When vitamins were first discovered at the beginning of the twentieth century, nobody had any idea what they actually did inside the body, but a clear picture of deficiency diseases emerged, with each vitamin linked to a disease. Vitamin A prevented night-blindness, vitamin B_1 prevented beriberi and vitamin C prevented scurvy, for example. Each vitamin was seen as a single substance and its deficiency was linked to a particular disease because that was how it was discovered – components of food were tested to see if they could prevent diseases that occurred when diet was restricted for any reason. In this context, vitamin D was discovered as the nutrient that could prevent the bone disease rickets.

No vitamin has been discovered as a result of studying the prevention of overweight. Indeed, overweight has been regarded as a result of over-nutrition – too much food – rather than malnutrition. Vitamin deficiencies are generally portrayed as a consequence of low-quality diets and are associated with poverty. It is easy to imagine that a person who gets so much food that they are overweight must get enough of all the nutrients they need, and to assume that vitamin deficiencies are a problem of the poor and not possible in affluent societies. In fact, it is possible to be deficient in vitamin D even if you have plenty of food and follow a healthy diet and lifestyle, and the reasons for this are explored in the first part of this book.

My definition of overweight

When I refer to overweight I mean any weight that is above normal, however you measure it, but it is the change from normal weight to overweight that is explored in this book. Weight gain is high in the first year of life, and then becomes steady, alongside height gain, until just before puberty when weight increase tends to outpace height increase until adult height is reached. By adulthood, the bones stop elongating and height remains stable. Weight should also remain stable, but we generally observe that, particularly in middle age, weight gain increases out of proportion with height. This is what is measured by an increasing body mass index.

In medicine, there is a clear-cut distinction between overweight and obesity. Normal weight is defined by a body mass index of 18.5 to 24.9. Overweight, described by a body mass index of between 25 and 30, is weight that is above normal but does not have any medical significance, whereas obesity, defined by a body mass index of above 30, is the level of overweight associated with health problems. This assumes that overweight becomes a medical problem at a particular cut-off point, but of course there is not a distinct point at which health problems begin. It would certainly vary from one person to another and there is a recent trend towards regarding any overweight as unhealthy, but in general, the higher the body mass index, the more severe the effect on health and life expectancy. The word obese comes from the Latin *ob*, which means intensive, and *edere*, which means to eat; the dictionary definition is 'fat or fleshy, corpulent', but literally obese means to overeat. It has a precise medical definition but is a word that has an unpleasant connotation. In this book, when I refer to overweight I generally mean any weight above normal including all categories of obesity. I use the terms obese and obesity only when I need to make the distinction between overweight and obesity as defined by body mass index. When I refer to the obesity epidemic, for example, I am really talking about the high prevalence of overweight and obesity combined. Overweight increases alongside obesity, but it is not called an *overweight* epidemic because overweight is not defined as a medical problem. It may turn out that there is a metabolic distinction between the two but the medical distinction is not helpful in understanding the cause of the recent increase in prevalence. My definition of overweight, as you will read in the second part of this book, is 'cold-adapted'. If you feel overweight, if you have some additional fat on your waist, or if you are unable to eat as much as you like without gaining weight, then you are affected by overweight.

This book gives my personal view of the origin of overweight. It is not a peer-reviewed, tried and tested scientific study. It is a hypothesis that I present to you so you can decide whether it makes sense of your experience of overweight. I have done my best to fully explore every aspect of it and to formulate a coherent and plausible biological explanation. For some of my assertions there is an abundance of evidence, others are speculative, and I have no doubt some will turn out to be wrong. I know how scientific research goes – something will turn up in the future that nobody could ever have dreamed of today. In the meantime, this book explores the relationship between overweight and vitamin D deficiency in greater depth and with a wider perspective than specialists are able to do at the moment.

What this book offers is a better understanding of overweight than we have ever had before. It explains why it is so easy to gain weight yet so difficult to lose it, why we have a wide range of effective drugs for other conditions but not for overweight, why overweight is more common in some regions than others, why overweight is associated with economic activity and why it has become so common in recent decades. It explains the individual experience of millions of people who, in different circumstances have gained weight, have lost weight, or have been unable to control weight. It gives us all the opportunity to take immediate steps to bring the epidemic to an end. It exposes the dark, muddy mire of overweight to the sunlight.

I hope this book will help you to make sense of your experience of overweight, whether your own or that of others around you. For me, this journey has left me with a new appreciation of the value of science and it has drawn my attention to one of nature's precious resources that has so far been either ignored or only regarded as harmful. I hope you too will recognise that to understand our human problems we need to appreciate the wider living world in which we live. Even if you disagree with me, if my book serves to make you begin to think about overweight in a different way, it will have been worth the effort.

Itinerary

I have arranged this book roughly in the order of my explorations. To begin with, I could see how there had been a gradual trend towards vitamin D deprivation in recent decades as we spent less time outdoors and reduced the amount of vitamin D-containing foods in our diets. Chapter 1 Helpful Radiation considers the many different things that affect our ability to make vitamin D, and the amount we can get from our diet. If you think we can get all the vitamin D we need from everyday sunlight exposure or from following a healthy diet you should read this chapter. It shows how easy it is to become deficient in vitamin D in our modern, urban-industrial lives.

From the moment I first got the idea, one of the most exciting prospects was that overweight could be reversed simply by taking a vitamin D supplement, but after taking a daily vitamin D supplement for several years I had a blood test that revealed my vitamin D level was still far from adequate in terms of bone health. By that time I had realised that we need to do more than just take a supplement for a few weeks if we want to reverse vitamin D deficiency. Chapter 2 Vitamin D Poverty enquires into how much vitamin D we actually need for good health. One of the biggest surprises I experienced on this journey of exploration was that vitamin D deficiency is much more widespread and severe than most people imagine. It is not a sign of poverty or nutritional neglect; it is not caused by the use of sunscreen, nor is it confined to a minority of people in industrial societies. These facts are important to understand before we can deal with vitamin D deficiency as a public health problem. This chapter starts with the difficulties in defining vitamin D deficiency and why it has crept up on us unawares. First you need to be able to measure vitamin D levels, and then you need to decide which levels are healthy and how low they can be before ill health results. It turns out that vitamin D experts agree that the cut-off point for deficiency is too low, the recommended intakes are too low, and the amount we can get from sunlight exposure has been overestimated. All these things, along with not fully understanding what vitamin D does, have contributed to our inability to detect the spread of vitamin D deficiency. At the other extreme, too much vitamin D can be harmful and this is one reason why policy-makers are reluctant to increase recommended intakes, and is why we need to be careful about getting carried away with the idea of vitamin D as a miracle cure for all ills. We need to reverse the deficiency and once we have enough, there is no benefit in having more. I would regard Chapter 2 as essential reading if you were tempted to take large doses of vitamin D.

Before we can accept vitamin D deficiency as the cause of overweight, we must be able to explain the dramatic increase in overweight since the 1970s and the spread of overweight around the world. Has there been an equally dramatic rise and spread of vitamin D deficiency and, if so, why? The preceding chapters explain how vitamin D deficiency has *gradually* increased. They outline the ways in which we are getting less sunlight and getting less vitamin D from food, and the fact that the problem was overlooked for a long time, but all these things did not explain, to my satisfaction, the dramatic rise in overweight and for a long time I had a nagging feeling that there was something missing from the list. The answer came much later when I was thinking about the effects of an aircraft ban on vitamin D, and Chapter 3 Atmospheric Obstruction examines how the atmosphere blocks ultraviolet radiation. Among the many things in the atmosphere that can block ultraviolet, including sand and volcanic emissions, the effects of fossil fuel emissions – in particular the increased emissions from transport – can potentially explain the dramatic rise in overweight in recent decades and the link between overweight and industrialisation. In essence, the cause of climate change could also be the primary cause of the recent rise in overweight.

One of the earliest questions I had was about the matter of sunlight exposure. On the one hand I was reading that we are suffering from vitamin D deficiency at least partly because we spend less time outdoors these days, which made sense to me. On the other hand, it was said that we are suffering from skin cancer because ultraviolet radiation has increased as a result of ozone layer thinning. If levels of ultraviolet are so high that we are suffering from skin cancer we should be getting plenty of vitamin D, but if not, then what is the cause of the increase in skin cancer? Could both these trends occur at the same time? Is sunlight exposure good or bad? Should we be sunbathing or not? Chapter 4 The Sunlight Paradox addresses these questions and suggests that we could be suffering from sunlight deprivation.

The second part of the book puts vitamin D aside and turns to overweight. For a long time before I got this idea, two things had really puzzled me about overweight – one was why weight seemed to be easy to gain yet so difficult to lose, and the other was why overweight had become so common in recent years. I had never accepted the popular view that the increase in overweight was caused by more food being available, by too many takeaways, or too much fat and sugar. Of course, we cannot gain weight if there is a severe food scarcity, but it doesn't follow that the converse must be true – that, normally, our weight is controlled by food availability. It did not make biological sense to me, especially since it does not explain the difficulty in losing weight. In fact, for decades our thinking about overweight was based largely upon supposition and it is only in recent years that the myths – such as the widely believed notion that if you eat fewer calories you will always lose an equivalent amount of energy in the form of fat – are being exploded by rigorous scientific analysis. I was astonished to find there was already abundant evidence that to keep our weight stable the body has fine control over its energy usage, which means that the popular notion that we can control our weight consciously is at best an overestimation of our abilities and, at worst, a downright deception. If you ever feel guilty about eating a doughnut, or a bar of chocolate, or a bacon sandwich, or you think people who are overweight should just eat less and do more, read Chapter 5 Fatstat Facts. This chapter shows how body weight is controlled by our physiology and demonstrates how the idea that overweight is just an excess store of energy doesn't make biological sense. The body controls its own weight and in this chapter I argue there is a body weight set point which explains why dieting can overcome the physiological forces in the short term by putting the body into starvation mode, but in the long term can make weight loss more difficult.

If the body is so good at controlling weight, why then does overweight ever happen? I thought there must be an advantage in being overweight and so I looked for its biological function. The answer came from memories of my school biology teacher, Mrs. Neary, who spent two lessons teaching us about surface area to volume ratio. When we gain weight our surface area gets smaller in relation to our volume, which makes it easier to keep warm in cold temperatures, so could overweight be an adaptation to cold? Overweight is associated with conditions such as high blood pressure, insulin resistance and high cholesterol. I realised that all these conditions could be understood as adaptations to cold, and the metabolic syndrome could actually be our natural winter metabolism. In Chapter 6 Ice Age Endurance, I show how important it is to keep warm in cold environments and I present evidence that overweight is an adaptation to the cold. This chapter builds a coherent picture that explains why overweight is associated with poor health and can lead to diabetes and cardiovascular disease. It also explains why people who are overweight can find exercise immensely difficult.

That still doesn't explain the link with vitamin D. If overweight is an adaptation to the cold, it can't be *triggered* by cold, as we have been increasing in weight while living in our artificial, centrally-heated environment. I was puzzling over this question when I saw an article about the lack of vitamin D in winter at northern latitudes and realised that vitamin D levels are seasonal – they fall as the sunlight becomes weaker in the autumn and increase as it becomes stronger in the spring. The first chapter of the third part of the book, Chapter 7 An Evolutionary Explanation brings us back to vitamin D. Vitamin D is our sunlight sensor, and when levels fall, our bodies get ready for winter. In this chapter I explore the biology of vitamin D and overweight in the context of evolution, human migration and history. The reason this book is called the *Origin* of overweight is because it traces the origin of overweight as a change in body size in response to falling vitamin D levels back to millions of years ago. It suggests that vitamin D originated as a sunlight sensor long before the evolution of the nervous system enabled us to see the sunlight and feel the warmth of the sun. Millions of years later, not only have organisms evolved into diverse animals including humans, but also the molecules that make up our bodies have evolved. Vitamin D has evolved to be converted to a hormone with many important functions in our bodies, but it still retains its original function as a sunlight sensor. When vitamin D is low, our body responds by getting ready for the winter. We store fat and make metabolic changes to help us to survive the cold. This chapter considers the survival of animals and humans throughout the ice ages, and shows how evidence from the changes in our skin colour and our differing abilities to digest milk in adulthood suggest that our ancestors had to adapt to low ultraviolet environments. In short, we have underestimated our need for ultraviolet and vitamin D.

One of the most appealing aspects of the link between vitamin D deficiency and overweight is that it potentially explains all that we know about overweight. Chapter 8 Weightonomics comes back into our everyday lives to see how my ideas can explain what happens when we gain weight and when we lose weight. On the one hand the cause of overweight is simple: vitamin D deficiency. On the other hand, the multitude of factors affecting how much vitamin D we can get makes it highly complicated. There are so many different influences on vitamin D levels and they can be explored to fully explain all the complexities of overweight. Chapter 8 demonstrates how we can use this new idea for a much better understanding of overweight. We can understand why, among other things, people gain weight with age, after illness or childbirth, why some population groups have higher rates of overweight than others, and how overweight is associated with poor health.

Chapter 9 The Reversal Strategy is the concluding chapter that explores what we can do in the future to eradicate overweight. I start this chapter with a retrospective look at how fixed ideas, or blind spots, have impeded our understanding of overweight. I then make suggestions for the many things we can do to make it easier to get vitamin D, deal with vitamin D deficiency and eradicate overweight.

Chapter 10 Crisps is a question and answer chapter summarising the main points in the book, plus a few not mentioned elsewhere. If you are pushed for time and can only read one chapter of the book, this is the one I would recommend. It provides a brief summary of the main points of the book in a question and answer format. You can dip in and out wherever you like and it should answer many, if not all, of your questions.

In the Notes, References and Further Reading section you can find references to work cited, including primary and secondary publications and website addresses, books for further reading, and some supplementary information, including fuller explanations of some points that may be of interest. All of these are presented in sequential order corresponding to the main text, so I hope you find this section easy to navigate should you need it.

PART I

VITAMIN D

Chapter 1

Helpful Radiation

JUST AS A SCRUMPTIOUS meal can be home-made or take-away, we can get vitamin D in two ways. We can prepare our own home-made vitamin D in our skin, or we can take it ready-made from our food from living things that have either made it themselves or got it from *their* food. Either way it was originally made in the sunlight. This chapter is all about the different things affecting how much vitamin D we can get, and how the way we live today means that most of us are not getting enough.

Make your own vitamin D

To make your own vitamin D, first you need to have a type of cholesterol called 7-dehydrocholesterol in your skin. Then you need to zap it with some energy in the form of photons of ultraviolet-B radiation. These photons need to have travelled on a very long journey of about 150 million kilometres before they come into contact with the 7-dehydrocholesterol, all the way from the Sun, through the atmosphere and through your skin. That long journey is full of obstacles to an ultraviolet-B photon and only a few of the photons leaving the Sun will, by chance, end up in your skin. How many ultraviolet-B photons are reaching your skin at the moment? Where are you reading this book – are you indoors or outdoors? Are you in bed, on a train, or in your sitting room? Think about where on the planet Earth you are at the moment – are you in the northern hemisphere or the southern? Do you know the latitude of the place you are in? Now think about how much sunlight is falling on your skin at the moment. How much of your skin is covered by clothes? How much sunlight did your skin get today – how much this week, this year?

If you wanted to make as much vitamin D as you possibly could, what should you do to maximise the chances of ultraviolet-B photons meeting your 7-dehydrocholesterol? The intensity of ultraviolet radiation falling on your skin depends first upon global factors – the time of year and time of day (where the Earth is in relation to the Sun) and latitude (where you are on the Earth). Then there are the local influences that include altitude, weather, atmospheric composition and building cover. And finally, there are the personal factors – your position, clothing and skin. All of these things influence how much vitamin D you can make.

The electromagnetic spectrum

We are familiar with energy as something that enables us to move about. The electromagnetic spectrum is a range of the kinds of energy, known as electric and magnetic, that travel in waves – a travelling form of energy. The energy travels all by itself not needing any form of transport, and it travels at a constant speed – it never speeds up or slows down. You might expect that with more energy it would go faster just like a car, but it never changes its speed. Instead, the more energy it has the shorter the wavelength because having more energy means it can bounce up and down faster – its frequency is higher – but the faster it jumps the shorter the distance it jumps (as if it had shorter legs), so it still goes at the same speed – the speed of light. With less energy it bounces slowly but takes longer jumps, i.e. it has a longer wavelength.

We think of this travelling energy as if it exists in quanta, or packets, called photons. The shorter the wavelength the higher the frequency and the more energy each photon of radiation contains. At one end of the electromagnetic spectrum are radio waves with a wavelength of a metre or more, and at the other end are gamma rays with wavelengths of less than a billionth of a metre. Radio waves make the longest and slowest jumps (low frequency and long wavelength) while gamma rays are the most energetic and make the shortest and fastest jumps (high frequency and short wavelength). Somewhere roughly in the middle are the wavelengths detectable by the human eye – the visible spectrum – which has wavelengths between 380 nm and 760 nm (i.e. 380 to 760 billionths of a metre). These wavelengths interact with the rods and cones in the retina at the back of our eyes and we see the different wavelengths as different colours. Either side of the visible spectrum is the ultraviolet radiation needed to make vitamin D and the infrared radiation.

The Sun emits radiation of every wavelength from X-rays to radio waves, but the strongest emission on Earth is in the visible region, which, presumably, is why our eyes evolved to detect it. The short wavelength radiation – X-rays and ultraviolet radiation less than 200 nm – don't get as far as the Earth and most of the radiation between 200 nm and 300 nm is absorbed by the ozone layer at the top of the atmosphere. Radiation in the red and infrared regions greater than 700 nm is absorbed to some extent by carbon dioxide, ozone and water in the atmosphere.

The scattering of the Sun's radiation by the Earth's atmosphere is the planetary albedo – earthshine – that is similar to the solar radiation being reflected by the Moon – moonshine – that we see in the night sky. Most of the scattering occurs in space and some occurs in our atmosphere due to clouds, dust and gases. About 33 per cent of the solar radiation that gets to the Earth is reflected back into space, mostly scattered by clouds; 22 per cent doesn't get to the surface because it is absorbed and scattered by the atmosphere; leaving 45 per cent to arrive at our level on the Earth's surface. In addition, we receive a little extra that is scattered by the atmosphere, i.e. some that didn't travel in a straight line.

What this means is that by the time sunlight reaches us it is made up of only a limited range of electromagnetic radiation, mostly in the visible, ultraviolet and infrared ranges. This is lucky for us because otherwise life would not be possible on Earth. Or, to put it another way, we wouldn't be what we are if the spectrum of radiation reaching the Earth was different.

Electromagnetic radiation travels in a straight line unless something gets in its way. Then it can either pass straight through, be absorbed, be reflected straight back in the direction from which it came, or it can go off in a different direction. In other words, when radiation interacts with molecules it can be absorbed, transmitted, scattered or reflected.

My physics tutor Graham Farmelo helped me to remember that ultraviolet radiation has lots of energy and a short wavelength by calling it ultra-*violent* radiation. It is the short and bouncy radiation. Because it has a short wavelength it is more easily absorbed than other parts of the spectrum. For example, in the winter as the sun sets it often appears more orange than when it is overhead. This is because the path travelled by the sunlight gets longer as the Earth turns, which means the blue and violet parts of the spectrum, as well as the ultraviolet light, are absorbed before they get to the Earth leaving a predominance of red, orange and yellow light. When there is a long distance to travel, the longer wavelength radiation – the red light – gets to the Earth's surface, but the short-legged blue and violet light bumps into objects and either bounces off in a different direction or gets stuck in the obstacle.

The longer the journey, the more likely it is that ultraviolet gets waylaid and in the winter, when the Sun is further from the Earth's surface, the short wavelengths just can't make the distance. Having a short wavelength also means that ultraviolet radiation is more able to interact with biological molecules, while the longer wavelength radiation can pass us by. This means that short wavelength radiation has the ability to cause damage to our molecules, but it is precisely this kind of damage that results in vitamin D. So as with all things in nature, the effects of ultraviolet radiation can be both good and bad.

Bands of UV

Ultraviolet radiation is divided into three bands: ultraviolet-A, ultraviolet-B and ultraviolet-C. The only difference is in the wavelengths, and the division is made simply to help distinguish between the general properties of different wavelengths. Some information about each band is given in the boxes on the following pages.

- Ultraviolet-C

- The shortest ultraviolet radiation is ultraviolet-C with wavelengths between 280 nm and 100 nm. Ultraviolet-C is defined as the band that does not reach the Earth's surface. The reason it doesn't reach the surface is because it is absorbed by ozone. Ozone consists of three oxygen atoms, while oxygen gas consists of two oxygen atoms. When oxygen is irradiated the molecule is split into separate oxygen atoms, which then combine to form ozone, and when ozone is irradiated two ozone molecules are converted to three oxygen molecules. The ozone layer is formed by a balance between the two reactions. Most ozone is in the stratosphere, the upper part of the atmosphere, and is normally thicker around the equator than at the poles. Lamps that emit radiation in the ultraviolet-C band are often used to purify air and water because the radiation kills bacteria. Ultraviolet-C can even be used to kill bacteria in wounds because the intensity of radiation needed to kill bacteria is much less than would damage human cells. For living things like us, ultraviolet-C is the most harmful part of ultraviolet radiation.

- Ultraviolet-A

- The band of ultraviolet radiation with the longest wavelengths is ultraviolet-A, sometimes called near-UV or black light. It has wavelengths between 315 nm and 400 nm, just outside of the visible spectrum. It has the least energy in the ultraviolet spectrum and was, until recently, thought to be harmless, although some people now believe that it is more likely to be responsible for skin cancer than ultraviolet-B. Most phototherapy and tanning lamps use ultraviolet-A radiation.

Although we humans cannot see ultraviolet-A, birds can. Birds have four photoreceptors (cones), compared to our three, and their fourth receptor can detect light in the ultraviolet-A range. This means that what appears to us to be a blackberry probably appears as a *violet*berry to a bird, and a blackbird is perhaps a *violet*bird. It also means that everything, including flowers, fruits and other birds' plumage, appears much more colourful to a bird than it does to us. If you imagine how things would look if you took out all of the red colour from the world, for example, not only would you be unable to see red, but orange would appear as yellow, you would see purple as blue, and the world would generally be less colourful. It is hard to imagine the reverse of this. Birds have an extra dimension to the colours they see and the colour perception of birds is beyond any human experience or imagination. (Please accept my apologies – this is not at all relevant to overweight or vitamin D but I find it so fascinating that I couldn't help but mention it.)

- Ultraviolet-B

- In between ultraviolet-A and ultraviolet-C is the ultraviolet-B radiation needed to make vitamin D. As far as vitamin D is concerned, the wavelengths between 315 nm and 280 nm are the most important to us. This is our helpful radiation. How much ultraviolet-B radiation do we receive? It is not easy to measure and in the absence of actual measurements we need to understand the large number of things that affect how much ultraviolet-B reaches our skin. The main consideration is how far ultraviolet-B has to travel. Remember that because it has a short wavelength it is easily absorbed and easily scattered, and the further it has to travel from the Sun the less likely it is to get here at the Earth's surface.

How much ultraviolet-B radiation do you need to make vitamin D? It has been calculated that we need 20 millijoules per square centimetre (mJ/cm^2 – see the notes) to convert 7-dehydrocholesterol into cholecalciferol (vitamin D_3) and these intensities have been confirmed in experiments using ultraviolet lamps where a minimum of 18 mJ/cm^2 was needed to produce an increase in the calcidiol concentration in the blood. (This is the test for vitamin D levels – see the notes at the end of the book for more details about the different forms of vitamin D.) Higher intensities of ultraviolet produced greater increases in calcidiol.

Do we get these intensities? According to modelling data it is certain that those of us at middle and high latitudes (above 40° N, which is roughly the latitude of the cities Barcelona, Beijing, New York, Naples, Thessaloniki and Yerevan) do not get these intensities in the winter. This means, if the models are correct, we cannot make vitamin D in the winter. As for real measurement of ultraviolet radiation intensities, there is little to go on at present. Much of the data available has been gathered using satellite measurements that don't tell us much about the intensity of radiation down here on the ground as, inevitably, the intensity at ground level will be lower because of absorption by the atmosphere. And, unlike temperature, for which we have records going back centuries, there is no historical data for ultraviolet radiation. A network of ground-based monitors has been set up in recent years but the intensity of radiation reaching any point on the ground depends on many factors differing not only by location, but also by time. Even the ground-based monitors cannot tell us exactly how much radiation is reaching every place at every moment. We must therefore make a judgment based upon the different factors affecting the path of ultraviolet radiation and make inferences about the intensity that reaches us wherever we are. The two most important factors are the time of day and whereabouts on Earth you are located.

The global factors

The time of day is obviously an important factor – you cannot make vitamin D in the middle of the night when there is no sunlight at all. As the Earth spins to face the Sun, the level of ultraviolet radiation builds up during the morning, reaches a peak and then declines in the afternoon. The time of the day when the intensity of solar radiation is strongest is when the sun is at its highest point in the sky – at solar noon, the midpoint between sunrise and sunset.

At solar noon, the closest point on the Earth to the Sun is the equator when it is facing the Sun directly. As you go further away from the equator and towards the poles, the sunlight has further to travel before it reaches the Earth's surface. At the equator the Earth's surface presents a relatively flat face to which the ultraviolet radiation arrives at a perpendicular, whereas at the poles, the Earth's surface is relatively angled because of the curve of the globe and the sunlight is spread over a larger area. So, all other things being equal (which they are not), ultraviolet-B radiation is at its strongest at the equator (latitude 0°) and becomes gradually weaker as the latitude increases and is weakest at the poles (latitude 90°). The closer the Sun is to the Earth's surface the higher it appears in the sky and the stronger the ultraviolet radiation coming your way.

The time of year doesn't matter very much in the tropics. But countries at higher latitudes are tilted away from the Sun in the winter and towards it in the summer. What this means is, while vitamin D can be made at any time of the year in the tropics, in regions far from the equator there is a vitamin D winter – a period in which little or no ultraviolet-B gets to us on the Earth's surface and when it is not possible to make much, if any, vitamin D. The northern hemisphere is tilted towards the sun from April to September and the southern hemisphere from October to March. In Boston, USA, latitude 42° N, the ultraviolet winter lasts for four months; in Edmonton, Canada, latitude 52° N, the ultraviolet winter lasts for five months; and in Bergen, Norway, latitude 61° N, it lasts for six months. In the southern hemisphere, because the Earth's orbit is elliptical, the solar radiation is a little stronger in summer than it is at the equivalent latitude in the northern hemisphere. This results in an even greater difference between summer and winter ultraviolet levels in New Zealand, for instance. At the North Pole, from April to September, daylight lasts for 24 hours. In spite of this, because of the distance travelled by the solar radiation (the sun is never more than 23.5° above the horizon) ultraviolet-B levels are low.

The latitude of the UK ranges from around 50° N to around 60° N. Over the period of a year we would expect that Birmingham, for example, would receive more ultraviolet-B than Glasgow, and the Isle of Wight more than the Isle of Man, purely because of the differences in latitudes. If you live in a middle latitude country, such as the UK, and holiday in a low latitude country, such as Spain, you are temporarily moving to an area with solar radiation that has a much stronger intensity of ultraviolet-B than in your home location.

We might generally expect that vitamin D deficiency would be higher at the most northern latitudes. But not all areas along the same line of latitude get the same amount of ultraviolet radiation, because the effects of latitude can be outweighed by local factors. Even in the tropics vitamin D cannot be made at all times without interruption, because incident ultraviolet-B radiation can be reduced by weather conditions – it is reduced during the monsoon rains, for example – as well as by other local factors.

The local factors

Pollution

Before it gets to your skin any photon arriving at planet Earth must go through the atmosphere. There are many obstacles in the pathway of ultraviolet-B photons in our atmosphere, and the atmosphere works like a filter. High up in the stratosphere there is abundant ozone, which absorbs ultraviolet-B, and lower down in the troposphere, the weather – rain, snow and clouds – can absorb or reflect ultraviolet-B. The further down you go towards the Earth's surface the thicker the atmosphere and anything that increases the amount of matter in the atmosphere that absorbs ultraviolet radiation will reduce the amount we receive down here at the Earth's surface. The atmosphere can contain aerosols, ash, dust, pollen, soot, salt from the oceans, emissions from volcanoes and sand blown up from deserts, all of which can act as a sunscreen. Emissions from industry and transport include pollutants that absorb ultraviolet-B, such as sulphur dioxide, nitrogen dioxide and ozone. Particles such as black carbon and PM_{10} (particulate matter of 2.5 to 10 micrometres – such as dust and pollen) are also known to reduce ultraviolet-B irradiance. The effects of the atmosphere on the blocking of ultraviolet will be explored in more detail in Chapter 3.

Altitude

The higher the altitude the stronger the intensity of ultraviolet radiation because the sunlight has less distance to travel and the atmosphere is thinner with fewer particles that absorb ultraviolet-B. Climb a mountain and you are lifting yourself above the thickest part of the atmosphere. It has been calculated that with each kilometre in altitude the ultraviolet radiation increases by around 10 per cent. And if the mountain is snow-capped it is even better, as snow-covered ground is the best reflector of ultraviolet-B and it can reflect it back to your skin.

Weather

The main effect of weather is that rain, wind, cold and snow keep us indoors or heavily clothed. But, even if you were to venture outdoors naked, rain and cloud may absorb much of the ultraviolet-B before it gets to you. For example, the west of the British Isles receives markedly more rainfall than the eastern regions. The Atlantic air rises over the high ground of the Welsh mountains, the Lake District and the Scottish Highlands and the east of England and Scotland is effectively in a rain shadow. For example, precipitation in highland Scotland can be more than 250 centimetres per year compared to 50 centimetres in the south-east of England. It is possible that this increased rainfall reduces the ultraviolet-B levels in Scotland compared with the south-east of England.

The effect of clouds on ultraviolet radiation is complicated and depends on the type of cloud. The cooling effect of some cloud can fool you into thinking that the sunlight is not strong, even when ultraviolet-B is actually quite intense. If you have very light skin you may have experienced sunburn when you underestimated the strength of ultraviolet-B on a cloudy day. On the other hand, when the sun is strong and you can feel it burning on your skin, it doesn't necessarily follow that you are getting any ultraviolet-B. We cannot necessarily tell how much ultraviolet radiation we are getting by seeing or feeling the sunshine.

Ground surface and building cover

Not all of the ultraviolet-B hitting our skin has arrived direct from the Sun. The ground, like the atmosphere, may absorb, scatter or reflect ultraviolet-B. Water, grass, concrete and asphalt absorb most of the ultraviolet-B and reflect very little. Dry sand and sea surf can reflect a little more, but the best ground cover for maximising your ultraviolet-B exposure is fresh snow, as it can reflect almost all of the sunlight. This means snow-covered ground can double the amount of ultraviolet-B you get. Buildings can also absorb or reflect ultraviolet-B. Concrete mostly absorbs solar radiation, while glass and white painted surfaces can reflect more. Scientists who study climate describe city areas with tall buildings as urban canyons, where ultraviolet-B irradiance and vitamin D production can be reduced to as little as a quarter of that in suburban areas.

In summary, the amount of ultraviolet-B reaching the surface of the Earth varies a great deal depending on where you are. We haven't mentioned the fact that it also depends on the amount emitted by the Sun, but of course there is nothing we can do about that. The amount of vitamin D you could make by sunbathing would depend on where you are in the world, the season, the time, the weather and the local landscape. To maximise the amount you can make, it would be best to be at the top of a snow-capped mountain on the equator at solar noon under a cloudless sky. But wherever you are on the Earth, waiting for photons to hit your 7-dehydrocholesterol, there is still quite a bit of travelling for the photons to do and how many get to be used for making vitamin D depends on personal factors.

The personal factors

Where are you exactly at the moment? Are you indoors or outdoors; in the sunlight or under artificial light; by a wall or a window? Remember we cannot see or feel ultraviolet-B. We have no conscious awareness of it. Still, we can imagine how the amount of ultraviolet-B reaching our skin depends on what objects are between the Sun and us because much the same thing happens to visible light. In a building with no windows it is dark because the visible light cannot penetrate the roof and walls of the building. If an object can block visible light it will also block ultraviolet-B, so if you cannot see without artificial light you can be sure that you are not getting any ultraviolet-B. But an object can be transparent to visible light while blocking ultraviolet-B, so if you can see without artificial light there may or may not be some ultraviolet-B present. On the other hand, ultraviolet-B can penetrate our skin, unlike visible light (if visible light could penetrate our skin we would, of course, be able to see through it). Indoors, ultraviolet-B cannot penetrate walls but it can sometimes get through windows.

If you cannot be outdoors to get your ultraviolet-B, it may still possible to get some indoors, especially if you are by a window, although you might have to open it first. Glass can be engineered to block all ultraviolet radiation – for example, the amber glass used for medicine bottles – and at the other extreme, quartz glass is completely transparent to ultraviolet radiation. Ordinary window glass probably absorbs or reflects most ultraviolet-B but may allow a little through, depending on the properties of the glass – for example, its thickness, the amount of iron impurities and whether it is laminated or tinted. It also depends on the strength of the ultraviolet irradiance, for example, you might get more ultraviolet through a roof window than a wall window. Modern changes to windows, including the increased use of double- and triple-glazing, and the use of low emissivity coatings, may have lowered the amount of ultraviolet-B, if any, getting to us through windows.

Artificial lighting

There is a tiny amount of ultraviolet given off by a light bulb, but it is so small that it is probably not enough to make vitamin D. But, of course, while light bulbs are designed to replace the visible radiation of the Sun and artificial heating replaces the heat of the Sun, we make no effort to provide an artificial source of ultraviolet radiation in buildings. The only artificial lamps designed to emit ultraviolet radiation are sunlamps and sunbeds used either to treat the skin conditions psoriasis and acne or for tanning. Most SAD lamps (used to ameliorate seasonal affective disorder) are designed to filter out most of the ultraviolet radiation. Germicidal lamps used for purifying air and water (such as in aquariums and ponds) are designed to produce short-wavelength ultraviolet-C. In fact, as far as I am aware, there is only one type of full spectrum sunlamp available that emits ultraviolet-B and is *specifically designed* for the purpose of allowing production of vitamin D – but this is designed for pet reptiles, not humans. How odd it is that the needs of pet reptiles are better facilitated than the needs of humans.

Clothing

The first part of your body to be hit by the ultraviolet radiation coming direct from the Sun is the top of your head, so any kind of hat will block a proportion of ultraviolet-B from your body and a wide-brimmed hat is an effective sun shield.

Can an ultraviolet-B photon get through your clothes? It can penetrate some clothing better than others. Tightly woven fabrics, dark colours and heavyweight fabrics block more ultraviolet radiation than light coloured clothing made of loosely woven, lightweight fabric. Wet clothing allows more ultraviolet radiation through than dry, and old, worn out clothing allows more through than new clothing. Some clothing has been designed to block ultraviolet and is labelled with a UPF – ultraviolet protection factor, a measure of the protection against ultraviolet radiation – in the same way as sunscreens indicate their sun protection factor (SPF). On the other hand, clothing can be made with fabric designed to allow 80 per cent of ultraviolet through so you can get an all-over tan without having to go naked.

Sunscreen

In a typical sunscreen some of the ultraviolet-B is absorbed by compounds in the cream and some is reflected. If you are wearing sunscreen there is little chance for ultraviolet-B to get inside your skin. A sunscreen with a sun protection factor of 8 or more will block almost all ultraviolet-B.

Position

Are you upright or prone? The best way to maximise your exposure, once you are in an ultraviolet-B hotspot, is to take off all your clothes, don't apply any sunscreen and lie down flat so as much of your body surface is exposed to the sun as possible. Some say you shouldn't wash after sunbathing as you may be washing off some of the vitamin D-containing oil from the surface of your skin. Don't let that deter you from washing the next morning though (*please*) as by then the vitamin D will have been absorbed.

Skin

Those photons that have managed to get all the way to the Earth, through the atmosphere and finally to our skin, still face obstacles before getting to our 7-dehydrocholesterol. The last leg of their 90 million mile journey is less than one millimetre of our skin. As far as a photon is concerned our skin is just another layer to travel through, like the atmosphere, with a lot of obstacles in its path. Just as happens in the atmosphere, when photons encounter the many compounds in our skin they may be absorbed or scattered. When they encounter a molecule of 7-dehydrocholesterol the energy of the photon breaks a bond and it is converted to cholecalciferol. Only a photon of ultraviolet-B will do the job – and it is a job that is only done in this particular reaction. The problem is that this photon of ultraviolet-B can also break bonds in other molecules such as DNA. While the damage to 7-dehydrocholesterol is beneficial to our health, the damage to DNA is not – the result can be mutations in the DNA that can lead to cancer. For this reason there are protective mechanisms in place to prevent photons entering the skin or reaching DNA, but they also prevent photons from reaching 7-dehydrocholesterol. There is a trade-off, then, between getting sufficient radiation to make vitamin D but not enough to damage our DNA.

What happens when our skin is bombarded with ultraviolet photons? It is common knowledge that if you take a group of people and expose them to exactly the same intensity of ultraviolet-B radiation the effect will be different. If, for example, you and I were to go sunbathing together, you might get sunburn while I get a tan, and in one afternoon on the beach last year my feet went pink while my hands went brown. The properties of the skin can vary between people because of genetics (for example, between a black and white person) and within an individual between different parts of the body (for example, the skin on the outer forearm is usually darker and thicker than the skin underneath the upper arm) and before and after sun exposure (with and without a tan). The differences depend mainly on skin thickness and skin pigmentation.

Skin thickness

The topmost layer of the skin is the epidermis in which some cells produce keratin, the tough substance that makes up our hair and nails. Keratin cells start life at the bottom of the epidermis – the basal layer – and gradually move up to the surface until they get to the top – the stratum corneum – and die, in a process that takes about a month. The more keratin cells you have, the thicker your skin. When you sunbathe the number of keratin cells increases making your epidermis thicker and, after two or three days, the stratum corneum gets thicker. Without further ultraviolet exposure the skin thickness will go back to normal again after about two months.

The epidermis is generally thinnest on our eyelids and thickest on the palms of our hands and soles of our feet. A child's skin is thinner than an adult's and therefore more photosensitive. Thinning of the skin can be caused by injury, steroid medication, and cosmetic treatments that remove the stratum corneum, such as dermabrasion, leaving the skin more sensitive to sunlight.

The thicker the skin the more the photons of ultraviolet-B are scattered and the fewer are able to get through to our 7-dehydrocholesterol. If we have thick skin, we make less vitamin D but we are also less susceptible to damage by sunlight. On the other hand, if we have thin skin, we can more easily make vitamin D but we are also more sensitive to the damage.

Pigmentation

Skin pigmentation (or skin colour) depends on the amount and type of melanin in the skin. Melanin is produced by branched cells called melanocytes. Through their branches, each melanocyte can deliver melanin to 30 or 40 keratin cells. Melanin does not have a specific chemical composition; in fact the mixtures of melanin are so complex and differ so much between individuals that they have not been very well characterised. Daniel Liebler, Professor of Biochemistry at the Vanderbilt-Ingram Cancer Center, compares melanin to wood because there are so many different types, but it can be divided into two main types – black melanin (called eumelanin) and red melanin (called phaeomelanin). Skin pigmentation depends on the type of melanin produced, and how much is made and transferred to the keratin cells. We all have a mixture of these two types of melanin but if you have dark, black skin with black hair you have mostly black melanin and if you have pale, fair skin with red hair you have mostly red melanin. Blond hair has little of either.

Melanin covers the DNA-containing nucleus inside the keratin cells, acting like a teeny-tiny sunshade to protect the DNA from damage by ultraviolet photons. When those ultraviolet-B photons come rushing into the skin there is, in effect, a competition between melanin and 7-dehydrocholesterol. If you have lots of melanin, the 7-dehydrocholesterol hardly gets a look in, but if you have little or no melanin, the 7-dehydrocholesterol can have its fill of photons. Given strong ultraviolet radiation it doesn't matter if you have lots of melanin, but when ultraviolet-B intensity is low the 7-dehydrocholesterol hardly gets any and little vitamin D can be made.

As a rough guide, if a white person needs 10 minutes of sunlight to make a certain amount of vitamin D, a South Asian person needs 30 minutes and a black person 2 hours. Melanin is the main reason for the difference. After exposure to ultraviolet radiation, there is an increase in melanin in our skin and some extra black melanin is produced – this is what happens when we tan.

In summary, to maximise one's vitamin D production it would be best to have fair, thin skin, to be outdoors lying flat on the ground with no sunscreen and no clothes on, at the top of a snow-capped mountain on the equator at solar noon under a cloudless sky. Unfortunately, this is also the best way to get sunburned and skin cancer. We need to get enough exposure to ultraviolet-B to make vitamin D, but not so much that we get sunburn and skin cancer. But we are a long way from making enough vitamin D to meet our needs.

Urban-industrial sunlight deficiency

You can see that the ultraviolet-B photon has many obstacles to overcome before it can be used to make vitamin D. If you follow a typical way of life in a mid-latitude country there is little opportunity for those ultraviolet-B photons to make the whole journey to make vitamin D in your skin.

Where I live in the UK, for example, I get little or no ultraviolet radiation between October and February. For the remaining months of the year I can get some ultraviolet-B between the hours of 11 a.m. and 3 p.m. if I go outside. But, however strong the ultraviolet radiation is high up in the atmosphere, much of it will be absorbed before it gets to me, especially when there is heavy cloud and rain. In addition, many of us live in an atmosphere with a high level of pollutants that absorb ultraviolet-B.

Most of us live in suburban and urban areas at low altitude where much of the ground is covered by buildings that shield the sunlight and with ground covered by asphalt or concrete that absorbs ultraviolet-B. Snow is the best ground cover in this respect as it reflects ultraviolet, but snow-covered ground occurs only in the winter at a time when ultraviolet-B is weak or non-existent at ground level.

On a working day you may typically travel to work by train, bus or car and spend the morning at work indoors, in a large building with air conditioning and artificial lighting and heating. Many workplaces are now like sheds in which natural light has been replaced by artificial light. You may work in a room with no windows, or a large room where your desk is far from a window and, in any case, the windows are tinted or covered in blinds. You may spend some time underground where there is no ultraviolet-B at all – on the underground railway system or in the basement or lower ground floor of buildings. At lunchtime you might walk outdoors to a deli or a café to buy a sandwich, but then you go indoors to eat it. You spend the afternoon indoors and by the time you go home from work there is no ultraviolet-B, except on the longest days of the year. This just leaves holidays and weekends. You spend most of the day indoors doing housework, DIY, eating, watching TV, gaming, or something else in front of a screen. Even when you go outdoors at the weekend you wear clothes; in cold weather you wear extensive clothing – gloves, scarves and hats – and in wet weather you use an umbrella. Most of your skin is covered by clothes and, for most of the time, only the face, neck, the top part of the chest, hands and forearms are exposed. On occasional hot days upper arms and shoulders, legs and feet may also be exposed and men may expose the whole upper body. The rest of the body – most of the chest, all of the back, tummy and bottom, all of the legs and feet – is almost always covered in clothing, often dark in colour and sometimes several layers thick.

For most of the time, then, your whole body is shielded from the sunlight and, for the rest, most of your skin is shielded. This means making your own vitamin D is something you do as a fair-weather hobby rather than the daily necessity it should be. When you think about it, it soon becomes clear that a proportion of the world's human population is exposed to very little ultraviolet radiation and it doesn't seem so surprising that this has resulted in widespread vitamin D deficiency.

It is getting darker

How has our accessibility to those ultraviolet-B photons changed over the period that overweight has risen? More people work indoors in shopping centres, call centres and office blocks and fewer people work outdoors – in agriculture, for example. People walk less as the motor vehicle has driven (excuse the pun) the development of out-of-town amenities such as shopping centres and leisure facilities. Improved lighting and heating technologies, along with air-conditioning systems, have allowed bigger buildings and enabled the building of indoor facilities with fewer windows and less natural daylight. Some sports that decades ago could only be done outdoors are now done indoors using, for example, indoor football pitches and tennis centres. Shops are inside shopping centres rather than along the high street. A typical household shopping trip involves driving to do one large supermarket shop for all our household goods rather than walking to the high street and going in and out of different shops as we did 40 years ago. Teenagers who would have spent their free time hanging around on the streets are now indoors gaming. Intuitively, we assume that driving contributes to overweight because it uses less of our energy but it may in fact be because we get less sunlight when we drive than when we walk, cycle or use public transport.

The official line is that you can get all the vitamin D you need from being exposed to sunlight while you go about your normal daily routine. This may be true if you live in the tropics, or at high altitude, wear little or no clothing and spend most of your time outdoors. But, for most of us, this is simply incorrect.

We don't notice the lack of sunlight too much because we use artificial sources to replace the light and heat of the sun, but not to replace ultraviolet radiation, which we cannot consciously detect. Without realising it we are living in the dark as far as ultraviolet-B is concerned; we are not getting enough sunlight and this means we are not getting enough vitamin D. Even if you live in the tropics, if you spend most of your time indoors, you won't get enough sunlight to make sufficient vitamin D.

With so little exposure, there is no adaptation of our skin to the sunlight and we become more photosensitive year after year. We become less able to tolerate the sunlight, closing the blinds and curtains when the sun shines through the window and wearing sunglasses outdoors because the sunlight seems too bright. If we then go on a holiday abroad to a place near the equator and expose our skin to levels of ultraviolet that are much stronger than at home, our skin is too thin and too pale to protect us from the danger of ultraviolet interacting with our DNA. It is perhaps not surprising that, with thin skin and little pigmentation, skin cancer results. Skin cancer campaigns that encourage sun avoidance, the wearing of hats, sunscreens and ultraviolet-protective clothing, mean that, even when we do go outdoors, we expose less of our skin to sunlight. But counter-intuitively, the answer may be to get more sunlight, not less. This question will be explored in more detail in Chapter 4, but for now we will turn to an alternative source of vitamin D.

Ready-made vitamin D

Does it matter that we don't get enough sunlight? Perhaps we have forgotten that vitamin D is a vitamin – a nutrient found in our food – and we don't need to make it ourselves as we can get it ready-made in our diet. Which foods contain vitamin D and how much do they contain? How much of these foods have you eaten today, this week, this year?

The changes to our exposure to sunlight in recent decades may have gone unnoticed, but the changes in the food we eat most certainly have not. The types of food we eat have changed – we eat more pizzas and pasta, for example, less fish and fewer eggs. But a more dramatic change can be seen in the methods of food production and preparation. The technology of food has changed our food beyond recognition. Today food is grown, stored, processed, preserved, transported and cooked on a huge scale.

My Aunt Vera was born in the 1930s and, when she was a housewife in the 1950s, she baked cakes by mixing flour, butter, eggs and milk together with her hands, fork and spoon. Later she got an electric whisk to make the mixing easier. Later still, she used prepared cake mixes, to which she needed only to add an egg, but today she buys her cakes ready-made. She is still uncomfortable with the idea of buying lettuce ready cut up in a bag or cheese already sliced. She is horrified at fast food and wouldn't touch it. Still, perhaps previous generations would have been aghast at the idea of buying potatoes when you could grow your own, or of buying pork chops when you could buy a whole piglet and fatten it in the back yard. Go back further still and our hunter–gatherer ancestors would have had a much greater depth of knowledge about food than we do today but would not recognise a Margherita pizza, a chicken tikka masala or a double bacon cheeseburger, either by sight or by taste. These massive changes in our food consumption are often blamed for the increase in overweight, as well as other health problems, but have the changes affected our vitamin D intake?

Vitamin D content of food

Vitamin D is a fat-soluble substance so it can only be found in the presence of fat or oil. It tends to be found with fatty acids along with vitamin A in many naturally occurring fats and oils. The main foods that contain vitamin D are:

1. Meat
2. Fish
3. Milk and dairy products
4. Eggs.

The information in the table below gives the vitamin D content of selected foods in micrograms per 100 grams. This information was taken from the UK's Department of Health Manual of Nutrition (Twelfth Edition).

Milk, whole	*0.0*
Cheese	*0.3*
Eggs, whole, boiled	*1.8*
Liver, lambs, fried	*0.9*
Salmon, canned	*8.0*
Butter	*0.9*

The trouble is that this information cannot be relied upon to tell us much about the vitamin D content of foods, except perhaps that it is extremely low. There are a lot of uncertainties when it comes to looking at the data on the amount of vitamin D contained in food.

Firstly, the information in the table shows there is no vitamin D in milk. If that is the case, where does the calf get its vitamin D? Sunlight perhaps, but I find it hard to believe that the milk produced for the rapidly growing calf does not contain any vitamin D at all. The table shows butter contains 0.9 micrograms and cheese 0.3 micrograms. If there is no vitamin D in milk, where did the vitamin D in butter and cheese come from? A previous edition of the Manual of Nutrition (Tenth Edition) showed 0.03 micrograms of vitamin D in milk. A 1978 paper states that milk contains 0.5 micrograms of vitamin D as cholecalciferol and a 2013 study conducted in Italy found the vitamin D content of cows' milk ranged from 0.3 micrograms to 1.9 micrograms per 100 ml. These different quantities could be explained by differences in methodology and sunlight exposure of the herd.

There is no mention of a seasonal effect in the food composition tables – the amount of vitamin D in the milk of a pasture-fed cow in a Devon farm, for example, will depend on how much ultraviolet-B reached the cow which will depend on (among other things) whether it is spring, summer, autumn or winter. We should expect the milk to contain more vitamin D at the end of summer than at the end of winter, but I have not seen any analysis of vitamin D in food that takes season into account.

Another problem is that vitamin D is not one substance, but includes different metabolites. Traditionally, only cholecalciferol (vitamin D_3) or ergocalciferol (vitamin D_2) is measured, meaning the amount of vitamin D in foods may have been underestimated (see the notes for more details about different forms of vitamin D). The technique (called high performance liquid chromatography) which detects calcidiol in foods has only recently been developed. Calcidiol is taken into account in Germany for assessing the total vitamin D content of milk, and in Finland and the USA for other foods, but because the technique is relatively new there is not yet agreement as to how to incorporate it into the food composition tables. Calcidiol is more potent than cholecalciferol because it is more easily absorbed from the diet. The potency has not yet been determined exactly, but is estimated to be between two and five times that of cholecalciferol. So a food labelled as containing one microgram of vitamin D may actually contain the equivalent of five micrograms if the vitamin D is present mainly as calcidiol.

Milk may actually be a good source of vitamin D because, even if its vitamin D content is low, it may be more easily absorbed, i.e. more bioavailable, than vitamin D from other foods. In addition, milk is used to produce many different dairy foods – butter, cheese, yoghurt, ghee, cream – and it is quite possible to have around a litre of milk every day in various forms, providing a daily source of vitamin D.

Because food has not been regarded as an important source of vitamin D, there has not been a great effort to analyse foods for their vitamin D content. As a result some foods have not been analysed at all for vitamin D content and those that have been analysed might not have had their vitamin D levels accurately assessed. In 2004 Tom Hill of the Vitamin D Research Group at University College, Cork re-analysed the vitamin D content of some everyday foods and found that turkey slices, which had previously been undetermined, contained 2.17 micrograms of vitamin D per 100 grams; a popular spread (Utterly Butterly), which previously had showed zero vitamin D content, contained 2.46 micrograms per 100 grams; and cod, which had been recorded as having a 'trace' (meaning it is present in such a low amount that it is either too low to measure or too low to be of any nutritional value), contained 1.49 micrograms of vitamin D per 100 grams.

Overall trends in diet

Celia Prynne, and her colleagues at the Elsie Widdowson laboratory in Cambridge, performed a detailed comparison of the diets of 4-year-old children living in England, Wales and Scotland in the 1950s and the 1990s to examine how diets have changed in the second half of the twentieth century. In 1992, children were eating foods that were unheard of by their 1950s counterparts. These included pizza, pasta, fish fingers, yoghurt and fromage frais. The standard diet in 1950 consisted of:

Breakfast – eggs or cereal with milk
Lunch – meat, potatoes, vegetable and a pudding (often stewed fruit with custard)
Supper – bread, butter and jam, cake and biscuits
Bedtime – milk.

In 1950 rice was eaten only as a pudding, but with the main course in 1992. Children ate less bread and butter, fewer vegetables but more fruit in 1992 than in 1950. The most dramatic change was in the type of drinks children had. Children attending nursery or school received one third of a pint (a gill) of milk each school day in 1950 but this had been discontinued by 1992. In place of the milk and tea drunk by 1950s children, the 1990s children drank fruit juice.

When the diets were analysed for their nutrient content, it is interesting that the 1990s diet had *fewer calories* and *less fat* than the 1950s diet. Daily energy intake dropped from 1445 kilocalories in 1950 to 1228 kilocalories in 1992, and fat intake dropped from 64 grams per day in 1950 to 48 grams per day in 1992. In addition, the 1990s child got less protein, carbohydrate, starch, calcium, iron and vitamin A, but, on the other hand, more sugar and vitamin C than the 1950s child. Overall the 1950 diet was assessed as better in terms of nutrient intake than the 1992 diet.

What about vitamin D? No assessment of the dietary intake of vitamin D was made, because it was not seen as important, but can we make any inferences about vitamin D? An analysis of vitamin A intake showed that it was 912 micrograms per day in 1950 and 473 micrograms in 1992. Why did it drop by half? Milk, dairy foods and eggs are rich sources of vitamin A. The fall in consumption of these foods could account for the drop in vitamin A. Both vitamin A and vitamin D are found together in the yolk of the egg and the fat of milk and dairy products, so if vitamin A intake dropped because consumption of these foods fell, then we can assume that vitamin D intake would also have dropped by half.

In fact *The Family Food Survey*, published in 2004 for the UK by the Department for Environment, Food and Rural Affairs, found that vitamin D intake fell by much more than half. According to the survey, during the period between 1974 and 2003, when obesity rose from 6 per cent to 23 per cent, vitamin D intake had fallen from 8.92 micrograms to 2.92 micrograms.

There can be no doubt that vitamin D intakes from food have fallen in the past few decades because of changes in our diet. In recent years foods containing vitamin D that were once popular because they were cheap such as sardines, kippers, liver and kidneys, have lost their appeal. Fatty meats have gone out of favour and been replaced by chicken and turkey. Fat is trimmed from the meat by both the butcher and the cook. Lard is no longer used for cooking and has been replaced by seed oils. Butter has largely been replaced by seed oil spreads and the consumption of eggs fell at the end of the twentieth century, although consumption levels have bounced back in recent years. Children's drinks based on fruit juices have been heavily marketed and the consumption of milk and milk-based drinks has gone into a decline.

Less fat means less vitamin D

One reason for these changes was the drive to lower the proportion of fat in the population's diet. Several reports from clinical studies in the 1950s and 1960s linked circulating cholesterol to dietary intakes of cholesterol and saturated fatty acids, and these links were reinforced by the correlation between dietary intake of these fats and mortality rates from coronary heart disease in populations in the USA and other countries. As a result, the emphasis of the *Dietary Guidelines for Americans*, published in 1980 by the US Department of Health and Human Services and the Department of Agriculture, was on reducing total fat, saturated fat and cholesterol in the diet. In 1994, the Department of Health made similar recommendations in the UK.

Data from national food surveys in the USA all show a decrease in the absolute quantity (in grams) and in proportions (in per cent of energy intake) of total fat and saturated fatty acid between the years 1971 and 1998. Between 1970 and 1996 food supply data showed a decrease in the consumption of red meat, eggs and milk (particularly whole milk). The fat content of meat was reduced quite substantially by modifying animal feeds, butchery techniques and fat trimming. The fat content of pork was reduced by 30 per cent, beef by 15 per cent and lamb by 10 per cent. For example, lamb loin chops contained 12 grams of fat per 100 grams in 1978 and 11 grams per 100 grams in 1995, and grilled bacon had 35 grams per 100 grams in 1978 compared to 23 grams in 1995.

Milk and dairy products accounted for 15 per cent of the total fat and 23 per cent of the saturated fat consumed in the UK, and similar proportions in the USA. Since 1980 there has therefore been a drive to reduce the fat in milk and dairy products, and switching from whole milk to skimmed or semi-skimmed is a common dietary change taken by people who are trying to lose weight.

Here is a typical low fat diet recommended for losing weight:

- Breakfast – low fat yoghurt mixed with honey, an apple, dried apricots and wholegrain cereal. Orange juice.
- Lunch – 2 slices of whole grain bread with 2 slices of ham, 2 tbsp of reduced fat cream cheese and mixed salad. One banana.
- Dinner – Baked chicken with honey and mustard, 4 small new potatoes and half a tin of ratatouille. One orange.
- Snack – Fruit salad.

And here is some typical advice for healthy eating:

- Trim all visible fat from meat and drain excess fat from cooked meat. Skim fat from foods such as stock, soup and stews.
- Use egg whites in place of whole eggs and replace up to one third of the fat or oil in many recipes with mashed banana or stewed apple.
- Swap saturated fats with moderate amounts of unsaturated fats; for example, swap butter with olive oil spread, cream cheese with guacamole and chocolate spread for peanut butter.
- Don't add extra fat when cooking and use healthy cooking methods – grill, steam or bake instead of roast or fry. Use non-stick pans, which don't need to be greased, or add a little stock instead of oil when cooking. When adding fat, use the minimum possible.
- Eat low fat cheese and skimmed milk.
- Remove the skin from chicken and turkey.
- Select low fat or non fat alternatives when they are available.

If you are overweight and try to lose weight by following this advice, you will also cut down on your vitamin D intake. Vitamin D is a fat-soluble compound. It cannot dissolve in water, only in fat or oil. When you trim the fat off meat, you are also trimming off the vitamin D, as well as the other fat-soluble vitamins – vitamin A, vitamin E and vitamin K. When the fat is skimmed off the top of milk, the vitamin D is also skimmed off. Low fat means low (fat-soluble) vitamins.

Cutting down on fat in the diet is the most common change to the diet adopted by those who wish to lose weight or improve health. In addition to the loss of vitamins, the overall fat content of the diet can affect the absorption of nutrients. For example, adding olive oil to the diet increases the absorption of vitamin A from other foods. So a very strict no fat or very low fat diet, like the one shown above – even one that contains all the essential nutrients – may result in vitamin D deficiency and other nutrient deficiencies because these vitamins and nutrients cannot be absorbed without fat.

Breast milk has a fat content of about 50 per cent, which is much higher than the typical adult diet of around 30 per cent. There is great concern about the fat content of diet generally (even though fat intake has gone down) and the increasing prevalence of overweight in children. These concerns combined have resulted in a trend towards lowering the fat content of children's diet too early. This adds to the problem of children not getting enough fat-soluble vitamins as well as not getting enough of the essential fatty acids required for development of the brain and nervous system.

The diet that is regarded as healthy today does not provide any vitamin D. In fact one study found that after six months on a 'healthy' diet, as part of a heart disease prevention programme, calcium and vitamin D levels were lower than before. Of course, in other respects the diet may have been healthier, but a key feature of the diet was to lower the intake of meat and dairy foods, both of which contain calcium and vitamin D, and no consideration was given to making up for the loss of these nutrients. Without realising it, we have all been getting less vitamin D from our diets. But these changes in the foods that make up our diet may not be the only reason we get less vitamin D from our food than we did years ago.

Has the amount of vitamin D in our food changed? The composition of foods naturally changes over time, even when production methods are the same. If you grow carrots in your allotment or back garden today in exactly the same place and exactly the same way as you did 30 years ago, the soil won't be exactly the same, so the mineral content of today's carrots will be slightly different from the mineral content of your carrots 30 years ago. Of course, food production methods have changed dramatically in the past 30 years and have inevitably changed the composition of foods even more.

Take the iron content of meat, for example. In 1950, 100 grams of chicken had an iron content of 2.1 milligrams and beef had 4.4 milligrams, while in the 1990s, chicken had an iron content of only 0.7 milligrams per 100 grams and beef 2.6 milligrams per 100 grams. (Note that we measure iron in milligrams and vitamin D in micrograms, which is a thousand times smaller.) A comparison of the mineral content of different foods recorded in food composition tables from 1940 to 2002, carried out by David Thomas, revealed that there was a significant loss of minerals and trace elements from food over that period.

Vitamin D and livestock

How does the vitamin D get into our food? The animals and birds that provide our food get their vitamin D in the same way that we do – they either make it themselves when exposed to ultraviolet-B, or they get it from *their* food. The mammals that provide our meat – mostly cows, sheep and pigs – make vitamin D when exposed to sunlight. If they are not exposed to sunlight, they need a source of vitamin D in their diet, otherwise they will be deficient in vitamin D and the food they provide will, in turn, lack vitamin D.

Inside the body of an animal vitamin D is stored in the muscle and fat, some circulates in the blood and some is in the liver and kidneys, so meat, offal and fat contain vitamin D. In addition, vitamin D can be found in the most nourishing food in nature – the food provided for young offspring. Milk is produced by the cow for its calf and eggs contain food produced by the hen to nourish the chick. These foods are rich in nutrients because they supply all that the young offspring needs. There are two reasons why a baby, whether a human baby, a chick, a calf or any other species, needs to be provided with its own 'packed lunch'. Firstly, its chances of survival are increased when it is not dependent in its first days of life on food that has to be obtained from the environment, bearing in mind that it cannot get its own. Secondly, it is in a phase of growth and needs nutrients not only to tick over, but also to grow new structures such as bones and muscles. So these foods also contain vitamin D and, in general, the bioavailability of nutrients is very good compared to other foods.

If we were to go back and eat a 1950s diet it is possible that we would still be getting less vitamin D because the amount of vitamin D in the food has gone down. How have modern production methods affected the vitamin D content? After the food shortages of the Second World War, national self-sufficiency in food production became an important goal. Industrialisation in developed countries was extended to include the industrialisation of farming, which has been extremely successful. Intensive farming means more food can be produced per unit area of land and it can be produced quickly and efficiently with minimum costs. The result is that problems with food supply simply do not occur in the developed world and many of us today have a continuous, plentiful supply of relatively cheap food. For us, famines have become foreign news or history.

Poultry

When I was a child, chicken was a luxury food to be eaten only on special occasions like Christmas, but it is now the cheapest meat available. The meat comes from broiler chickens kept in huge quantities in broiler houses where the light, temperature and feed are controlled automatically and the chicks grow to full size in 42 days. Layer hens are kept in similar conditions and pigs and calves may also be kept in intensive animal units.

This factory farming has caused great concern for those interested in animal welfare, but has also presented problems for the producer. Keeping animals close together and in the same place as their faeces and their dead allows diseases to spread quickly. In the 1980s this problem of disease became public knowledge after a series of Salmonella outbreaks was traced to eggs.

Diseases became a problem in poultry farming when hens were first kept in hen-houses in the early twentieth century, and various perforated flooring systems were developed to separate the hens from their faeces. But infectious disease was not the only problem. Another problem for egg producers was cage layer fatigue caused by bone disorders following a high rate of egg production. The condition results from the withdrawal of calcium from the bones for formation of the eggshells. But broiler chickens (raised for meat rather than eggs) also suffer from bone disorders. In fact as many as a third of caged hens may suffer from a fracture at least once in a lifetime. Another health problem only found in caged hens is fatty liver syndrome. In addition to these diseases, farmers noted an increase in behavioural problems including hysteria, feather-pecking and cannibalism. There can be no doubt that the hens suffer in these conditions and the concern has been directed on the welfare of the hen, but intuitively we know that a sick bird cannot be producing healthy food. If the animal or bird from which we get our food is suffering from ill health, its food cannot be healthy to eat.

Where does vitamin D come in all of this? It is possible that vitamin D is a major factor in the health of intensively farmed animals and birds. From the point of view of vitamin D, the main problem with factory farming is that the animals and birds that would live outdoors if they were kept in their natural environment are instead kept indoors. Layer hens, for example, were bred originally from the Asian jungle. In the 1940s just 2 per cent of eggs were produced from hens kept indoors, but by the 1980s the figures had reversed and almost all eggs were produced from hens kept indoors.

How severe is vitamin D deficiency in the layer and broiler hens that produce our eggs and chicken meat? It is beyond question that vitamin D deficiency causes the type of bone disorders that are common in farmed poultry and it can also impair the immune system, which means infections cannot be fought off easily. At the moment we do not have the information we need to tell how farming practices affect the vitamin D content of eggs or chicken meat. For example, the official vitamin D content does not specify whether the egg was produced by a caged hen or a free-range hen, but then again, do we even need to measure vitamin D in poultry or is it not plainly obvious that they are suffering from severe vitamin D deficiency? If so, this means, of course, that the meat and eggs they produce will have less vitamin D than that produced by free-range poultry. I have concentrated here on poultry but the same can be said for any livestock kept indoors.

As a result of the welfare concerns in recent years, efforts have been made to provide better housing conditions for layer hens in the form of enriched cages or barn systems, and free-range conditions are gradually replacing battery farming. But improved housing that provides bigger cages with more room for the hen to move will not solve the problems caused by vitamin D deficiency. The solution to this problem is to ensure that hens are exposed to sunlight, to provide vitamin D in the feed, or to provide lighting that emits ultraviolet radiation. It is well known among pet owners that reptiles, such as iguanas, are at risk of vitamin D deficiency when they are housed indoors and need to be provided with a lamp that emits ultraviolet radiation, so why not provide the same for livestock?

Fish

Fish have little or no 7-dehydrocholesterol in their skin, so cannot make vitamin D even when exposed to sunlight. Since they are unable to make their own vitamin D, they must get all their vitamin D from their diet. Vitamin D is made by plankton in the upper layers of water penetrated by sunlight. This vitamin D then passes along the marine food chain. The plankton is eaten by krill, small fish and crustaceans, which are eaten by bigger fish and crustaceans and so on along the food chain.

Tai C. Chen, Professor at Boston University School of Medicine, analysed fish and found that 100 grams of farmed salmon contained 6 micrograms (240 IU) of vitamin D, while wild salmon contained 25 micrograms (981 IU). (Like other vitamins, vitamin D can be measured in micrograms or International Units, abbreviated to IU. One microgram of vitamin D is equivalent to 40 IU. In this book I use micrograms.) What explains the difference? Sunlight exposure of the livestock is not an issue when it comes to fish farming since they are cultivated outdoors and, in any case, are thought not to make their own vitamin D. They are therefore wholly dependent on food for vitamin D intake and it is food that may be the problem. Wild salmon eat zooplankton, small fish and krill. Cultivated fish are fed with fish oil and fishmeal pellets made from larger fish, so it could just be that the vitamin D is further along the food chain by the time the farmed salmon get their food and the concentration of vitamin D is lower in the farmed salmon feed than the wild salmon diet. Even though the vitamin D content of farmed salmon is only a third of that of the wild salmon, farmed salmon still represents a rich source of vitamin D compared to other foods.

Haring in't land, dokter aan de kant

An Old Dutch proverb meaning: 'If herring is around, the doctor is far away'.

Overall, although we don't at present have all the information we would like, there can be no doubt that trends in food production must have reduced the amount of vitamin D in foods. Keeping livestock indoors means there is a lack of sunlight exposure and a lack of vitamin D synthesis. In summary, not only are we eating less of the foods that contain vitamin D than we did 30 years ago, but also those few foods that contain vitamin D now contain even less vitamin D than they did in the past. Furthermore, when we try to lose weight, or to eat healthily by cutting down on fat, we are also cutting down on vitamin D. While sunlight has been disappearing from our daily lives, vitamin D has also been disappearing from our food.

Chapter 2

Vitamin D Poverty

WE ALL LIKE TO think of ourselves as healthy, and no one wants to hear that they are deficient in vitamin D. The previous chapter considered how our modern, urban–industrial life has reduced the amount of vitamin D we get in many different ways and it is pretty clear that we have been getting less vitamin D than we did in the past. But we need to assess the extent of vitamin D deficiency. Are we just a little short of vitamin D, like going slightly overdrawn at the end of the month, or are we severely deficient, like being on the verge of bankruptcy? Is there an epidemic of vitamin D deficiency underpinning the obesity epidemic? To answer these questions we must know how much vitamin D we need and how much we are getting. When I began gathering the facts about vitamin D deficiency, I expected the answers to be easily available, with well worked out official guidance on recommended intakes based on robust scientific evidence, but, as it turns out, the metrics lack certainty and are undergoing revision. There is some official guidance on vitamin D but there are several problems with it: It is not easy to work out how much vitamin D is necessary for good health; the recommended intakes of vitamin D are inadequate by any realistic standards and even these inadequate recommendations are not put into practice.

Our vitamin D requirements

How much vitamin D do we need? Deciding how much vitamin D is required for good health is not an easy task. First, you need to be able to measure it and then you need to determine what amount is too little and how much is too much. After vitamin D was discovered in the early twentieth century, several decades passed before it became possible to measure it in people. Since 1997 it has been agreed that best way of assessing vitamin D status is to measure the concentration of calcidiol in the blood. Calcidiol is measured in nanomoles per litre (nmol/l). To keep things simple, I won't use the units in the text, so when I say the average calcidiol level is 50, I mean 50 nmol/l. Sometimes calcidiol is measured in nanograms per millilitre (ng/ml): to convert nmol/l to ng/ml, divide by two and a half. For example, a calcidiol level of 50 nmol/l is the same as 20 ng/ml. This is not quite precise but good enough for most situations.

Defining vitamin D deficiency

There is a range of values of calcidiol concentration regarded as normal. Deficiency is defined by values that fall below the lower limit of this range and values above the upper limit define toxicity. The normal range of calcidiol is defined as the mean value plus and minus two standard deviations. These values are determined from the analysis of blood samples taken from healthy volunteers. But what if the volunteers don't have a normal level of calcidiol, even though they appear to be healthy?

To illustrate the problem, consider finding the normal range of height. If you were to measure the height of, say, 50 people, you could work out the average (mean) height, which for men would be around 1.75 metres (5 ft 9 in). Suppose you tried to determine average height by measuring 50 short men, you would then think that short men are average and the truly average men would seem to be tall. What if the majority of the population is deficient in vitamin D? Then there is a high risk that at least some, and possibly all, of the 'healthy' volunteers whose calcidiol was used to work out the upper and lower limits will be deficient. There are two meanings of normal – *common* is one, and the other (in this case) is *healthy*, and this is exactly the problem we have as far as vitamin D is concerned. It might be normal to have a calcidiol level of 50 in the sense of being common, but is it normal in the sense of being healthy? There is a growing view among experts that when it comes to vitamin D, perhaps it is normal (common) to be abnormal (unhealthy). In 1971, when the first of these analyses were done for calcidiol, the mean calcidiol for 'normal' volunteers was 68. Until recently, the accepted normal range for calcidiol was between 12.5 and 75. If you had less than 12.5, you were almost certain to suffer from bone disease. At the other end of the range, anything more than 75 was thought to be toxic. But for several years now, vitamin D researchers have been finding that these cut-off points are actually too low.

In the 1980s, when calcidiol was measured in people who get more exposure to sunlight than most people who live in urban–industrial environments, the values were in the 'toxic' range, often between 135 and 225, yet people with these levels were healthy. For example, in Puerto Rico (latitude 18° N) hospital personnel averaged 105, whereas farmers averaged 135 (with the highest level at 225) and in lifeguards in St. Louis, Missouri (latitude 38° N) the average was 163.

Bruce Hollis, of the Medical University of South Carolina, Reinhold Vieth, Director of the Bone and Mineral Laboratory at Mount Sinai Hospital in Toronto, Canada, and other vitamin D experts believe that the values obtained from people in sun-rich environments are normal and the 'normal' values for people in other environments are actually deficient. They believe that the 'healthy' people, whose calcidiol levels were used to define the normal range, were actually suffering from vitamin D deficiency. So why not simply find some more people, such as the lifeguards and the Puerto Rican farmers, who are healthy and not vitamin D deficient and then work out a new normal range? The trouble is, search as long as you like, you will be hard pressed to find many people living at medium and high latitudes, such as Europe and North America, who are getting all the vitamin D they need.

Neil Binkley, of the University of Wisconsin Osteoporosis Clinical Center, attempted to solve this problem by measuring vitamin D levels in Hawaiians. More than ninety volunteers were recruited either from the University of Hawaii at Manoa or by advertising in a skateboard shop in Honolulu. All the participants were young adults who had at least three hours of sunlight exposure per day for at least five days of the week and many did not use sunscreen. Binkley's idea was to find people who get enough sunlight exposure to make all the vitamin D they need so that we can see what level of calcidiol is a normal, healthy level. The results of this study were a surprise – in spite of the high sun exposure, the calcidiol levels were not particularly high. In fact, about half had a calcidiol level lower than 75 – the level that many now regard as the deficiency threshold, in other words about half seemed to be deficient in vitamin D. On the other hand, the highest level was 155 – substantially higher than found in Europe and mainland North America.

But why were the levels lower than expected? It was assumed in this study that sunlight exposure means ultraviolet-B exposure, but the study did not take into account the problem of vog that besets Hawaii. Vog is volcanic smog and is caused by sulphur dioxide emitted from volcanoes. It results in a brown haze, which can reduce the amount of ultraviolet-B at ground level. In Hawaii vog is produced by the volcano Kīlauea, which has been erupting continuously since 1983. So the young adults in the study who were spending a lot of time outdoors may not have been exposed to as much ultraviolet-B as had been assumed. Until we can relate calcidiol specifically to ultraviolet-B irradiance, we cannot find out what the healthy calcidiol level is by using this approach. In the meantime, perhaps the best indicator of the normal, healthy level of calcidiol comes from a study by Martine Luxwolda and colleagues at the University Medical Center, Groningen. They measured calcidiol in 35 Maasai and 24 Hadzabe people living in Tanzania. The Hadzabe are hunter–gatherers and the Maasai are semi-nomadic pastoral people, both living mostly outdoors in a region close to the equator where there is plenty of sunlight all year round. Luxwolda found the average calcidiol to be 115 – around double the average for urban–industrial dwellers and falling into what was until recently thought to be a toxic level.

Since it is not easy to find healthy volunteers, we need an alternative method for deciding what level of calcidiol is healthy. Several studies have been done to determine the level of calcidiol associated with disease. Here we are on more solid ground as the effect of vitamin D deficiency on markers of calcium and bone health is well understood. When calcidiol goes down, you absorb less calcium from your food, so the amount of calcium circulating in your blood also goes down. This fall in calcium kick-starts your parathyroid hormone gland to produce parathyroid hormone. So when you are short on vitamin D, your blood levels of calcidiol and calcium go down while your level of parathyroid hormone goes up. Eventually, bone mineral density lowers and you develop rickets or osteomalacia. If you take vitamin D supplements everything goes into reverse.

To find the lowest level of calcidiol required for normal calcium and bone health, trials have been conducted in which volunteers are given vitamin D supplements or sunlight exposure and the resulting increase in calcidiol levels are related to bone health markers. This has been done for calcium absorption, parathyroid hormone levels and bone mineral density. When calcidiol is at 80, calcium and parathyroid hormone become normal. So, as far as calcium is concerned, 80 seems to be the level to aim at, but bone mineral density continues to rise when calcidiol rises above 80 to more than 100.

All this indicates that if you can get your calcidiol above 100, you should have no problems with your calcium and bone density – but what about other aspects of your health? We now know that vitamin D has many other effects, which include helping the immune system to fight infections but we don't yet know the minimum level of calcidiol necessary to provide for all-round good health. As a result of the recent studies, Bruce Hollis believes that a calcidiol level of below 80 should define vitamin D deficiency. As the evidence that the original normal range is too low has gradually accumulated over recent years, most researchers have agreed that the cut-off points should be higher and most now define deficiency as below 50 and toxicity as above 250. Although the new deficiency cut-off level of 50 is considerably higher than the previous level of 12.5, it still falls short of the average for the Maasai and Hadzabe of 115 and the levels of 80 or more required for good bone health, and I have no doubt that as the research to determine the ideal level of calcidiol continues, the cut-off points will rise again. In the meantime, it is reasonable to say that most people living at mid and high latitudes would benefit from an increase in their vitamin D level.

The recommended intakes

Now we come to the recommended levels. If your vitamin D status is low, the most straightforward thing to do is to take a supplement – but how much? It is not surprising that, since the range of calcidiol levels defined as normal is too low, the recommended intakes are also too low. The problem is not just that they haven't been updated to take into account the current view that calcidiol levels should be higher than previously thought, but the recommended intakes are still mostly based on evidence obtained before it was even possible to measure calcidiol. In addition, the recommendations were designed to prevent rickets, but this fails to take into account the wider role of vitamin D in health. Finally, it has been assumed that we get all the vitamin D we need from sunlight but this is incorrect and does not take into account the fact that we get less sunlight these days. All in all, the recommended intakes need to be updated.

Recommended Dietary Allowances (RDAs) were introduced during the Second World War to ensure that adequate nutrition could be achieved during food shortages. Recommended dietary allowances are defined as: *the average amount of the nutrient, which should be provided per head of a group of people if the needs of practically all members of the group are to be met.* Since we all have different bodies and our lives involve different activities we all have different nutrient needs – some people require more protein than others; some more iron than others – and the word 'recommended' has largely been replaced by the phrase 'reference value' since the values are not meant to apply to individuals. Nevertheless, they are used extensively in providing nutritional recommendations to organisations such as schools, early-years childcare providers and care homes, where the provision of healthy menus is – rightly – taken very seriously.

Most nutrients have a Reference Nutrient Intake or Dietary Reference Intake – an amount thought to be sufficient for most of the population. Reference intakes may be different for men and women or for different age groups. For example, the reference nutrient intake in the UK for calcium per day is 450 milligrams for children aged 4 to 6 years, 1,000 milligrams for boys aged 11 to 18 years, and 800 milligrams for girls aged 11 to 18 years. In addition, 'lower reference nutrient intakes' are set for vitamins and minerals. This is the amount that is enough for a few people who have low needs.

What are the reference nutrient intakes for vitamin D? Essentially there are none because it is assumed you can get all you need from sunlight exposure. In most countries there is, however, a level that is designed to prevent rickets in children and osteomalacia in adults for those who are not exposed to sunlight and it is usually around 5 or 10 micrograms per day, varying with age and between countries. Lower levels are sometimes recommended for babies and children and higher levels for the elderly. Recommendations in the UK, for example, are (at the time of writing) 10 micrograms per day for the elderly and for pregnant and breastfeeding mothers, 8.5 micrograms for infants between birth and 6 months old, and 7 micrograms per day for babies and children up to 3 years old in the winter. For those aged between 4 and 65 years, it is assumed that summer sunlight provides adequate vitamin D. Upper levels are sometimes set to prevent people from taking too much. These are thought to be the highest levels at which anyone can take a daily dose without suffering adverse effects. In the USA, Canada and Europe these are 25 micrograms per day for infants up to 6 months old, rising to 100 micrograms per day for adolescents and adults. In Australia, the upper levels are 5 micrograms for infants and 80 micrograms for all other groups. These recommendations are shown in the table on the next two pages. I give these examples for discussion purposes and ***you must not rely on them for accuracy***. If you need the information, you should check with your government for the recommendations in your country.

The recommendations have been revised upwards slightly in the past ten years to reflect updated knowledge, but they are still based on recommendations determined before it became possible to measure calcidiol, when the only way of measuring vitamin D in people was to see whether they had bone disease or not. If bone disease was not present, it was assumed that there was no vitamin D deficiency. Around the time vitamin D was discovered, rickets in children could be prevented by a spoonful or two of cod-liver oil each day, containing around five micrograms of vitamin D. This is how the amounts of 5 to 15 micrograms came to be regarded as sufficient for people who were unable to get out in the sunlight. These levels were set with the assumption that if you did not display any obvious signs of rickets or osteomalacia, you must be getting sufficient vitamin D. Michael Holick says that the bone disease osteomalacia may be more common than thought as it is not easy to diagnose. It causes aches and pains and he thinks it might sometimes be mistakenly diagnosed as fibromyalgia. But it is now evident that vitamin D is needed for general good health and not just for preventing bone disease.

Examples of recommended intakes of vitamin D

	Micrograms	International Units (IU)
Amount in human milk (per litre)	0.25 to 2	10 to 80
Infants		
Netherlands	10	400
Australia	5	200
USA & Canada	10	400
Children		
Netherlands	10	400
Australia	5	200
USA & Canada	15	600
Pregnant women		
Netherlands	10	400
Australia	5	200
USA & Canada	15	600
Adults		
Netherlands	10	400
Australia (up to 50 yrs)	5	200
Australia (51-70 yrs)	10	400
USA & Canada	15	600
Elderly		
Netherlands	20	800
Australia (over 71 yrs)	15	600
USA & Canada	20	800

Examples of recommended upper levels of intake of vitamin D

	Micrograms	International Units (IU)
Upper level (infants)		
Europe	25	1,000
Australia	5	200
USA & Canada (0-6 mths)	25	1,000
USA & Canada (6-12 mths)	37.5	1,500
Upper level (children)		
Europe (1-10 yrs)	50	2,000
Australia	80	3,200
USA & Canada (1-3 yrs)	62.5	2,500
USA & Canada (4-8 yrs)	75	3,000
Upper level (adolescents)		
Europe (11-18 yrs)	100	4,000
Australia	80	3,200
USA & Canada	100	4,000
Upper level (adults)		
Europe	100	4000
Australia	80	3200
USA & Canada	100	4000

Mothers, babies and children

Do babies and children need more or less vitamin D than adults? On the one hand they are smaller so if they need the same amount per body weight as adults, then of course they need less in total, but on the other hand they are growing and developing new tissues, including bone, so it is possible that they need more vitamin D for their body weight than adults.

The age group of 1 to 5 years is the one in which food preference is most likely to be out of the ordinary. This faddiness is a cause for despair for many mothers. A friend's child went through a phase of eating only bread sticks and yoghurt, another of eating only macaroni cheese, bananas and toast with butter. My mother told me that as a small child, I went through a phase of eating only cheese spreads and evaporated milk and I now wonder if I was trying to raise my vitamin D levels since both these foods were fortified with vitamin D. I wonder if children are faddy eaters because they are trying to get the nutrients they need most at a particular stage of development.

Babies deserve a special mention when it comes to the inadequacy of the recommendations regarding vitamin D, not just because they are small, lovely and need looking after, and not just because their nutritional needs are important for growth and development, but because they are the section of the population most likely to be suffering from – not just a deficiency – but a *complete absence* of vitamin D.

Recommendations are that babies should be kept out of direct sunlight, wear protective clothing and sunscreen outdoors to minimise sunlight exposure. If these recommendations are followed, infants will fail to make any vitamin D in their skin in the first year of their lives and are entirely dependent on milk for their supply of vitamin D. But can they get the recommended amount from milk? All formula milks contain vitamin D but breastfeeding is strongly recommended, so how much do breastfed babies get? A review of studies found that the content of human breast milk ranged from 0.25 to 2 micrograms (10 to 80 IU) per litre. A baby that is not exposed to sunlight and entirely breastfed (both in accordance with official recommendations for the best possible care) would need to drink a staggering 28 litres per day to obtain the 7 micrograms of vitamin D per day recommended in the UK, or 40 litres to obtain the 10 micrograms recommended in North America, if the concentration of vitamin D in the breast milk is at the lower end of the range. Even at the highest concentrations, 3.5 to 5 litres per day would be required. Since a typical intake of milk is half to one litre per day in the first few months, we can conclude that we cannot rely on breast milk as an adequate source of vitamin D for babies.

Supplements are recommended for breastfed babies, but this message rarely gets passed on to mothers. A baby who is breastfed for the first 6 months, shielded from sunlight and not given any vitamin D supplements will have hardly any vitamin D at all.

How much vitamin D is needed for a pregnant woman? Calcitriol (the hormone derived from vitamin D) rises during pregnancy, until it becomes twice as high in late pregnancy than before pregnancy. It is thought that this increase in supply is necessary to meet the demands of the growing and developing foetus. The UK Department of Health, in response to advice from the Scientific Advisory Committee on Nutrition, advises that pregnant women should have 10 micrograms per day of vitamin D yet the National Institute for Health and Clinical Excellence (NICE) recommends (at the time of writing) that healthy pregnant mothers should not be routinely supplemented with vitamin D. Nevertheless, Elina Hyppönen, Reader in Epidemiology and Public Health at the Institute of Child Health in London, has called for pregnant women to be given free supplements of 10 micrograms of vitamin D per day.

It is probable that much more than 10 micrograms is required for a healthy pregnancy but further trials and safety assessments need to be carried out before recommending more. Bruce Hollis and Carol Wagner, both of the Medical University of South Carolina, have spent many years researching vitamin D and are conducting a major study to determine how much vitamin D is needed during pregnancy and lactation. In their study, 350 pregnant women took vitamin D supplements of 10 micrograms, 50 micrograms or 100 micrograms per day in the second and third trimester of pregnancy. The higher supplements were five and ten times the recommended amounts, yet there were no adverse effects.

In summary, no reference nutrient intake for vitamin D is set because it is thought that almost everybody can get enough from sunlight exposure and only a few people need vitamin D in their diet. The recommendations for children do not take into account any additional needs for growth and there are no differences in the recommendations for girls and boys, simply because there is no data available on which to base a decision. The vitamin D requirements of the developing foetus, infant and growing child are not known. Essentially we have to acknowledge that the recommendations are inadequate because no one really knows how much we need. We will now turn to the fact that even when there are recommendations for vitamin D supplements they are not put into practice by health professionals.

Implementation

Every so often there is a flurry of research papers on a particular nutrient and both professionals and the public give this nutrient a lot of attention. A few years ago, for example, vitamin C was promoted as something of a cure-all and then it was the omega-3 essential fatty acids. An unfortunate side effect of this is that other nutrients tend to be overlooked, cloaked in the shadow of whatever the current celebrity nutrient is. Vitamin D was in shadow for several decades. Many studies have shown fish oils to be beneficial and these beneficial effects are attributed to the omega-3 fatty acids, but the role of vitamin D is usually ignored, even though fish and fish oils are also a rich source of vitamin D. It is quite possible that the key to the power of fish oils as a good source of nutrition is either omega-3 or vitamin D or the combination of both.

There is a danger that, as we become more aware of its importance, vitamin D will become the celebrity nutrient and will be seen as a panacea with the ability to cure all ills, while other nutrients fade into obscurity, only to rear their heads in 20 years' time when we are all suffering from some awful disease caused by a severe deficiency of whatever it is. That time seems a long way off yet. For now, if you read any general nutritional text about vitamins you will find that vitamin D hardly gets a mention.

Vitamin D was not considered in the 1990s when the routine provision of cod-liver oil to pregnant women was stopped because of concern about vitamin A toxicity. It was not considered when the sun protection campaigns advised people to stay out of the sunlight. It is still not considered when advising people to have low fat dairy products or to switch from whole milk to semi-skimmed or skimmed milk (not even for growing children).

When I started writing this book it was impossible to buy vitamin D from a shop in any form except as part of a multivitamin preparation, with calcium, or as cod-liver oil. To buy vitamin D as a single supplement, you needed to go to a specialist health shop or a website and there was little choice as to the formulation or dose. The maximum dose you could buy was 10 micrograms and there was no vitamin D supplement designed for children and for babies. This situation has improved since, but there is still limited choice and availability so that if you want to ensure that you and your family has the recommended amount of vitamin D to prevent bone disease, you will not find it easy to find a bottle of capsules, chews or drops that suits you. I do hope that in future it will be possible to go into any pharmacy or drugstore and find an array of vitamin D supplements of various doses and in different formulations.

It has always been assumed that most of the vitamin D we need can be obtained from sunlight and supplements are only necessary in certain circumstances. While it is true to say that we get most of our vitamin D from sunlight, this is not the same as saying that we get most of the vitamin D that *we need* from sunlight. Most of us living in urban-industrial societies are certainly not getting enough vitamin D from sunlight. The assumption that you can make all the vitamin D you need when in sunlight has led to a failure to appreciate the importance of diet and supplements as a source of vitamin D.

According to the scholarly textbooks, vitamin D supplementation is recommended for breastfed babies, the elderly and those in institutions. In practice, such supplementation is almost never carried out. During stays in institutions such as hospitals or nursing homes, patients are not given vitamin D supplements, vitamin D-rich foods, or exposure to sunlight. Indeed, if you want to become even more vitamin D deficient than you already are, what better place to go than a place that is supposed to improve your health – a hospital – where you will be undernourished, get no supplements and no sunlight? Of the many elderly people I know, only one has been given a vitamin D supplement (for the treatment of osteoporosis) and it was no more than the recommended 10 micrograms, even though she had bone disease.

Why is the official guidance not carried out? One reason is the celebrity effect mentioned above – people simply forgot about vitamin D. If you go to your physician – even with a bone problem such as a fracture or bone pain – the chances are it will simply not occur to him or her to check your vitamin D status. Nor will you have your vitamin D checked if you have been housebound by illness and unable to get outdoors. Nor will you have your vitamin D checked if you have suffered from burns or a skin condition that might reduce your ability to make vitamin D. Vitamin D testing has not yet become a standard piece of kit in the physician's toolbox, but another reason that the professionals are reluctant to recommend supplements is the fear of vitamin D toxicity.

Vitamin D is a poison

What happens if you take too much vitamin D? Excessive vitamin D is diagnosed by its effect on calcium levels. Calcium levels inside the cells are used to control many different functions, including the contraction of the heart, so any excess can be dangerous. The symptoms of vitamin D toxicity are lethargy, headaches, abdominal pain, thirst, nausea and vomiting. In babies, it can cause irritability, feeding difficulties and constipation. Toxicity has been studied in rats, rabbits, dogs, pigs, cows, horses and humans and no differences have been found among animals – the amount that is too high in one animal is also too high in another.

Some cases of toxicity in humans occurred when patients were given vitamin D as a treatment. Between the 1930s and 1950s it was common to give patients large doses of ergocalciferol (vitamin D_2), or a pharmaceutical version of it (called ertron), as a treatment for rickets, arthritis and other conditions (vitamin D was a celebrity nutrient in those days). Other cases of toxicity occurred when food was accidentally fortified with the wrong amount of vitamin D and others when supplements contained more than was shown on the label – in one case the supplement contained 430 times the amount it should have had. In the UK in the 1950s, there were reports that vitamin D overdoses caused by incorrect food fortification caused a condition in babies called infantile hypercalcaemia. You can read more about this in the notes.

By the late 1950s, there were understandable concerns that high doses of vitamin D were causing serious problems. As a result, it was agreed at a Medical Research Council Conference on Hypercalcaemia held in 1957 that 10 micrograms of vitamin D was adequate throughout infancy and the levels of vitamin D in national cod-liver oil and fortified foods were later reduced. For the rest of the twentieth century, the fear of widespread poisoning by vitamin D limited the recommendations regarding vitamin D intake.

This concern was not limited to the UK. In other countries, fortification was lowered. In Finland, the recommended intake of vitamin D for infants was 100 to 125 micrograms per day from the mid-1950s until 1964, but was reduced in 1964 to 50 micrograms per day, then again in 1975 to 25 micrograms per day and again, in 1992, to 10 micrograms per day. And yet, no cases of infantile hypercalcaemia were recorded in Finland, even at the highest intakes. But at the end of the twentieth century it was thought that anything above 50 micrograms per day was toxic and a calcidiol level above 100 was a sign of vitamin D poisoning.

How much further have we got in our understanding of whether we can have too much vitamin D and, if so, exactly how much is too much? Most reports of vitamin D poisoning occurred before it was possible to measure calcidiol in the body and it is now much easier to study the effect of vitamin D intake on the level of calcidiol and its derivative hormone calcitriol. Recent studies that have done so have cast doubt upon the earlier studies that formed the basis of decisions about the recommended intakes and the limits are being revised in the light of more recent studies. There can now be no doubt that the early studies and reports of hypercalcaemia in babies – in whom the amounts of vitamin D actually ingested were not known – were misleading.

Nevertheless it is known that calcitriol is poisonous in excess. *Solanum glaucophyllum* is the waxyleaf nightshade, a flowering plant found in South America. This plant causes a disease called enteque seco (also called enzootic calcinosis), which results in emaciation, spinal arching, stiffness and death in grazing animals that eat it. The cause is an overdose of calcitriol causing excessive calcium that becomes deposited in the blood vessels, heart, lungs, tendons and ligaments. The disease has also occurred in milk goats in Switzerland where the poisonous plant is yellow oat grass. The calcitriol is found in the form of glycosides in the leaves of the plant.

It is important to understand that this disease results from an ingestion of the hormone *calcitriol,* not cholecalciferol, ergocalciferol or calcidiol. The amount of the hormone calcitriol that we have in our bloodstream is normally tightly controlled, but in enzootic calcinosis there is no control and the affected animals end up with far too much active calcitriol floating around in their blood causing problems in just about every part of their body. This serves as a reminder that calcitriol is a hormone and, like all hormones, it can be highly dangerous in excessive amounts.

Of course, any substance can be poisonous in the wrong amount. You can compare vitamin D to warfarin, which in large doses is used to kill rodents, but in small doses is used as a medicine – an anticoagulant to treat thrombosis and other blood coagulation conditions. The difference is that, unlike warfarin, vitamin D is essential for everybody's health and we must understand how much we need and how much is too much. We also need to understand how vitamin D is absorbed and processed in the body, so that we can understand how excessive doses can be harmful.

Vitamin D in the body

When vitamin D is absorbed from food it goes into a little vehicle, like a bus, called a chylomicron and is then transferred on to a smaller vehicle, like a taxi, called the vitamin D-binding protein. When we make our own vitamin D it goes directly on to the vitamin D-binding protein. This home-made vitamin D tends to stay in our bloodstream for longer than the vitamin D we eat and this seems to be because while the vitamin D is in chylomicrons muscles, liver or adipose tissue can easily take it up. It has also been noted that the more fat you have, the more vitamin D is stored. For this reason, Michael Holick advises that people who are overweight or obese need more vitamin D than people of normal weight. Robert Heaney argues that it is a matter of dilution – a bigger body has more tissue and requires more vitamin D to maintain the same concentration and it is the concentration that is important. Whatever the cause, experts agree that people who are overweight require more vitamin D than people who are of normal weight and the bigger you are, the more vitamin D you need.

Cholecalciferol, whether it is home-made or absorbed from food is taken to the liver to be converted into calcidiol, which also travels through the bloodstream on the vitamin D-binding protein taxi. There is enough vitamin D-binding protein to carry much more vitamin D than is normally carried. Even so, the amount of vitamin D-binding protein increases in pregnancy and it is possible that this is so that more vitamin D can be provided for the baby. Some of the calcidiol is converted to the hormone calcitriol. It seems that this conversion can be done in the cells that need it – i.e. for local use – but the kidney is the 'national' producer of calcitriol.

It is clear from enzootic calcinosis that it is the hormone calcitriol that is responsible for the high levels of calcium that result from vitamin D toxicity. Normally, calcitriol is very carefully regulated so that there is always the same amount in the blood, even if calcidiol is high. Calcitriol concentration is mainly a reflection of calcium deficiency. When calcium is low, higher calcitriol is needed to allow more calcium to be absorbed and retained, but if calcitriol increases when calcium is not low, excessive amounts of calcium can accumulate. The reason that calcitriol is controlled so carefully is precisely *because* too much calcitriol is dangerous, whereas cholecalciferol and calcidiol do not act as hormones (as far as we know) and do not need to be so carefully controlled.

So how do high levels of cholecalciferol and calcidiol lead to hypercalcaemia? Based on a variety of studies, calcidiol has to be in excess of 375 to cause hypercalcaemia – note this is considerably higher than the level of 250 now thought to be the maximum – and much higher than the 100 that was previously thought to be too high. Accidental overdoses of vitamin D, in which calcidiol was measured, were well above this amount – more than 700 and the highest being 1,652. It is still not understood how high calcidiol with normal calcitriol causes hypercalcaemia, but it might be because somehow you end up with too much calcitriol in the cells, even when it is at a normal level in the blood, or it is possible that calcidiol can act like calcitriol when it is present in very high amounts.

Another way in which vitamin D poisoning can occur is if there is a problem with the enzymes that are involved in vitamin D metabolism. A liver enzyme is necessary to remove vitamin D, for example, and if this enzyme is not working properly for some reason, you will not be able to remove vitamin D properly and may suffer from vitamin D poisoning even at low intakes. The enzyme is the product of a gene called *CYP24A1*. It converts calcitriol into a water-soluble form of vitamin D called calcitroic acid – this form can be excreted. On the other hand, if you have too much of this enzyme, you remove it too quickly and will need more vitamin D to avoid becoming deficient.

There is no doubt that there can be too much of a good thing and once a deficiency is rectified – once you are vitamin D-replete – there is no benefit to be had in increasing the dose any further. It was understandable that practitioners got carried away with giving high doses of vitamin D to treat disease and fortifying foods to improve the nation's health. But once it was realised that too much vitamin D could be harmful, the situation went into reverse. Subsequently, vitamin D almost got forgotten and everyone was scared of toxicity. Now the pendulum is beginning to swing back towards the middle as we realise that this fear of toxicity has resulted in a deficiency that is much more profound and widespread than we realised. There will then be a danger of going too far back again and causing widespread vitamin D poisoning. But we have the advantage over previous generations of being able to measure calcidiol and monitor the effects of increasing the dosage. It is still important to ensure that we do not get carried away with the idea that vitamin D is a cure-all and that just because a little helps we should try taking a lot more. There is a spectrum of vitamin D status ranging from deficiency to toxicity and we need to be somewhere in the middle. Until we know more about vitamin D, perhaps we should remember the wisdom of Paracelsus:

'Alle Ding' sind Gift, und nichts ohn' Gift; allein die Dosis macht, daß ein Ding kein Gift ist.'

'What is there that is not poison? All things are poison and nothing is without poison. Solely the dose determines that a thing is not a poison.'

Phillip von Hohenheim, aka Paracelsus, alchemist-physician 1493–1541.

Recent studies of vitamin D requirements

So far, we have established that we need more vitamin D than previously thought because, in the past, the amount of calcidiol thought to be normal was too low, the recommended intakes were too low and the amount thought to be toxic was too low. Today we have the ability to relate the intake of vitamin D to the amount of calcidiol circulating in the blood and are beginning to have a better understanding of how the body deals with vitamin D. Reinhold Vieth, Robert Heaney, Bruce Hollis and other vitamin D scientists, have conducted studies in which volunteers given vitamin D supplements have been carefully monitored to see how their levels of calcidiol are affected. These studies are still few and far between and are not sufficient to tell us *exactly* how much vitamin D you and I need to take to stay healthy (or to maintain our weight) but they do allow us to make some conclusions, as follows.

Larger doses

The dose–response studies have shown that larger doses can be taken safely in the short term. In Robert Heaney's study, one group of volunteers took 125 micrograms per day and another took 250 micrograms per day without any ill effects and in a study by Carol Wagner and Bruce Hollis, women who were breastfeeding took 160 micrograms per day with no ill effects for either mother or baby.

In some studies, the volunteers were given a single large dose of vitamin D rather than the usual daily capsule or tablet. In one study by Robert Heaney and his colleagues, 30 healthy participants received one oral dose of 100,000 IU of cholecalciferol and their calcidiol levels were measured regularly for 112 days. This dose was the equivalent of 2,500 micrograms, which over the whole period works out to roughly 25 micrograms per day and proved to be safe and effective at raising calcidiol. There is interest in giving a single large dose intermittently as it can be easier and cheaper than taking capsules every day and overcomes problems for people who have difficulty in taking daily doses.

It is important to remember that in these studies the volunteers were closely supervised and tested for adverse effects. Furthermore, these trials only lasted for weeks or months (Heaney's study lasted for 5 months, for example) and we don't yet know the consequences of taking these amounts for *years*.

Recommended intakes do not treat deficiency

In most of the studies, volunteers took a daily vitamin D supplement of different amounts. The results show, without doubt, that the recommended 5 or 10 micrograms per day is not enough to reverse vitamin D deficiency. Even more troubling, they indicate that these amounts are not enough to stop calcidiol levels falling in the winter.

Robert Heaney analysed the results of a study involving 67 men and calculated that, on average, one microgram of vitamin D caused a rise of less than one unit (nmol/l) of calcidiol. This has been confirmed by others who performed similar studies (and more about Robert Heaney's review of supplementation studies can be found in the notes). Given that the average calcidiol level is under 50 in the UK, for example, to get up to 80 (the minimum required for normal levels of parathyroid hormone and calcium) we would need to increase it by 30. It is evident that a supplement of 10 micrograms per day would not be able to do this and would not make a noticeable difference to vitamin D status. Even the large single dose described above did not result in a calcidiol level of 80 in some of the participants. It should be noted that although 10 micrograms makes little difference in adults, it does have a significant effect in babies.

In the light of these studies, in 2007 no less than 13 vitamin D scientists wrote an editorial in the *American Journal of Clinical Nutrition* entitled: *The urgent need to recommend an intake of vitamin D that is effective,* in which they argued that higher daily intakes of vitamin D were required. In a report in 2010 the Institute of Medicine in the USA duly increased their Dietary Reference Intakes for vitamin D (e.g. the Recommended Dietary Allowance was increased from 5 micrograms per day to 15 micrograms per day for most adults) but this increase was not enough to satisfy many clinicians and scientists who responded with fierce criticism of the report.

Some people need more vitamin D than others

While you are taking a supplement, you may also be making some vitamin D, and the amount of vitamin D you make differs for the many reasons outlined in the previous chapter. To avoid one of these complications, most of the studies were conducted in winter. Even so, all of the studies found that the amount by which calcidiol levels change in response to supplementation is variable from one person to another.

Aside from the vitamin D that you make, there are other possible sources of variation in the way that the body deals with the supplement. There are differences between individuals in the amount of vitamin D-binding protein and the enzymes that process vitamin D. People with variants in the gene for the vitamin D-binding protein, for example, tend to have lower calcidiol levels even when given the same amount of vitamin D supplements.

In general, it seems that the lower your calcidiol to start with, the more you need to achieve a given level. It also appears that older people need more than younger and people who are overweight need more than people of normal weight. We know little about the other factors that might influence the response to supplementation in different people. It is clear that even if you and I take exactly the same amount of a vitamin D supplement, we won't necessarily end up with the same level of calcidiol.

Prevention vs. treatment

We need more vitamin D to raise calcidiol status than to maintain it. The recommended amounts of 5, 10 or 15 micrograms per day are not enough to raise calcidiol by any appreciable amount. This means they are not enough to treat vitamin D deficiency.

We need to be careful when thinking about how much vitamin D we need to distinguish between our regular daily needs and the amount we need to get our calcidiol from a deficient level up to a healthy level. This confusion between the maintenance of healthy calcidiol – in other words, *prevention* of deficiency – and *treatment* of deficiency, partly explains the conflicting reports you might hear about vitamin D. Many trials of vitamin D have involved giving participants a fixed amount of a vitamin D supplement – often 10 or 20 micrograms – and have little or no effect. These trials are doomed to failure as the participants who have vitamin D deficiency at the start, still have vitamin D deficiency at the end of the trial. It could be that the recommended amounts of 10 or 15 micrograms are sufficient to maintain a healthy vitamin D status if it serves only as a top-up because you get most of the vitamin D you need by making it in the sunlight and if you take it *every day of your life.* The trouble is that few people today have obtained the vitamin D they need from sunlight exposure and few people have taken a vitamin D supplement regularly throughout their lives. This means most of us need to get a lot more vitamin D than we are getting now, one way or another, to get ourselves out of vitamin D poverty.

Vitamin D in the diet

Some studies have worked out how much vitamin D people get from their food. These studies are based upon the amount of vitamin D as measured in food, but these measurements may not be terribly reliable. One way of assessing whether a food is a good source of vitamin D is to see whether it increases the amount of calcidiol in people who eat it. Even if we know a food contains vitamin D, it doesn't necessarily mean that we will benefit from it. In Chapter 5 I discuss absorption of food and how we can get more magnesium from kale than from spinach, even though spinach contains more magnesium than kale – *we are what we absorb.* Does the vitamin D in the food we eat get into our body – is it bioavailable? For example, do people who eat lots of fish have higher levels of calcidiol than people who never eat fish?

A few studies have examined the effects of certain foods in the diet on calcidiol levels. One studied Korean men and found that those who ate more fish had higher levels of calcidiol. Another found that people who ate more meat were less likely to suffer from rickets and osteomalacia. In another study, people who ate wild chanterelle mushrooms had a slightly lower increase in calcidiol than those who had vitamin D supplements, while those who had neither supplements nor mushrooms in the study experienced a fall in calcidiol. Elderly Japanese women who ate fish more than four times per week had calcidiol concentrations of just over 60, higher by 10 than those who ate less fish, and those who ate eggs more than once per week had higher calcidiol concentrations than those who did not eat eggs at all. In a study of 613 adults aged 18 to 65 years in the Netherlands, the consumption of fatty fish was a significant determinant of calcidiol level, making a higher contribution than supplements.

Unfortunately, there are only a few of these kinds of studies in which the levels of calcidiol are related to diet. Other studies rely on estimating vitamin D intakes from the food composition data. Some of these are detailed below:

- In a study of Irish adults, intakes were 4.2 micrograms on average, with men having 4.4 compared to 4.0 in women. Meat and meat products, fish and fish products and eggs were the main contributors.

- Among people who had a Mediterranean diet in Northwest Spain, intakes were 2.2 micrograms on average.

- Japanese women in a nursing home had an average intake of 7.1 micrograms. The main contributors were fish (more than 90 per cent), mushrooms, eggs and meat.

- In the National Diet and Nutrition Survey in Britain, average intakes were between 2 and 4 micrograms for adults with older adults having higher intakes than younger adults.

- Other studies have shown that in Germany the mean daily vitamin D intake is 3 to 4 micrograms per day; in the Netherlands, below 5 micrograms; and in Finland, 4.7 to 5.6 micrograms. In Finnish children, where most babies have vitamin D supplements, intakes started at an average of 11 micrograms per day, but fell to 4 micrograms by the age of three years, mainly because supplements were stopped by that age.

One thing is clear: in all these studies the amounts of vitamin D obtained from diet are tiny and most people do not get as much as the recommended daily intakes (low as they are) from food.

I would not be surprised if future studies will reveal that the few micrograms we are talking about here are miniscule amounts. It is perhaps worth thinking about just how small these amounts are. A milligram is a thousandth of a gram and a microgram is a millionth of a gram. To illustrate, a spoonful of sugar weighs 4 grams and to obtain 10 micrograms of sugar you would need to divide the spoonful by four hundred thousand. The recommended intakes of most micronutrients are measured in milligrams or hundreds of micrograms. Only a few nutrients apart from vitamin D are measured in smaller quantities. These are trace elements (e.g. the average daily intake of cobalt is 12 micrograms per day), vitamin B_{12} (the average daily intake is around 5 micrograms per day) and vitamin B_7 (average intake around 30 micrograms per day). Vitamin D is unique, however, because we can make it in our skin. It would not be surprising if we can make hundreds of micrograms in our skin and only need small amounts in our diets as a top-up. Similarly, the amounts in food could be low because the living things that we eat can provide their daily vitamin D needs by making it in sunlight. If so, we might need hundreds of micrograms in supplements to compensate for the lack of sunlight in winter.

The trouble is that although we now have many studies relating supplement intake to calcidiol levels, there have been only a few studies that relate sunlight – or specifically ultraviolet-B exposure – to calcidiol levels, and these are not sufficient to make any conclusions. I have no doubt that when more of these studies are done, they will add to the evidence that we need much more vitamin D to be healthy than was previously believed.

With regard to toxicity, even if we can make hundreds of micrograms of vitamin D in our skin each day, we don't yet know for sure that it is possible to safely compensate for the times we lack ultraviolet-B by taking hundreds of micrograms as supplements. In this respect, we still have knowledge gaps to be filled:

- We don't know much about the role of vitamin D in the developing foetus and the effects of supplementation of more than 10 micrograms during pregnancy (although recent trials suggest ten times this amount is healthy for both mother and baby).

- We don't know the effects of long-term supplementation of 50 micrograms or more. Recent trials have indicated that 100 micrograms is safe but the trials lasted only for weeks or months – what about years?

- We don't know about any effects of vitamin D toxicity that are not related to calcium.

- We have no means of identifying those people who have problems with metabolising vitamin D.

Assessing vitamin D deficiency

This chapter began by discussing the difficulties in defining vitamin D deficiency. Many researchers now define deficiency by a level of calcidiol below 50 and some use the term insufficiency to mean vitamin D levels that are less than healthy but distinct from the deficiency levels associated with bone disease. Robert Heaney argues that you either have enough vitamin D to be healthy or you don't – any less is deficient and there is no need to have a category of insufficiency. We can understand the problem if we imagine trying to determine the healthy level of body weight by taking measurements of the general population *today* in countries where the majority are overweight. It is now normal (common) to be overweight. We defined healthy levels of weight before overweight became prevalent, but we were not able to define healthy levels of vitamin D before deficiency became common. We now have the means to measure vitamin D status, but without having an established definition of vitamin D deficiency it is impossible to estimate the extent of vitamin D deficiency in a population. Nor can we assess trends in vitamin D deficiency because we have only recently been able to measure it. I know of just one study that has looked at this question. Adit Ginde, Director of Research at the University of Colorado School of Medicine found that the average calcidiol level measured in the National Health and Nutrition Examination Survey in the USA fell from 75 to 60 between surveys taken in 1988–1994 and 2001–2004. What else can we learn from measurements of calcidiol in the population?

Calcidiol is seasonal

Many of us follow a similar diet throughout the year but the amount of sunlight exposure is very dependent on the season. Elina Hyppönen and Chris Power at the Institute of Child Health took month-by-month measurements of calcidiol between September 2002 and March 2004 from more than seven thousand 45-year-olds in the UK. The calcidiol levels were at their highest at the end of the summer in August, September and October and gradually fell until they reached their lowest in the winter and early spring in January, February and March, then gradually rose again. The calcidiol levels taken in September were about twice the levels taken in January. Similarly, in the 1980s, children in Germany (latitude around 50° N) had levels of 84 in summer but only 43 in winter.

This seasonal variation indicates that we depend on sunlight for our vitamin D and not on food. If most of our vitamin D could be obtained through our diet, we would not see this variation. It confirms that we are deficient in winter and need to get vitamin D from our diet, supplements or artificial ultraviolet, just to maintain a steady level of vitamin D. At the moment it appears that anyone who lives in a temperate climate might experience a fall in vitamin D *every year*.

Even at their lowest levels in January when there is no or little ultraviolet-B, the average level of calcidiol measured in the study in the UK was above 30 which suggests that it is not *just* a reflection of recent intake and synthesis, unless almost everybody takes enough from their diet to keep it above 30, which seems improbable. More likely, this level is maintained by taking from the body stores.

Eric Lawson, of the Dunn Nutritional Laboratory at Cambridge, found a correlation between calcidiol levels in summer and winter. In other words, the higher your vitamin D in the summer, the higher it will be in the winter. The reason is that some of the vitamin D you get in the peak of vitamin D supply in the summer is stored away for the winter. In fact, Ann Webb and colleagues, in a study of 125 adults in Greater Manchester, found that to maintain calcidiol concentrations above 50 in February it was necessary to have a calcidiol level in September of at least 75 in women and 85 in men.

Other factors

The vitamin D status of various groups of people has been measured in other studies. In addition to the seasonal variation, it has been noted that, in general, calcidiol varied with clothing. For example, a study conducted in Turkey (latitude 39° N) found the average level was 56 in people wearing clothing that exposes the face, neck, hands and arms, but in people who wore traditional clothing with only the hands and face exposed it was only 32, and in people wearing traditional Islamic-style clothing which covers the whole body including hands and face it was as low as 9. In Denmark, Muslim women had levels of only 17.5 even though they had an oral intake of 13.5 micrograms (which is higher than the recommended intake). Calcidiol also varies with skin tone. In the UK in the 1990s, for example, dark-skinned children of Asian descent had winter levels of 36 compared to fair-skinned children whose winter levels were 52. Several American studies comparing calcidiol in ethnic groups have found that calcidiol tends to be highest in non-Hispanic whites and lowest in non-Hispanic blacks, with other groups having intermediate values. In a study of elderly people in Boston, for example, the percentages of people with calcidiol levels less than 50 at the end of the summer were 30 per cent of whites, 43 per cent of Hispanics and 84 per cent of blacks.

The extent of vitamin D deficiency

In the National Diet and Nutrition Survey, adults in the UK between 19 and 64 years old were surveyed for a year between July 2000 and June 2001.

The average calcidiol levels were 48.3 in men and 49.6 in women. Only 2 per cent of men and 3 per cent of women had levels over 100. There was of course a marked variation with the seasons, with just above a quarter having a calcidiol level below 50 in summer but three quarters in winter.

According to these figures, only a small minority of people have sufficient levels of vitamin D. The same survey measured body mass index and more than half were overweight and about a quarter were obese. In short, 57 per cent of men and 54 per cent of women had low levels of vitamin D in their blood (defined as below 50), and 66 per cent of men and 53 per cent of women were overweight. But if we define a healthy calcidiol level as 100 and above, these data suggest that only 2 to 3 per cent have healthy levels. Could this mean that only 2 to 3 per cent of this population are healthy?

Overweight has been associated with a multitude of illnesses and medical conditions. It is usually assumed that overweight is the cause and that if you lose weight you will be less likely to suffer from them. But it is possible that vitamin D deficiency causes both overweight and these other conditions. Putting aside overweight and the metabolic syndrome for a moment, there are essentially three ways in which vitamin D deficiency might possibly cause disease. The first is the classical mechanism that without vitamin D calcium absorption is impaired, leading to a lack of calcium. This causes problems that are most obvious in the formation of bone, causing rickets and osteomalacia. Secondly, the hormone calcitriol, which is derived from vitamin D, is a gene regulator and it is a reasonable assumption that vitamin D deficiency can impair the development of cells. If so, it could conceivably cause problems in any part of the body when the tissues do not develop or are not renewed properly. Thirdly, it is now known that vitamin D is involved in the immune system where it helps to kill infections and acts as an anti-inflammatory agent.

All this means that, conceivably, just about any disease could be more likely to develop when there is a lack of vitamin D. There are now thousands of studies that demonstrate a link between vitamin D deficiency and various diseases of different types, including cancers, autoimmune and infectious diseases. Many of the studies found that patients with a disease tend to have lower levels of calcidiol than people without the disease; some found that patients with lower calcidiol are less likely to recover, and others that a disease is more common in regions with less sunlight than others.

With the exception of rickets, osteomalacia and fracture risk there is, as yet, no evidence that vitamin D supplementation can prevent or cure these diseases and until this evidence is produced, the link remains speculative in every case. *Vitamin D Deficiency* is not recorded as a cause of death. It would appear that vitamin D deficiency, like any malnourished state, might render us more susceptible to disease, but it does not seem to be a direct *cause* of any disease. Even rickets and osteomalacia – the so-called classic diseases caused by vitamin D deficiency – can result from lack of calcium rather than from lack of vitamin D. However, we are still in an early learning stage when it comes to vitamin D (and even in our understanding of the causes of disease). That vitamin D deficiency underlies a significant proportion of the ill health that exists today has not yet been proven, but the weight of evidence so far suggests it is a realistic possibility, and that raising the vitamin D status of the population could potentially alleviate a great deal of suffering. It is clear that levels of calcidiol regarded as healthy have been too low and need to be increased, that we obtain little vitamin D from food and that current recommendations do not prevent population-wide falls in calcidiol in the winter every year.

The previous chapter showed that the amount of vitamin D we get from sunlight and food has been overestimated. This chapter has shown that the amount we need to be healthy has been underestimated. Combine the two and it is easy now to see how vitamin D deficiency crept up on us while we weren't looking.

We were complacent that unless there are outbreaks of rickets in our children, there was no need to worry. It is not at all surprising that the amount of vitamin D we need for good health was underestimated, because before 1980 we had no idea that vitamin D was involved in the immune system. As far as we knew its only biological action was on bone and the only way of measuring vitamin D in people was by looking at their bones. We thought that an absence of rickets meant an absence of vitamin D deficiency. In addition, there is the problem that we have been getting less vitamin D in our food and have been making less in the sunlight.

But while these facts account for the failure to *recognise* vitamin D deficiency, do they explain the cause of the current vitamin D deficiency epidemic? Suppose for a moment, that 5 or 10 micrograms really was enough for most people 50 years ago, but, for some reason, it is no longer and that a higher dose that might have been toxic 50 years ago might now be the minimum necessary for good health?

If vitamin D deficiency is the primary cause of overweight it would certainly explain the complexities in the epidemiology – why overweight is higher in some regions and population groups than others and so on. How vitamin D deficiency accounts for these complexities is explored in Chapter 8 Weightonomics. But can it account for the huge increase in prevalence of overweight in the past few decades? If we accept that vitamin D deficiency is the cause of overweight, then the massive rise in the prevalence of overweight suggests that there has been an equally massive fall in vitamin D availability that needs to be explained. Chapter 3 considers the role of recent atmospheric changes.

Chapter 3

Atmospheric Obstruction

VITAMIN D IS THE sunshine vitamin and we assume that sunny places must be ultraviolet-rich so people who live in low latitude countries must get plenty of vitamin D. Whether we get our vitamin D by making it in our skin, from the food we eat, or in the form of supplements, it was originally made using ultraviolet. If there is no ultraviolet there can be no vitamin D. Although, intuitively, sunny places in the world should be getting more ultraviolet than wintry places, it is not necessarily so. The two studies from Iran and India, described below, show that even in low latitude countries pollution can result in low calcidiol levels.

- *In India,* Kishore Agarwal and colleagues at St. Stephen's Hospital, Delhi measured calcidiol in babies and toddlers living in Mori Gate and compared the levels to babies and toddlers living in Gurgaon, a less polluted area on the outskirts of Delhi. Delhi (latitude 28° N) is a highly polluted city and in Mori Gate the pollution haze is visible.
- The researchers found that the babies and toddlers from Mori Gate had only half the calcidiol levels of those from Gurgaon.

- *In Iran,* Farhad Hosseinpanah and colleagues of the Obesity Research Centre in Tehran compared calcidiol levels in 100 women living in the east of Tehran with calcidiol levels in 100 women living in Ghazvin city. Tehran (latitude 35° N) is the capital city of Iran and has a higher level of pollution than in Ghazvin. As a result, Tehran has lower ground-level ultraviolet-B than Ghazvin.
- The women in Tehran had lower calcidiol and higher weight than the women in Ghazvin.

Ultraviolet-B photons have to negotiate a veritable obstacle course before they get to our skin and most of the obstacles are in the lower part of the atmosphere. Substances in the atmosphere can absorb or scatter ultraviolet-B before it gets to us on the surface of the Earth. Sometimes you can see things in the air that absorb ultraviolet. If you can see haze, fog, vog, smog or smoke, it is almost certain to be blocking some of the ultraviolet. The chances are that when the air looks clear, the sky looks blue and you can feel the heat of the sun, there is some ultraviolet getting to you, but there is no guarantee. You cannot see or feel ultraviolet – you see visible light not ultraviolet – and, most of the time, you cannot see the substances in the atmosphere that absorb ultraviolet. The only way to tell how much ultraviolet you are getting down on the street, if any, is by using an instrument that can measure ultraviolet. This chapter examines what we know about these ultraviolet-absorbing substances, how they affect ground-level ultraviolet-B and asks whether they have they changed in recent decades. In essence, this chapter asks what at first sight seems a ridiculous question: is bad air the cause of weight gain?

Ozone

It might be true to say that vitamin D was overlooked in the late twentieth century but the same cannot be said for ultraviolet radiation. On the contrary, it received a lot of attention because stratospheric ozone thinning put scientists on the alert for increasing ultraviolet.

Most ultraviolet reaching the Earth is absorbed by ozone in the stratosphere – the ozone layer – before it reaches the lower part of the atmosphere. Ozone is a molecule consisting of three oxygen atoms, whereas the oxygen gas that we need to breathe consists of two atoms. Ozone is formed by ultraviolet radiation interacting with oxygen, which then absorbs ultraviolet radiation to form oxygen again. This turning from ozone to oxygen and back again is normally in balance in a continual cycle so that the stratosphere (from 10 km to 50 km altitude) contains a constant amount of ozone overall.

Much of what we know about the atmosphere and how its composition affects ultraviolet comes from studies of the depletion of the ozone layer, which was expected to cause a dramatic increase in ultraviolet on the ground. Problems with the depletion of the ozone layer were first reported in 1985. It was apparently caused by the reaction of ozone with chlorine from the chlorofluorocarbons (CFCs) widely used in aerosol sprays, refrigerators and solvents. Depletion was expected to result in an increase in ultraviolet radiation at the Earth's surface since less would be absorbed in the stratosphere. It was feared that this would lead to increasing skin cancer, eye cataracts and damage to the immune system in humans, as well as other detrimental biological consequences. It was vital, therefore, that efforts were made to monitor stratospheric ozone and its effects on ultraviolet radiation.

Stratospheric ozone was measured by TOMS, the Total Ozone Mapping Spectrophotometer, flown on the Nimbus-7 satellite between 1978 and 1993 by NASA. The instrument measured total ozone column and produced data for ultraviolet radiation taking into account humidity, rainfall, temperature or elevation. It did not take into account pollutants at low altitude. The measurements were collected mostly before the time when ozone depletion was at its most severe. The Ozone Monitoring Instrument on NASA's Aura satellite has since superseded the TOMS instrument. Overall these measurements suggest that ultraviolet radiation increased during the period that the ozone layer thinned. So it would appear that ultraviolet-B increased as a result of lower stratospheric ozone. The Montreal Protocol in September 1987 (and its subsequent amendments) was an agreement between the EEC and countries elsewhere to phase out the use of CFCs. As a result, the concentration of chlorine in the atmosphere stopped increasing and the ozone has been recovering since the late 1990s.

If we assume that ozone reduction results directly in an increase in ultraviolet-B, we would expect ultraviolet-B to have increased since the 1970s and to continue to be higher than before 1970 for several decades yet until the stratospheric ozone completely recovers. If so, with more ultraviolet-B available, we should have been able to make more vitamin D, so how can it be possible that vitamin D deficiency has been increasing to the extent that it is epidemic? One explanation is that we get less from our food and supplements than in the past. It is also quite possible that as ultraviolet-B has increased we have been less exposed to it for the reasons given earlier in Chapter 1 Helpful Radiation – we spend more time indoors and covered with clothes and sunscreen. Even if the exposure we get when outdoors is higher it might still not be enough to compensate for our increasingly indoor lifestyle. However, the relationship between stratospheric ozone and ultraviolet radiance at ground level is not as straightforward as it appeared at first and is particularly complex when we consider the effects at a local and regional level. Indeed, it is quite possible that, while global ultraviolet has increased at the top of the atmosphere, regional ultraviolet at the bottom of the atmosphere – in the places where we live – has *decreased* during this period.

Is ultraviolet increasing or decreasing?

One of the problems with the satellite measurements is that they overestimate the amount of ultraviolet radiation reaching the ground. The data are adjusted to take into account the absorption and scattering in the atmosphere lower down and the effects of the surface. But there is still little known about these effects because our understanding of them is really only just beginning. What about measuring ultraviolet-B on the ground instead of relying on satellite measurements? The trouble with ground-level measurements is that they are not easy to obtain. Ground-level monitoring is difficult to maintain – instruments need to be kept clear of debris and away from changing surfaces that may either shade or reflect ultraviolet. Ultraviolet on the ground is highly variable because it can be affected by so many things. Not only does it vary from one region to another, but also within a day and even within an hour. To overcome these difficulties ground-level ultraviolet has been predicted using theoretical models. The problem is that these models, though highly sophisticated, cannot take into account all the things that affect ultraviolet, particularly clouds. You need only to look at the clouds in the sky to appreciate these difficulties – how high are the clouds, how dense, how broken, what gases and particles do they contain, how fast do they change and move across the sky, how much of the sky is covered?

Until recently, there was little interest in monitoring local ultraviolet-B. The aim of monitoring was to assess the *global* ultraviolet changes in response to ozone thinning. The local variations were interference. In addition, the wavelengths measured often include a wider band than the narrow band of ultraviolet-B that we need to make vitamin D. Most of what we know about ultraviolet comes from measurements of ozone obtained from satellites. But the amount of ultraviolet-B we receive is affected by things on or close to the ground, far below the satellites. This explains why ground measurements of ultraviolet radiation are always lower than those estimated by the satellite measurements, particularly in polluted regions. It is now recognised that we need better ground-based data and should not depend on satellite estimates because of the uncertainty. It is also recognised that we need better geographical coverage by ground-based monitors and long-term monitoring to understand the ultraviolet climatology and to detect the long-term trends. Measurements of ultraviolet have also been made using research aircraft such as the NSF/NCAR C-130 aircraft run by the Earth Observing Laboratory in the USA, and the Cessna 182 at the University of Manchester. These can measure ultraviolet at different elevations.

The fact is that monitoring of ultraviolet is a relatively new activity with the techniques and interpretation of the data still under development and there is virtually no data available from the pre-ozone thinning days, i.e. before 1995. This means we cannot tell whether ultraviolet-B has increased or decreased in the places we live over the period from the 1960s in which overweight has increased. Concerns about ultraviolet-B specifically and its effects on vitamin D availability have only just begun to be addressed.

What we really need, from the point of view of making vitamin D, is local monitoring to compare ultraviolet between regions where people live. When you go outdoors, how much ultraviolet-B will you get? Is it more, less, or the same as your friend in the next town? And will you get more, less, or the same as 30 years ago? At the moment nobody can answer those questions because we don't have the information we need. We may have to wait a few more decades before we can get accurate measurements of ground-level ultraviolet-B and before we can see trends. In the meantime, what can we infer about ultraviolet-B from our knowledge of the lower atmosphere?

The atmosphere

The stratosphere, where most of the ultraviolet-B is absorbed by the ozone layer, starts 11 kilometres above us, which is two or three kilometres above the top of Mount Everest. The bottom layer of the atmosphere where we live, the troposphere, is the thickest part. Any ultraviolet-B photons that manage to get through the stratosphere must then travel another 11 kilometres before they reach us down on the ground and on that long journey they must be able to dodge all the dust, gases, aerosols, soot and clouds that are in their way. The thinning of the ozone layer might increase the amount of ultraviolet-B way above our heads, but does that ultraviolet-B go on to make the journey all the way down to us?

In the stratosphere the majority of ultraviolet radiation is absorbed by ozone, but ultraviolet-B can be absorbed and scattered by lots of different substances in the atmosphere at all levels. The atmosphere is mostly a mixture of gases (mainly nitrogen, oxygen and argon), water in the form of vapour, droplets and ice crystals and particles including dust, soot, ashes, pollen and salt from the oceans. The composition of the atmosphere changes at different locations and at different times, varying with the weather and the amount of pollution. Close to the Earth's surface, substances produced by industry and transport are recognised as problematic both because they are a health hazard and because they contribute to an enhanced greenhouse effect that is causing global warming. In addition, the atmosphere contains sand and dust, smoke from fires and volcanic emissions.

Sulphur dioxide, to take one example of a pollutant, is recognised as a health hazard. It can irritate the skin, eyes, nose and airways. When the concentration of sulphur dioxide in the atmosphere is high, people with respiratory conditions, such as asthma, emphysema, or bronchitis, are advised to stay indoors. In addition, in the presence of water, sulphur dioxide can form sulphuric acid that causes rain to become more acidic and harms freshwater life and trees. But does sulphur dioxide reduce the amount of ground-level ultraviolet-B irradiance? Sulphur dioxide certainly absorbs ultraviolet radiation – indeed its presence is detected by its absorbance of ultraviolet – but its effect on the amount of ultraviolet-B reaching the Earth's surface is unknown because it has never been considered in this respect.

It makes sense that if there are more particles and pollutants in the air, such as sulphur dioxide, less ultraviolet can get to us on the ground, but what is the evidence? Only a few studies have examined the effects of atmospheric composition on ultraviolet by directly measuring it using ground-level instruments.

Ultraviolet irradiance at ground-level

Hamdy Elminir of the National Research Institute of Astronomy and Geophysics in Cairo studied the effects of different atmospheric compositions on ultraviolet irradiance in Egypt. He found that between 1998 and 2003, even though stratospheric ozone reduced by almost 5 per cent, and would be expected to result in an *increase* in ultraviolet, at ground level it had actually *lowered* by almost 15 per cent. He also found that the ultraviolet irradiance at semi-urban Aswan was higher than at rural El-Kharga, in part due to the sandstorms in El-Kharga. At Aswan, dust reduced ultraviolet by, on average, almost 7 per cent on dusty days and sometimes as much as 20 per cent. In Cairo, a population-dense urban area, the effects of pollutants were studied. On days when the amounts of particulate matter (PM_{10}) were high ultraviolet radiation was 40 per cent lower.

In another study, Bill Barnard and his colleagues at the Department of Marine, Earth and Atmospheric Sciences, North Carolina State University directly measured ultraviolet and the effects of five pollutants at the University of California, Riverside. In this study, the sulphur dioxide and nitrogen dioxide levels were not high enough to reduce ultraviolet, and ozone reduced ultraviolet but not by a significant amount. But black carbon (or soot) reduced ultraviolet by as much as 35 per cent. In fact, Barnard calculated that every microgram of black carbon blocks 150 J/m^2 of ultraviolet each day from the Earth's surface.

Similar results have been found in Mexico City – when pollution is high, ultraviolet is low. The emissions from industry and transport constitute a major source of pollution since the Industrial Revolution but, as we saw above, the sandstorms of Egypt also reduced ultraviolet at Aswan in Hamdy Elminir's study. Before we consider the effects industry and transport have on ultraviolet in more detail, we will consider volcanoes, plankton and fires.

Volcanoes

On 12 June 1991 Mount Pinatubo in the Philippines erupted. This was the second largest volcanic eruption of the twentieth century (the largest was Novarupta in Alaska in 1912). It is estimated that about 20 million tonnes of sulphur dioxide went into the stratosphere where it was transformed by solar radiation into sulphuric acid and sulphate particles that gradually fell into the lower atmosphere. It caused a fall in the amount of solar radiation of about 2 per cent.

Volcanic eruptions produce gas and dust which blow up into the lower stratosphere and are rapidly distributed around the world by the strong winds. The main gas produced by volcanoes is sulphur dioxide that combines with oxygen and water to form sulphuric acid gas. This gas forms into fine droplets that form a haze. Ninety-nine per cent of gas molecules emitted during a volcanic eruption are water vapour, carbon dioxide and sulphur dioxide.

One of the best-studied volcanoes is Kīlauea on Hawaii. Scientists measure the sulphur dioxide by measuring the amount of ultraviolet radiation absorbed by a volcanic gas plume as the sun shines through it. In June 2008 they measured a total of 2,000 to 4,000 tonnes of sulphur dioxide emitted from two active vents from the Kīlauea volcano on Hawaii, which has been erupting continuously since 1983. Occasionally the emission reaches as much as 7,000 tonnes per day.

Vog – volcanic smog – is a visible haze formed by the reactions of volcanic emissions when they interact with sunlight, atmospheric oxygen, moisture and dust. It is formed under certain conditions of air temperature, humidity and rainfall. Vog is the change in atmosphere you can see, but if there is no haze that doesn't meant there is no sulphur dioxide. Much of the sulphur dioxide is blown by the trade winds out to sea but some reaches the west side of Hawaii Island resulting in a haze along the Kona coast. When the winds blow from the south the vog can spread throughout the Hawaiian Island chain.

In Chapter 2 Vitamin D Poverty, I mentioned a study in which scientists measured the calcidiol in volunteers from Hawaii expecting them to have high levels, but, despite getting at least 3 hours of sunlight per day for at least 5 days per week, their average calcidiol levels were not particularly high. One possible explanation for this is that although they were getting plenty of sunshine they were not getting plenty of ultraviolet-B because it was blocked by vog.

There are around 50 to 70 volcanic eruptions going on around the world each year. Some volcanoes emit gas in between eruptions as well. Recent volcanoes that have affected people because of persistent sulphur dioxide emissions include Nyiragongo (DR Congo), Masaya (Nicaragua), Poás (Costa Rica), Mount Oyama, Mount Aso and Sakurajima (Japan). At any one time, it is estimated that at least 20 volcanoes are erupting. Stromboli in Italy has been erupting for more than a thousand years.

In May 1784 Benjamin Franklin wrote about a 'dry fog' that had happened the previous year; he deduced that the effect of the fog on the sunlight reaching the Earth was the cause of the unusually cold winter in 1783/4. Some say this bad winter contributed to the onset of the French Revolution. It is now thought that the fog may have been caused by eruptions in the Laki volcanic fissure in Iceland, which may have resulted in more than 10,000 deaths. It has been hypothesised that mass extinctions are caused by reductions in solar radiation as a result of either meteorite impacts or volcanic activity. Either of these might be responsible for a fall in ultraviolet-B at the Earth's surface. I wonder if it is even possible that the extinction of the dinosaurs, as well as their preceding increase in size, was due to a fall in ultraviolet-B caused by an increase in absorbers such as sulphur dioxide.

Plankton

The familiar smell of the seaside is caused by a compound called dimethyl sulphide, which is emitted from marine algae in response to ultraviolet. It is thought that algae produce this gas for protection against strong sunlight. Any increase in the amount of dimethyl sulphide in the atmosphere could also reduce the amount of ultraviolet-B reaching other organisms. This effect has been little studied, but it is possible that the amount of ultraviolet-B we can get in sunny coastal areas is lower in hot weather when dimethyl sulphide levels are high.

Fires

In Australia the average UV index is 9 to 10 whereas in the UK it is 2 to 3. There are several reasons for this. Compared to the UK, Australia is at a lower latitude, is closer to the equator, has less pollution in the atmosphere, is in the southern hemisphere, which means that the summer solstice occurs at perihelion (when the Earth is closest to the Sun) and, finally, has a thinner ozone layer in the stratosphere, at least in the spring and summer. With a population that is mostly fair-skinned (largely of British ancestry) nobody is surprised that the incidence of skin cancer in Australia is the highest in the world.

Although Australia has low levels of urban pollution, it has two naturally occurring aerosols in the atmosphere absorbing ultraviolet-B – smoke and mineral dust – and these were studied by Olga Kalashnikova of the Jet Propulsion Laboratory at the California Institute of Technology, USA. To study the effects of smoke, Kalashnikova and her colleagues chose Darwin, located in northern Australia. Fires occur in winter and spring in northern Australia and in summer in southern Australia and the area around Darwin has the greatest number of fires. Darwin has very low background of aerosol loadings and is affected by smoke during the local fire season (September to November). To study the effects of dust, Kalashnikova chose Alice Springs in central Australia because dust is present in central Australia and may come from the Great Artesian Basin, or possibly the Simpson and Strzelecki deserts. At Darwin, they found that smoke affected ultraviolet-B more than it affected other wavelengths of ultraviolet. They found that smoke from strong fires could reduce ultraviolet-B by as much as 45 per cent – almost half – and also blocked up to 30 per cent of ultraviolet-A. The study at Alice Springs was less conclusive, but they were able to conclude that smoke has a greater effect on ultraviolet-B than dust.

The Industrial Revolution

It is clear that when the composition of the atmosphere changes ultraviolet irradiance is affected. We are more familiar with the idea of the atmospheric changes that cause global warming, so how does this information fit in with climate change?

Global warming is caused by an enhanced greenhouse effect that results from a higher concentration of gases in the atmosphere emitted mainly from fossil fuel burning for transport and industry. Conventional power stations burn coal, oil or gas to produce electricity. Petrol, diesel and kerosene used for transport are also fossil fuels. The burning of fossil fuels produces sulphur dioxide, nitrogen oxides, carbon monoxide, particulate matter and volatile organic compounds such as hydrocarbons.

Coal produces more sulphur dioxide than does oil or gas. Coal was the first fossil fuel to be used on a large scale at the beginning of the Industrial Revolution. After the Industrial Revolution coal burning was a major source of pollution, producing smoke and sulphur dioxide that resulted in smogs. In the twentieth century, cleaner coals were produced to reduce the sulphur dioxide emissions and the Clean Air Acts controlled pollution by introducing smokeless zones and tall chimneys for factories burning coal and other fuels to reduce the amount of pollution at ground level. In addition, the replacement of coal fires by electric and gas heating reduced pollution in the second half of the twentieth century. By then, however, the amount of pollution produced by transport had increased.

The main greenhouse gases are carbon dioxide, methane, nitrous oxide and ozone. These are responsible for the warming of the atmosphere. Carbon dioxide does not absorb ultraviolet-B (except at burning temperatures), nor does methane (it absorbs at 125 nm which is ultraviolet-C) and nor does water vapour. Ozone, sulphur dioxide, nitric oxide and nitrogen dioxide, however, do absorb ultraviolet-B (indeed ultraviolet-absorption can be used to detect these gases) and particles such as dust, soot and ash may absorb or scatter ultraviolet-B. So although not all greenhouse gases absorb ultraviolet, the burning of fossil fuels produces other gases and particles that *can* block ultraviolet-B.

It is reasonable to suppose, then, that with increased emissions due to the Industrial Revolution there should be more stuff in the air that can absorb and scatter ultraviolet. It seems logical that increased emissions should lower ultraviolet on the ground, yet these effects were overlooked until recently as all attention was directed towards the effect of the depletion of the ozone layer. Now, because there is no clear evidence that the decrease in ozone in the stratosphere has resulted in the expected increases in ultraviolet radiation (at least not in most populated areas) attention is turning to the composition of the lower atmosphere.

How can we study the effects of the Industrial Revolution and transport on ultraviolet-B? When it comes to temperatures, records have been compiled of the temperature of land and sea since 1856 and temperature records in Central England go back as far as 1659, but measurements of ultraviolet only started in the 1980s – indeed we didn't even know ultraviolet existed until it was discovered in the nineteenth century – and it has been difficult to work out whether ultraviolet has been increasing or decreasing in the past two decades, so how can we possibly know what ultraviolet was like for the previous two centuries? It is possible to work out what the temperatures were before records began from historical documents and proxy data as from tree rings and ice cores. Can we do the same for ultraviolet? In his book *The Little Ice Age*, Brian Fagan, Professor Emeritus of Archaeology at the Department of Anthropology at the University of California at Santa Barbara, says that Hans Neuberger studied paintings completed between 1400 and 1967 and noted that there was a gradual increase in clouds up to 1850, after which the sky became less blue. Brian Fagan noted other ways in which the Industrial Revolution affected the climate and marked the end of the Little Ice Age.

For a detailed analysis Maria Kvalevåg of the University of Oslo, Gunnar Myhre of the Center for International Climate and Environmental Research in Oslo, and Cathrine Lund Myhre of the Norwegian Institute for Air Research, estimated the effect of pollutants on ultraviolet-B using a computer simulation. They wanted to calculate the effects of known emissions from industry and transport in the period 1750 to 2000. They studied three gases (ozone, nitrogen dioxide and sulphur dioxide), aerosols (sulphate, organic carbon and black carbon), clouds, surface albedo and aviation vapour trails (contrails). These emissions have been increasing since the beginning of the Industrial Revolution, but ozone thinning, so far as we know, has only occurred in the past few decades.

When it comes to ozone, the analysis showed that, although the amount of ozone in the stratosphere has fallen, tropospheric ozone (closer to the Earth's surface) has increased. Taking both together, the result is an increase of 4 per cent in *global* ultraviolet at the surface, but *regionally* ultraviolet has decreased at low latitudes. Nitrogen dioxide and sulphur dioxide both strongly absorb ultraviolet and they are also precursors of ozone. Organic carbon and black carbon were shown to reduce ultraviolet by as much as 12 per cent in Central Africa due to biomass burning (natural fires and agricultural burning).

Altogether, these simulations suggest that the only area where ultraviolet has increased is at high latitudes. Elsewhere there has been a *fall* in ultraviolet radiation at the surface and it has been reduced by as much as 20 per cent since the beginning of the Industrial Revolution. The strongest reductions have been in South East Asia, Europe and North America and the most populated regions have experienced the biggest reductions in surface ultraviolet. The stratospheric ozone thinning has resulted in an increase in ultraviolet only at high latitudes and everywhere else it has been more than offset by the increased absorption in the lower atmosphere, particularly in the places where we live. In other words, we are getting less ultraviolet than our forebears did 250 years ago.

Bad air

Finally, we come to the question posed at the beginning of this chapter. Could any of these changes in the atmosphere explain the rise in overweight? Our concern is with the past 40 years or so when overweight rose so dramatically. Is it possible that the amount of ultraviolet-B reaching us on the ground has lowered because of changes in the atmosphere?

The fact is that we simply don't have the information at the moment to make a reasonable, evidence-based judgment. It would be wrong to assume that the amount of ultraviolet-B reaching us at the surface is decreasing, but it would be equally wrong to assume that it is increasing.

Studies of ultraviolet-B have been focused on the global climatology and efforts have been made to filter out the local variations. However, these variations are exactly what we need to know to find out how ultraviolet-B is changing where we live and to see how it is affected by local conditions. In the studies of the effects of ozone on ultraviolet irradiance, the effect of sulphur dioxide as an absorber of ultraviolet is an interference. Local areas with high levels of pollution will have more sulphur dioxide. For this reason, ground measurements tend to be taken in places where there is a low level of pollution and at the top of buildings, for instance, to reduce the effect of the absorption by pollutants. But, from the point of view of finding out how much ultraviolet is falling on our skin, we need to have this information. The global effect of a pollutant on ultraviolet may be small, but if we live and work near an airport, a motorway, a power station or an industrial site, the effects on the amount of ultraviolet we are getting as we go about our daily business might be very high indeed.

As we have seen, ultraviolet-B at the ground level is highly variable because the composition of the atmosphere is highly variable. It is difficult to measure ultraviolet and almost all studies look at a broader range of wavelengths of ultraviolet radiation than ultraviolet-B. It is worth emphasising that the UV index is a calculated value; it is not directly measured. Most measurements of ultraviolet come from satellites and ground-level monitors are usually placed at the top of buildings. The focus of ultraviolet studies has mostly been global and not local and it is quite possible that ultraviolet-B could be increasing in one place while decreasing in another.

In short, it is generally the case that ultraviolet radiation *has not been studied from the perspective of making vitamin D*. It is vital that, particularly in urban areas, we have a better understanding of ultraviolet not least because the current drive to reduce greenhouse gas emissions may lead to increased ground-level ultraviolet radiation, and we need to be able to monitor ultraviolet levels. In the meantime, allow me to make a highly speculative conjecture about how a loss of ultraviolet-B may have occurred in the past few decades.

How a volcano drew my attention to the effect of aircraft on ultraviolet

In April 2010 a volcanic ash cloud, emitted by an eruption of the Eyjafjallajökull volcano in Iceland, drifted over northern Europe. The ash was a mixture of glass, sand and rock particles. If the ash gets into the engines of an aeroplane, the particles accumulate and clog the engine causing it to cut out. To prevent the potential damage to aircraft, and subsequent danger to passengers, a ban on air traffic was implemented in the affected area resulting in a complete no-fly zone over northern Europe. Hundreds of thousands of travellers were stranded, or were forced to take a slow, circuitous route home by land and the cost to airlines was estimated at 200 million dollars a day. Many people felt the disruption caused by the ash cloud was symbolic – a reminder that we cannot control the planet or nature – and was particularly apt when attempts to reduce greenhouse gas emissions were being held back by climate change denialists, and by politicians who had been diverted by a recession caused by the global banking crisis of 2008.

I was reading about how severe and widespread vitamin D deficiency has become when I heard about the volcanic ash cloud and I was concerned that it would reduce ground-level ultraviolet-B. But the resulting flight ban appeared to have had the opposite effect. The sky seemed to be a deeper blue and the sun felt better, but was it my imagination or just part of the normal variation in the weather? Many people enjoyed the clear blue skies without the usual contrails emitted from aircraft. April 2010 was a dry and sunny month with warmer days and colder nights than average. Shortly after the flight ban a friend of mine experienced sunburn for the first time in her life and newspapers reported the case of a baby taken to hospital with severe sunburn. Was it because the flight ban reduced the amount of absorbing compounds in the atmosphere allowing more ultraviolet-B to reach the ground? Nobody warned us that ultraviolet radiation would be stronger because there were no planes in the sky – how could they, when nobody knows how ultraviolet radiation is affected by aircraft?

The increase in transport

The use of road and air transport has increased over the past 40 years. In 2008 in the UK, for example, 52 million tonnes of fuel were used by transport, 37 million tonnes by road transport and 12 million tonnes by air transport. On the next page are some more statistics for Britain taken from the 35th Edition of *Transport Statistics Great Britain*, showing how transport increased between 1975 and 2005. Transport is the largest single source of emissions in the UK and emissions from cars are greater than any other form of transport. However, while car emissions have been stable since 1990, air travel emissions have continued to increase because of rising demand. Transport emissions grew between 1990 and 2005 even though there was an overall fall in emissions in the UK.

- *Road Transport*
- *In 1975,* there were 16.5 million total road motor vehicles including 12.5 million private cars. *In 2005,* there were 32.9 million total road motor vehicles including 26.2 million private cars.
- *In 1975,* 44 per cent of households had no car and 11 per cent had two cars or more. *In 2005,* 25 per cent of households had no car and 31 per cent had two cars or more.
- *In 1975,* 48 per cent of adults had a driving licence. *In 2005,* 72 per cent of adults had a driving licence.

- *Air Transport*
- *In 1975,* there were 701 take-offs or landings, 42 million passengers and 638 thousand tonnes of freight handled.
- *In 2005,* there were 2,300 take-offs or landings, 227 million passengers and 2,361 thousand tonnes of freight handled.
- *The number of* passengers increased every year since 1950 with the exception of 1974 and 1991 and the average growth rate was 6 per cent.

This trend is, of course, not confined to the UK. Globally, aviation is one of the fastest growing and least regulated sectors of the global economy. The output of the air transport industry increased by a factor of 23 since 1960 during which period the total GDP increased by 3.8.

Both road and air transport depend on burning fossil fuels and emit a mixture of substances. As described above, sulphur dioxide, nitric oxide, nitrogen dioxide and particles such as dust, soot and ash may absorb or scatter ultraviolet-B, and some lead to an increase in ozone which absorbs ultraviolet-B. Carbon monoxide and hydrocarbons are the largest emissions during idling and taxiing. Emission of nitrogen oxides are at their highest during take-off. Since the 1950s air emissions have been increasing and are now increasing faster than emissions from land vehicles. Air transport has enormous potential to grow even further in the future especially in poorer countries because, as economies grow, so too does the use of transport.

Aircraft emissions

Thirty years ago the concerns about aircraft emissions were all about the air quality around airports. These concerns led to international standards regarding emissions below 915 metres, chiefly during landing and take-off. There are no standards to control emissions from aircraft during cruise because, understandably, there were no concerns about the air quality in the upper troposphere and lower stratosphere where nobody lives. Later, the contribution of aircraft emissions to the enhanced greenhouse effect became a matter of interest. But aviation fuel only accounts for a small proportion of the total fossil fuel use – about 13 per cent of the fossil fuel used for transportation and only about 3 per cent of the total for all uses. In terms of its contribution to global warming, then, aviation fuel usage is relatively minor and international aviation emissions are not covered in the Kyoto protocol because of the difficulty in allocating flight emissions to specific countries (although domestic aviation emissions are included). However, the effects of aviation emissions on ultraviolet may be more significant.

Today's aircraft are more efficient than those produced 40 years ago and efficiency is expected to increase even further in the future. Improvements in technology aimed at improving the fuel efficiency and reducing noise have reduced the amount of greenhouse gases emitted by aircraft. But these improvements have increased the emissions of nitrogen dioxide and nitric oxide, which cause increases in ozone and block ultraviolet. Therefore, what might be good news for global warming could be bad news for ultraviolet.

A special report about aviation and the global atmosphere was written in 1999 for the Intergovernmental Panel on Climate Change. This considered the effects of aviation on global climate change. Although it also considered the effects on ultraviolet, this report didn't fully take into account the effects of soot, sulphate aerosols and the formation of cirrus clouds and it took a global, rather than a regional, perspective. Nevertheless, the report concluded that, overall, the effect of aircraft is to increase ozone and reduce ultraviolet-B mainly due to nitrogen dioxide and nitric oxide emissions. Other emissions and effects on the atmosphere from aircraft (contrails, aerosols and cloudiness) were expected to be small. Aircraft emissions of nitrogen dioxide and nitric oxide were estimated to have increased ozone in northern mid-latitudes by up to 6 per cent. Emissions during cruise increase the concentration of nitrogen dioxide and nitric oxide at altitudes between 9 and 12 kilometres. Unlike carbon dioxide and methane, which mix with the atmosphere and become widely distributed, the gases and particles that reduce ultraviolet irradiance (nitric oxide, nitrogen dioxide, sulphur dioxides and soot) stay concentrated near the flight routes. The effect on ultraviolet is therefore likely to be greatest in localised areas.

The impact of cruise emissions on ultraviolet may be greater than those at take-off and landing, because at high altitudes there is a lower background level of emissions and because the pollutants stick around longer. There is no rain up in the stratosphere to wash out the pollutants nor any trees or shrubs to absorb them. It means that it is possible to live in a place that has good air quality because ground-level pollution is relatively low but suffer from low ultraviolet because of high cruise-level pollution.

As aircraft took off, so did overweight

Could the growth in transport, and particularly air transport, explain the rise in overweight? The use of air transport expanded dramatically after the 1970s, by which time the jet aircraft had replaced the piston-powered aircraft. Before then, air travel had been the preserve of the affluent. Jet engines produced large thrust, could climb higher and cruise faster than the piston-powered aircraft they superseded. The jet engine was developed in England and the first commercial jet flight was the Comet 1 built by de Havilland and flown by the British Overseas Aircraft Corporation. The Comet flew at 772 kmph (480 mph) compared to the top speed of the piston engine aircraft of 290 kmph (180 mph). In 1958 the Pan American airline flew the Boeing 707–129 with 111 passengers. American Airlines used the first domestic jet service for a flight from New York to Los Angeles in 1959. Airlines around the world were quick to replace piston-engine aircraft with jets.

The 1960s was the age of the Jet Set – wealthy people who took advantage of the speed and comfort of jet flights to get from one country to another merely for social gatherings such as weekend parties. By the 1970s aircraft had got larger – both longer and wider – to accommodate a greater number of passengers. The Boeing 747, a four-jet aircraft 56.4 metres (185 ft) long, could carry between 365 and 490 passengers at 1,000 kmph (625 mph). In 1978 the Airline Deregulation Act in the USA removed government control of fares, routes and airlines. As a result the average fare per passenger mile was 9 per cent lower in 1994 than it was in 1979. Airlines were able to fly larger aircraft on longer routes.

It was in the USA that air transport first became widely used, where it was used for both internal and international travel, and it was in the USA that overweight first became severe and widespread. Almost all aviation fuel is used in the northern hemisphere and most in the middle and polar latitudes above 30° N. The largest changes in the composition of the atmosphere caused by aviation are at northern mid-latitudes at altitudes of 10 to 12 km – above the first nations to experience widespread overweight, namely USA and UK. Since the 1970s air transport has steadily increased and so has overweight. The twentieth century ended with jumbo jets and jumbo people.

Of course this correlation is not sufficient evidence to assume a causal relationship. There is no direct evidence that aviation causes vitamin D deficiency and it is speculative to suggest that aviation is the primary cause of the increase in overweight since the 1970s. But the possibility needs to be investigated, particularly as it has the potential to explain the following:

- The increase in overweight in the second half of the twentieth century.
- The fact that the USA was the first country to suffer from a high prevalence of overweight.
- The association of overweight with economic activity.
- The geographical distribution of overweight.
- The low concentration of vitamin D in food.

At the beginning of this chapter I said that sunny places are not always ultraviolet-rich. The effect of aircraft emissions on ultraviolet has the potential to explain why overweight is high in some regions that on the face of it should be ultraviolet-rich environments including, for example, some Pacific Islands which have a high prevalence of overweight.

In a compilation of data by the World Health Organization, the nation with the highest prevalence of overweight is Nauru. Nauru is the smallest island nation in the world, where, with an area of 21 square kilometres, it is impossible to live far from the airport. Indeed, much of the island is uninhabitable and the majority of the population live on the south-west coast of the island, close to Nauru's international airport. The island is surrounded by coral reef and there is no seaport, so the island is dependent on aviation for tourism, to export phosphate and to import all basic (food, water and fuel) and manufactured goods. Regular scheduled services started in 1972. Like Nauru, many Pacific Islands have extremely high rates of overweight, but no previous history of overweight before they became heavily dependent on aviation for tourism, exports and imports. The high rates of overweight in the Pacific Islands could conceivably be due to increased ozone produced by aviation. A 2013 study by Steven Barrett and colleagues at the Massachusetts Institute of Technology used a computer-based model to examine the variability of ozone produced by aviation around the globe. The model showed that aviation–generated ozone was highest in the Pacific Island region. The peak sensitivity was at a point 1,000 km north-east of the Solomon Islands where an emission of 1 kg of nitrogen oxides emitted by aircraft would result in an increase in ozone of 15 kg over a year. This is 5 times higher than the sensitivity in Europe and almost 4 times higher than North America.

The reason ozone production peaks in this region is thought to be because, paradoxically, the cleaner atmosphere over the remote Pacific region makes it more sensitive to production of ozone by the nitrogen oxides emitted by aircraft, compared to the more polluted atmospheres over Europe and North America, for example, where the production of ozone is counterbalanced to some extent by the loss of ozone as it reacts with background pollutants. An added problem for the Pacific region is that the flights in Southeast Asia tend to be very long so burn more fuel.

This problem of cleaner atmospheres being more sensitive to aviation-generated ozone combined with their dependence on aviation could perhaps also explain the higher rates of overweight in islands in general when compared to mainland nations. And for island nations, shipping emissions may just add to the problem. The World Health Organization has a Global Infobase available online showing the prevalence of obesity around the world. The following refers to overweight and obesity in men. Seven of the ten countries with the highest rates are island nations, the other three being USA, Greece and Argentina. In the African Region, the Seychelles has the highest rate (63.8%) and Mauritius has the second highest rate (44.8%). In Europe, Malta (73.3%) and Greece (77.5%) have the highest rates. Greece has around 1400 islands, 227 of which are inhabited. In the UK, itself an island nation, the islands of Orkney, Shetland and the Western Isles are reported to have the highest prevalence of overweight.

Concern about emissions and air quality has been mainly about two issues. The first is the air that we breathe – do pollutants cause asthma and hay fever, and are we more likely to get respiratory disease if we live near to a main road? The second issue is the enhanced greenhouse effect that results in global warming. Now, perhaps, we should be thinking about a third effect of emissions – that of blocking ultraviolet. Could overweight be a direct effect of atmospheric changes on our bodies? I can't help wondering if in future we shall see overweight as the canary in the climate change coalmine. We are accustomed to being protected from all but the most extreme changes in weather by our clothing and buildings, but perhaps we would be naive to think that they could protect us from the cause of climate change.

This chapter has shown how difficult it is to work out how much ultraviolet-B we are getting on the ground, when there are so many different things affecting the composition of the atmosphere. On the other hand, local measurements are not helpful in understanding the global levels of ultraviolet-B and how they are changing. One of the problems we have is that ultraviolet has been studied from the point of view of the harm it does to living things, particularly as a carcinogen in humans, and not as the essential environmental condition for making vitamin D that it is. If ultraviolet-B is low, animals make less vitamin D and we get less from both our exposure to sunlight and from our food. It is vital that we study ultraviolet from the vitamin D perspective. It is vital that we are aware of the effects of reducing greenhouse gas emissions on ultraviolet. Ultimately we can defend ourselves against any increase in ultraviolet by using clothing and shelter, but we have little defence against a fall in ultraviolet.

Chapter 4

The Sunlight Paradox

PERHAPS WE REALLY SHOULD get out more. It seems that we make less vitamin D in our skin than we did a few decades ago for many reasons, and we can explain the rise in overweight in this period at least partly by our trend for spending less time outdoors. If we want to make more vitamin D it would help if we try to get outdoors more and expose as much skin as possible. It might also help to use a sunbed, particularly if the ultraviolet is low in the area in which you live and work, and especially in winter. But some people regard sunbathing and the use of sunbeds as harmful, and regard those who practice such activities as guilty of reckless behaviour. While in many countries overweight has increased since the 1980s, so too have other diseases and medical conditions, and one that has increased monumentally is skin cancer. To avoid skin cancer we are advised to protect ourselves against sunlight falling on our skin. But to improve our vitamin D status we need to get more sunlight.

This is highly confusing – is sunlight safe, is it harmful, or is it beneficial? Should you go out in the sunshine, and if so when, and for how long? Should you let your children go out without sunscreen? Should you take your baby out or not? Perhaps, if you want to do all you can to avoid skin cancer, it might be sensible to avoid sunlight exposure. But, supposing you want to avoid vitamin D deficiency and overweight, then perhaps you should get as much sunlight as you can. But what if you want to avoid skin cancer, as well as vitamin D deficiency and overweight?

Our instinct is to get out in the sunlight, but we now see it as dangerous – you might read that sunburn can double your risk of skin cancer and the statistics show that melanoma is increasing at an alarming rate. This is all scary stuff indeed. When it comes to babies and children, the problem is even more vexing than it is for adults as, on the one hand, their need for vitamin D may be greater than for adults but on the other hand, sunlight exposure for children seems to be more damaging than for adults because their skin is more delicate. If you want to do the best for your child's health, it seems at the moment you just can't win no matter what you do.

There is a view among dermatologists that we can get vitamin D in other ways – from our diet or by taking supplements – and sunlight exposure is not necessary. The solution is therefore to avoid sunlight exposure completely and to get all our vitamin D by other means. The American Academy of Dermatologists, for example, once took this view and recommended extreme sun protection measures, including the use of sunscreen by people of all skin types, every day, *even when indoors.* (Descriptions of skin types can be found in the notes) But at the moment, sunlight exposure is the main way we get vitamin D – we can see that plainly from the seasonal ups and downs of calcidiol. The amount available in food is limited and it might be difficult to eat enough vitamin D-rich foods to meet our needs. We are not sure at the moment how much we need to take in the form of supplements to prevent deficiency, or indeed, whether it would be safe to take the amount necessary to compensate for loss of sunlight exposure. In the future it might be possible to develop drugs that help to raise our vitamin D levels, but, for the time being, if you want to increase your vitamin D status, increasing your skin's exposure to sunlight is probably the best approach.

Skin cancer is not the subject of this book and, to be honest with you, I wanted to avoid saying much about it at first, but I find that it is a subject that needs to be addressed, not just to clear up some of the confusion about sun protection, but because there is a fundamental question to be asked that has not been addressed elsewhere: *How can vitamin D deficiency be increasing at the same time as skin cancer if the first is caused by too little ultraviolet while the second is caused by too much?*

Skin cancer is increasing

Around the world, one in every three cancers diagnosed is a skin cancer. In fact, it is so common that non-melanoma skin cancers (mainly basal cell carcinoma and squamous cell carcinoma) are left out of any summary of cancer statistics because their frequency makes other cancers seem rare by comparison. There are about 70,000 new cases of skin cancer diagnosed each year in the UK, for example, and of these about 11,000 are malignant melanomas. Worldwide, it is estimated that 200,000 cases of melanoma were diagnosed in 2008.

Like overweight, the incidence of melanoma has been increasing since the late 1970s in the countries of North America, Australasia and northern and western Europe. In these countries with predominantly fair-skinned populations the incidence of melanoma is rising fast, approximately doubling every 20 years. It is no surprise then that there is great concern, and efforts being made to try to prevent skin cancer.

Sunlight protection vs. sunlight exposure

Campaigns to reduce sunlight exposure began in Australia because Queensland has the highest incidence of malignant melanoma in the world. The state of Queensland lies within the tropics in the north-eastern part of Australia and most of its inhabitants are fair-skinned descendants of migrants from the UK. In the 1960s the incidence of melanoma was 16 per 100,000, and, in the 1970s and 1980s, efforts were made to educate medical professionals, with the aim of detecting and treating it earlier, and to educate the public, with the aim of both detecting it earlier and preventing it altogether by avoiding sunlight. The campaigns then spread to Europe and North America.

The general theme of the advice to the public is to avoid sunlight exposure, and particularly to avoid sunlight when ultraviolet radiation is at its most intense. These campaigns sent out a clear message that sunlight causes skin cancer, with a particular emphasis on malignant melanoma. By the end of the twentieth century there were numerous campaigns including *Slip! Slop! Slap!* used in Australia and New Zealand, *Sun Know How* in Britain, *Care in the Sun* in Northern Ireland and *Choose Your Cover* in the USA.

At the time I started writing this book the message was very clear – ultraviolet radiation was a harmful, cancer-causing agent and sunlight exposure was dangerous. The need for sunlight exposure for making vitamin D was ignored at first, but in time, as the problem of vitamin D deficiency became recognised, the voices of the vitamin D scientists were impinging on the sunlight protection campaigns. They were concerned that these campaigns worsened the problem of vitamin D deficiency that, they argued, had greater consequences for public health than skin cancer.

There seemed to be a boxing match between opposing health advice with 'sunlight is dangerous' in one corner and 'sunlight is beneficial' in the opposite corner. Their proponents seemed to have nothing to do with each other and were so opposed that, in 2004, Michael Holick was asked to resign from his position as a Professor of Dermatology at Boston University for suggesting that unprotected sunlight exposure for short periods was necessary for good health.

The position at the time of writing is that, although some health advisers still recommend extreme sun protection, much of the advice has been modified to take vitamin D into account. In Australia and New Zealand it is now recommended that unprotected exposure for a few minutes a few times a week should be allowed to make vitamin D. Similarly, in the UK it is now recommended to have some unprotected exposure to sunlight around noon, on a little-and-often basis, to allow for vitamin D to be made.

There is a shift, then, towards recognising that we need *some* exposure to sunlight to make vitamin D but not *too much,* which can cause sunburn and skin cancer. The opponents in the boxing match are coming together to form a consensus that is refereed by the question of dosage. But this consensus still does not address the fundamental question posed above.

We appear to have a paradox. How can it be resolved? Perhaps it is no coincidence that we are getting less sunlight, more overweight and more skin cancer at the same time. The cause of skin cancer is not known and there is currently a great deal of research taking place that will improve our understanding in the future. In the meantime, in this chapter I would like to explore the possibilities by asking some straightforward questions.

Could it be that skin cancer and vitamin D deficiency are unconnected, occurring in different places, or in the same places but in different people?

Or is it that the two are separated in time – first, higher ultraviolet levels caused increases in skin cancer, and then the sun protection campaigns took effect and caused or exacerbated vitamin D deficiency?

Different Places

Are skin cancer and vitamin D deficiency occurring in different places? In general, it is reasonable to expect that in tropical and subtropical countries, at low latitudes where the sunlight is strong, the prevalence of skin cancer should be high, whereas that of vitamin D deficiency should be low or even absent. On the other hand, in temperate and polar regions at mid and high latitudes, where the sunlight is weaker and there is no vitamin D to be made in the winter, we would expect skin cancer to be absent or low and vitamin D deficiency to be high.

With the exception of South Africa, melanoma is rare in Africa, because, it is thought, the population is mainly black with skin less susceptible to damage by ultraviolet than white skin. South Africa may be the exception because it has the highest white population in Africa as well as being at higher latitude. Melanoma is also rare in Asian countries. The two countries with the highest rates are Australia and New Zealand. These countries have a combination of strong sunlight and a largely fair-skinned population. For many people this fact alone is sufficient to explain the link between sunlight exposure and skin cancer. The five countries with the next highest rates of melanoma are Switzerland, Denmark, Norway, The Netherlands and Sweden. More details about melanoma incidence can be found in the notes.

No one is surprised that melanoma has increased in Australia, but why has it also increased in Denmark at latitude 55° N? In fact, as well as having the fourth highest rate of melanoma of the world, Denmark also has a high rate of non-melanoma skin cancer – squamous cell carcinoma doubled and basal cell carcinoma trebled between 1978 and 2007. In general, skin cancer is higher in northern Europe than in southern Europe – the opposite of what you would expect if skin cancer were caused by sunlight exposure. Even Iceland, at latitude 64° N just south of the Arctic Circle, has a relatively high rate of skin cancer. It seems that on a regional basis, there is not a direct link between skin cancer and sunlight availability.

What about vitamin D deficiency? It has been studied mostly in middle and high latitudes – for a long time it was assumed that no one can be deficient in vitamin D in tropical or subtropical countries such as Australia. One of the first questions I was asked when I told others of this idea that vitamin D deficiency is the cause of overweight was, 'Why are Australians overweight when they get so much sunlight?' In fact, both overweight and vitamin D deficiency are common in Australia and New Zealand, the two countries with the highest incidence of skin cancer, and vitamin D deficiency is now recognised as a growing problem there. We have already seen in this book that sunlight does not equal ultraviolet and that the assumption that people who live in sunny places get more ultraviolet is incorrect for many reasons – ground-level ultraviolet is affected by altitude, the built environment and atmospheric pollutants as well as the more obvious latitude and season. It is not surprising, therefore, that vitamin D deficiency is present in Australia and New Zealand. In summary, it appears that skin cancer and vitamin D deficiency can occur in the same places, but do they occur in the same people?

Different people

With regard to behaviour, we would expect the people who get skin cancer to be the ones who sunbathe, use sunbeds, don't use sunscreen, get tanned, and go on sun seeking holidays abroad, while another group of people get vitamin D deficiency because they don't sunbathe, never use sunbeds, always use sunscreens, and avoid sunlight exposure as much as possible. It is difficult to measure this kind of activity objectively, so there is no way of knowing this at present. We would expect to find that patients with skin cancer should have plenty of vitamin D and people with low levels of vitamin D are less likely to get skin cancer, but some studies have found quite the opposite.

What about skin colour? We might reasonably assume that those with the lightest skin should have the greatest risk of skin cancer but also the highest vitamin D levels, while those with the darkest skin should have the highest vitamin D deficiency and the lowest risk of skin cancer. Relatively recent migrations have resulted in light-skinned people living at low latitudes – for example, the white descendants of the British in Australia and New Zealand, who we expect to be susceptible to skin cancer – and dark-skinned people at high latitudes – for example, the black descendants of Africans and Caribbeans in Europe, Canada, and the USA, who we expect to be susceptible to vitamin D deficiency. In general most studies find that this is correct. Skin cancer is mostly a disease of white people and those with the lightest skin are the most susceptible. It is also true that vitamin D deficiency tends to be more common in black people than white people living at high latitudes. But Daniel Glass, of King's College London, found some surprising results when he studied more than one thousand women, with skin types 1, 2, 3 and 4 (from very pale, Celtic type skin that never tans to the darker Mediterranean– or Chinese–type skin that tans easily). Those with the darkest skin had the highest vitamin D levels. The women in the study who had more holidays abroad and used sunbeds tended to have darker skin and higher vitamin D levels. This is interesting because it suggests that people with the fairest skins, who we presume can make the most vitamin D in a given time, may not have the highest vitamin D. In fact, it suggests that very fair skin could possibly be a consequence of vitamin D deficiency.

In summary, it is clear that the population can be divided on the basis of skin colour for risk of skin cancer. But we should be careful about making assumptions that fair-skinned people are less likely to be vitamin D-deficient, or that skin cancer and vitamin D deficiency cannot occur in the same person or population group.

Timing

Did the rise in skin cancer come first, followed by vitamin D deficiency? Perhaps higher ultraviolet exposure due to ozone thinning caused increases in skin cancer at first, and then the sun protection campaigns took effect and caused vitamin D deficiency. This could explain how both vitamin D deficiency and skin cancer occur in the same places, but would they occur at the same time?

We might expect the rise in vitamin D deficiency to come after the rise in skin cancer, but whereas we know that calcidiol rises and falls within a few weeks of any change in sunlight exposure, we don't know how long it takes for the damage that causes skin cancer to become detectable. Based upon the increase in risk of melanoma in people who suffered sunburn in childhood, and the fact that melanoma is rare in children (although it does occur in young adults), it is thought that there could be years or even decades between the time of the damage (e.g. sunburn in childhood) and the first appearance of a skin cancer (e.g. melanoma in middle age). A skin cancer diagnosed today might result from exposure that took place in the 1970s or 1980s.

Perhaps the main way in which we have been exposed to more ultraviolet in the past 50 years has been by going abroad on holiday. In 2008, 18.5 million people went on package holidays abroad, compared to 2.7 million in 1970. In some quarters it is thought that this is the main cause of the increase in melanoma, which has been particularly high in older people – those people in their 60s and 70s who went on their first package holidays, when in their 20s and 30s, in the 1970s before the campaigns for sun protection began.

Could vitamin D deficiency be caused by sun protection? Any measure we take to block sunlight from our skin, whether it is wearing clothing, wearing a hat, using sunscreen, staying in the shade or staying indoors, will prevent ultraviolet photons from getting to our skin and stop us from making vitamin D. There can be no doubt that sun protection can contribute to vitamin D deficiency. In confirmation, Jörg Reichrath, Professor at the Clinic for Dermatology at the University of Homburg, studied the calcidiol levels of patients with xeroderma pigmentosum and kidney transplant patients, who are advised to be extra careful about protecting their skin from sunlight because they have a much higher risk of skin cancer. He found that they had extremely low calcidiol levels (less than 30). One assumes that they were not advised to take vitamin D supplements, or at least, not enough to compensate for the loss of sunlight exposure.

In summary, it is quite possible that skin cancer increased first and was then followed by an increase in vitamin D deficiency. If this is correct, there could be a dramatic fall in skin cancer incidence in the years to come. However, there are many contributing factors to vitamin D deficiency, and sun protection can only have a minor role.

Sunlight exposure or skin sensitivity?

Is skin sensitivity more important than sunlight exposure? The relationship between skin cancer and sunlight exposure may not be entirely consistent, but one thing we can be sure about is that many of the common risk factors for skin cancer relate to photosensitive skin. Pale skin, freckles, blond hair and a history of sunburn are all related to sensitivity and there is no doubt about its importance as a risk factor for skin cancer. The fact that most skin cancer occurs in white people, particularly those with the palest skin, and that there is a link between sunburns and skin cancer, along with the low incidence of skin cancer in Africa compared to Australia and New Zealand, tell us that susceptibility is more important than sunlight exposure.

In Chapter 1 Helpful Radiation, I talked about the properties of the skin and how differences in the thickness and colour of the skin can present obstacles to the penetration of photons of ultraviolet into the cells of our skin. The thicker the skin, the more likely it is that photons will be reflected before they can do any damage inside your cells. And when they do get inside the cells, melanin acts like a sunshade for DNA, absorbing ultraviolet before it gets to DNA, so the more melanin you have, the less likely it is that photons will do any damage.

What factors affect skin sensitivity? The main factor is heredity – we inherit our skin properties, but within limits, the skin can adapt to become more or less sensitive. When exposed to sunlight, photoadaptation takes place – a phenomenon we see as tanning.

Sunburn and tanning are opposing reactions – if your skin tans easily it doesn't burn, and if it burns easily it doesn't tan much. Tanning involves an increase in the amount of melanin in your skin and a thickening of your skin. Both these changes stop ultraviolet photons from getting into your skin. They don't stop ultraviolet completely – you can still make vitamin D even with the darkest black skin – but you might need to be outdoors for longer or in stronger ultraviolet to make the same amount as you would if you had pale white skin. The trouble with pale white skin is that although you have the ability to make more vitamin D in a given time in the sunlight, you may actually make less in practice because, without the natural defences of black skin, you need to artificially protect your skin from the sunlight to avoid sunburn.

The opposite process to photoadaptation is photosensitisation. If you spend little time outdoors, your skin becomes thinner and contains less melanin to maximise the amount of ultraviolet radiation allowed to enter, so that you can make vitamin D in low ultraviolet conditions. This also increases the susceptibility to the damage that can lead to skin cancer and other conditions. This is why sunburn is more likely to occur in people on holiday or on a day off from work and is less likely in people who spend a lot of time outdoors, such as gardeners and golfers.

Photoadaptation changes your skin to ensure that your body gets the same effects from different levels of sunlight. There is a trade-off between sensitivity to ultraviolet, which increases your ability to make vitamin D but makes you more vulnerable to damage, and resistance to ultraviolet, which protects your skin from harm but makes less vitamin D.

Within our inherited limits, skin is self-regulating. It makes biological sense that if we lack vitamin D, our skin becomes thinner and lighter to enable us to make more when exposed to ultraviolet. It is reasonable to assume that those of us with fair skin have ancestors who experienced vitamin D deficiency. When we sunburn easily it might be because we have become sensitised to sunlight. On the other hand, when you have plenty of vitamin D, your skin can thicken and darken more quickly. This is not to suggest that you can get a tan by taking vitamin D supplements, but if you can raise your vitamin D status in this way you might find that you tan more easily and do not burn so easily when you are exposed to sunlight. Indeed there is some evidence that diet can affect the photosensitivity of the skin.

One of the risk factors for skin cancer is sunburn, and the best way to avoid sunburn is to get some regular sunlight exposure so that your skin adapts, whereas sunlight protection makes sunburn more likely. So could it be that, counter-intuitively, our attempts to protect our skin from skin cancer by avoiding sunlight exposure are actually making it more sensitive? And is it possible that vitamin D deficiency can explain the rise in skin cancer?

Are we becoming more photosensitive?

When my friends return from a holiday with a suntan they look good. When I've been out in the sunlight and look a little browner than usual, people tell me I look well. And it isn't just about colour, since fake tan doesn't look good (at least in my opinion). When the sun is shining, we want to get the barbecue out, or go down to the beach, and let our young children run around with little or nothing on. The fact that many of us feel that getting outdoors on a sunny day is a good thing, and that we believe that a suntan is a sign of good health, is a problem for the sun protection campaigns. We are told by the experts that what seems natural is abnormal, harmful and even reckless behaviour. But perhaps our instincts are right and the sun protection campaigns are wrong.

Skin cancer is not the only disease, and not the only cancer to have increased in recent decades. If it were the only type of cancer to be increasing, it might be more likely due to sunlight exposure alone. However, other cancers, for which there is no suggestion of sunlight as a contributory factor, are also increasing in incidence. The incidence of breast cancer, for example, has increased since the 1970s, in many countries, including Australia and New Zealand. The cause of this increase is not known, but there is no suggestion of a connection to sunlight exposure. There is always a possibility that improved detection has caused these increases, and it is generally thought that an ageing population can explain much of the increase, but what if there is a common risk factor? Some people think it could be vitamin D deficiency.

The brothers Cedric and Frank Garland, both Professors of Preventive Medicine at the University of California, San Diego, became interested in a possible link between vitamin D deficiency and cancer in the 1970s when they attended a seminar about cancer and noted how death rates from breast and colon cancer were higher in northern states of the USA than in south-western states. In 1980 they published a hypothesis that vitamin D and calcium could prevent cancer. Since then they have published around 50 papers linking sunlight to cancer prevention, which run counter to the mainstream view that sunlight causes skin cancer and question the use of sunscreen as a preventive measure. Edward Giovannucci, Professor of Nutrition and Epidemiology at Harvard School of Public Health, calculated that raising calcidiol would prevent more than 85,000 deaths from cancer in men in the USA. Compare this to the 7,000 deaths in men caused by melanoma and you can see why vitamin D experts think we should get more sunlight.

Ultraviolet starvation

Perhaps the reason we have become so keen on sunbathing and sunlight is precisely because we are not getting so much in our daily lives. Richard Hobday, in his book *The Healing Sun*, describes how sunlight was used as medicine at the beginning of the twentieth century, a practice that became forgotten once antibiotics became widely available. Within a century, our view of sunlight had swung from healing to hazardous. He also points out that in agricultural societies pale skin was desirable, as tans were associated with the working class. Today, in our modern, urban-industrial society, a tan has become highly desirable and seems to have become more popular over the past decades, perhaps because it is associated with holidays abroad, which not so long ago were the preserve of the rich.

But is there more to the desire for a tan than looking rich? Dermatologists seem to be puzzled at what they regard as reckless behaviour. As we have learned more about the risk of skin cancer, some of us still want to tan and keep on sunbathing. Could it be that as the availability of ultraviolet has declined, we need to make an effort to get some, just as we might go to the gym before going to work in an office? Exercise for its own sake is not necessary if you do a physically demanding job, but when you spend all day sitting in a chair you benefit from intensive exercise for a short period for a few days each week. Similarly, if you get little ultraviolet as you go about your everyday life, you might go out of your way to get a strong burst of it whenever you get the opportunity. The practice of sunbathing in a bikini or swimming shorts, or using a sunbed to get a tan, is not necessary in agricultural societies where work is mostly done outdoors.

Suppose, for a moment, ultraviolet at ground level declined dramatically in the second half of the twentieth century so that today we make just a fraction – perhaps a half, or even a tenth – of the amount of vitamin D we could previously make just by walking to the station. Perhaps in the past, even people who did not work outdoors were still able to get sufficient ultraviolet as they went about their daily business, and perhaps today we are getting less and less and must instead make an effort to compensate by deliberate sunbathing. Making all the vitamin D we need is no longer a passive procedure – instead we need to go out of our way to make it. If we don't, we become hypersensitive to sunlight, so that the harm it can do may outweigh the benefits, and – quite sensibly – we avoid it. Is it possible that counter-intuitively, a reduction in ultraviolet has caused both the rise in vitamin D deficiency and the rise in skin cancer?

Should we strip off or cover up?

At present, we can only speculate on the cause of skin cancer, which is not the subject of this book. There is much research going on into skin cancer and we should have a much better understanding of it in the future. In the meantime what do we do? Exposure to ultraviolet radiation confers both health risks and benefits. Sunburn, skin cancer and vitamin D are not the only effects of sunlight exposure. Other conditions can be caused, triggered, or worsened by sunlight exposure, including heatstroke, migraines, eczema, rosacea, sun rash, and lupus. And for all we know, the benefits of sunlight exposure may not be confined to raising vitamin D. For most environmental risk factors, zero exposure results in minimal disease incidence; however, for ultraviolet radiation this is not the case – we know that zero exposure causes disease. Even if there is a direct link between sunlight exposure and skin cancer, reducing ultraviolet exposure to zero is not an option.

Robyn Lucas, of the Australian National University, and her colleagues calculated the disease burden of ultraviolet exposure in the year 2000 and compared it to the disease burden if ultraviolet exposure was lowered, resulting in bone diseases caused directly by vitamin D deficiency. They estimated that ultraviolet exposure was the cause of 50,000 deaths, and that, in total, 1.6 million years of life were lost either to premature death or poor health, mostly due to cutaneous malignant melanoma and cataracts. They then calculated what would happen if ultraviolet exposure was reduced and found that the disease burden would rise to 3.3 *billion* years of healthy life lost. Their calculations included only the increase in rickets, osteomalacia and osteoporosis and did not include any of the other diseases that might increase with vitamin D deficiency. They concluded that, overall, ultraviolet exposure is a minor contributor to the world's disease burden and that it is essential to avoid vitamin D deficiency.

Just as both underweight and overweight are associated with health problems and the ideal weight is somewhere in the middle, so too does underexposure and overexposure to ultraviolet radiation result in ill health. The work of Robyn Lucas suggests that overexposure is less dangerous than underexposure, at least on worldwide population basis.

Our skin protects the rest of the body from sunlight but it is on the front line. Can it protect itself? On the one hand, we have delicate skin, on the other, we have physiological mechanisms for protecting it. When we compare our skin to other land-living animals, there is no doubt that we humans have sensitive skin that is susceptible to damage. We have no fur or feathers to cover our skin, our hair is sparse and fine, and our skin is thin and fragile. Elephants cover their skin with mud, which dries and acts as a sunscreen (and also helps to avoid infection from biting insects). Baby elephants stay in the shade of their mothers to protect their skin from the sun. It is not unreasonable to expect that we should have a particular need to protect our skin from everyday sunlight. But perhaps we should make the most of our in-built mechanisms for protecting our skin and we may need to be exposed to sunlight in order to be protected from it.

PART II

WEIGHT

Two Humans and Two Habitats

Two men

There are two men: one is thin and the other is fat. The thin man eats whatever he wants and never gains weight. He has three meals a day. He doesn't think about food much at all – when he is hungry he eats as much as he likes and then he forgets about food until the next meal. The fat man is always hungry. He has three meals a day – but it is never enough and he is always going to the fridge or cupboard in between meals for something else to eat. He never wants to do any exercise and when he does try it he finds it very difficult.

Two men in a hot habitat

A thin man and a fat man went on a hunting expedition on the tropical savannah to hunt an animal for food. The thin man's body was muscular and agile. He could run fast and far, jump long and high, throw rocks and spears, swing on branches and climb trees. He could easily crouch behind bushes and jump over obstacles. He was strong and could lift heavy weights with ease. The fat man might have had muscles but they were hidden under a mass of wobbly fat. He could throw a rock or spear quite well, but he could only jog a little way before he had to stop to get his breath back and he was too fat to jump at all. Although he found the heat uncomfortable he wore full-length trousers and a shirt because he was too embarrassed to expose his fat body, while the lean man wore just a pair of shorts. The fat man was useless at hunting. Instead, he became the hunted animal and was caught and eaten by a lion, while the thin man carried home an animal to feed his tribe.

Two men in a cold habitat

A fat man and a thin man went on a polar expedition. The weather turned bad and they got stuck in a blizzard. There was no shelter, food was scarce and the temperature dropped well below freezing. The two men began to starve. The thin man had only his own muscles to provide his body with energy. The thin man had a higher surface area to volume ratio, so he lost heat quickly and started to shiver first. His core temperature dropped quickly and before long he suffered from hypothermia. The fat man, on the other hand, had a low surface area to volume ratio, so he was better at retaining heat. He could use his stores of fat for energy before he needed to break down his muscle protein. His core temperature was protected by the constriction and dilation of his blood vessels. He had plenty of triglyceride in his muscles to provide fuel for shivering and a higher proportion of the best shivering muscle fibres. His cells produced more heat by increasing thermogenesis. By the time rescuers found them, the fat man was no longer fat but he was alive and well, while the thin man had died long before.

Chapter 5

Fatstat Facts

FOR A LONG TIME, the cause of overweight seemed obvious to all – eating too much and not doing enough exercise results in an excess of energy that is stored on the body as fat. Why *do* people eat too much if it is making them fat? Ask anyone why they are overweight and you will get an answer personal to the individual. Here are some examples:

- Janet
- Janet, 61, has always been overweight, although she has gained most weight in the past three years since giving up her nursing job to take care of her elderly mother. She blames her grandmother, who would bake cakes and stodgy puddings for her as a child, and her father who, separated from her mother, would always bring a big bag of sweets and chocolates when he visited, both leading her to associate high-calorie food with the feeling of being loved.

- Ken

- Ken is aged 56 and weighs 102 kg (16 stone or 225 pounds). He says that he started putting on weight ten years ago when he stopped smoking and instead of reaching for a cigarette he would eat cakes and biscuits when he was at home, or sweets and chocolates when he was out and about. He also puts his weight gain down to cycling less than he did when he was younger.

- Emma

- Emma, 30, gained weight rapidly when she was made redundant from her job. She found it difficult to find another job and quickly sank into a depression. She felt that food became a comfort at a difficult time and although she now has a new job, is over the depression and eating less, she can't shift the excess weight.

- Rebecca

- Rebecca is 46 and has been overweight for almost all her life. She says most of her family were overweight and she got sucked into a culture of hysteria about weight, dieting and food. In her forties she had hypnotherapy, which established that she had always had a low self-esteem because she had dyslexia and was bullied at school. She would eat when she was anxious, or when she was happy or when she was angry.

- Keiran

- Keiran, 25, says he eats out of habit. He doesn't try to explain it – he just doesn't know why he keeps eating and why he can't stop, or why he can't just eat less. He's tried exercise but he suffers from knee and back problems.

Keiran is unusual in not offering an explanation for his overweight. Most people put their weight gain down to their upbringing or a change in their personal circumstances, and the predominant theme is psychological. *Self-esteem, emotional eating, stress, comfort eating, anxiety, feelings, relationship with food* – these are the words and phrases that are commonly used by people when they talk about overweight.

For a long time, the *solution* to overweight seemed obvious to all – simply reverse the cause of overweight by eating less and doing more exercise to restore the energy balance. If things were really so simple, of course, there would be no epidemic of overweight and this book would never have been written. It sounds easy enough, yet it seems to require momentous effort and extensive management.

- Samantha

- Samantha, 36, was 95 kg (15 stone or 209 pounds) and lost 33 kg (just over 5 stone or 73 pounds) by going to a weekly slimming club. As well as dieting, she took up walking and, after a while, started running. She is now 62 kg (9 stone 10 lb or 137 pounds), and runs 5 km three times a week. She says she felt the time was right for her to re-educate herself about food. She still keeps a food diary and keeps in regular contact with her fellow slimmers from the club, which helps her to keep the weight off.

- Lucy

- Lucy is aged 27 and weighs 76 kg (12 stone or 168 pounds) after losing 18 kg (almost 3 stone or 40 pounds) on a weight loss programme. She had started to gain weight at university, lost the weight by dieting, but then regained it when she was in her final year. Since then she continually monitored her eating habits and tried diet after diet. She says she had tried every diet, including the grapefruit diet and the cabbage soup diet, until this new programme finally succeeded. The programme involved sticking to a regime, weighing food, counting calories, planning meals and keeping a food diary. She has now stopped drinking alcohol completely but still eats chocolate, although no more than ten grams at a time and only as an occasional treat. She believes that this time she has really conquered control of her weight and will keep it off. She says, '*this time I was determined to stick to it. I truly believe that anyone can lose weight if they really set their mind to it.*'

- Harry

- Harry lost almost 10 kg (1.5 stone or 22 pounds) and 20 cm (8 inches) from his waist after attending a slimming club. He was unable to comment as he is a Labrador dog.

Words and phrases that are often associated with losing weight are *determination, motivation, willpower, discipline, personal goals, identifying barriers, making the right choices*. You can read similar stories to those above in any slimming magazine, many women's magazines and newspapers. The stories give the impression that the slimmer has finally done it and there is a happy ending – 'and so he/she lived happily and slimly ever after'. But the truth is that most successful slimmers face a lifetime of effort to keep the weight off – that means a lifetime of hunger – otherwise they will regain the weight and, when they do, no one has an interest in publicising their unhappy story, least of all the slimmers themselves who have 'failed' where they previously 'succeeded'. Nevertheless, some people do lose weight fairly easily *and* keep it off in the long term without going hungry. Did they have all the right personal characteristics, or did they just get lucky?

We don't need to control our weight

People don't like restricting their food intake. Why? What is it about food? Well, for a start, it is absolutely essential to survival. Every living thing needs to eat, and to eat sufficient nutrients to function properly. Even an amoeba with a body consisting of just one cell can find its way to food. Is it so surprising that trying to lose weight goes against our natural instincts? Perhaps we underestimate the power of our survival faculties and overestimate our ability to command conscious control over vital functions. We should be able to eat what we need – what we *like* – without worrying about our weight. People sometimes talk about how food has changed over the past ten thousand years or so but hunger has evolved over *millions* of years. Every living thing needs to eat but does every living thing need to understand what constitutes a healthy, balanced diet?

Food isn't just a source of fuel to be burned or stored, like a litre of petrol in a car. It is also needed to provide the building blocks for our bodies. Muscle, skin and bone need to be constructed in childhood, and throughout life they need to be renewed and repaired in a continuous process. Food provides the materials for making new blood cells and the lining of our digestive system and lungs. We need food to fight off infections, dispose of toxins, and to convert molecules from one into another. We need food even to digest food. Of course we need food for energy, not just for exercise but also for every process in our bodies, and we need energy to maintain our core body temperature. Would our bodies allow control of food intake to be easily affected by our conscious mind, our state of psychological well-being, and social and cultural factors, when it is so important?

When overweight was confined to a minority of the population it was thought that certain individuals had a propensity for overweight, either because of their genotype or because of their 'learned behaviour' and, until the 1990s, the study of overweight was dominated by studies of monogenic disorders and behaviour. There was a significant change of direction towards interest in the physiological control of energy upon the discovery of a hormone called leptin. Leptin was first discovered in 1994 in mice by Jeffrey Friedman at the Howard Hughes Medical Institute. He called it leptin from the Greek word *leptos* for thin. Mice that were deficient in leptin gained weight and suffered from the problems of metabolism associated with overweight in humans, such as diabetes and high blood pressure. When these mice were given leptin injections, they lost weight and their metabolism went back to normal. The discovery of leptin made big news as it was thought that 'the fat gene' had finally been isolated.

You can appreciate the excitement at this discovery. It was thought that perhaps overweight humans were deficient in leptin just like the laboratory mice, and since the mice could be cured of overweight by treatment with leptin, it would be possible to use leptin as a simple treatment to reverse overweight in humans. Unfortunately, it didn't work, but it did serve as a jump-start as far as research into overweight was concerned and prompted efforts to look for other factors that might be responsible for controlling weight. Much research has been done in the years since the discovery of leptin, which has uncovered a number of different signal molecules and pathways involved in weight control. This has resulted in the emergence of a new branch of science called *energy homeostasis.*

The idea of energy homeostasis has been around for a long time. Food intake tends to increase when we are more active and we become less active when food is scarce. So there seems to be a natural process at work – at least in normal circumstances – to keep our weight stable and our energy in balance. It turns out that leptin acts on neurons in an area of the brain called the hypothalamus that has long been known to be involved in appetite.

Research has also revealed that fat cells are not just inert storage depots but instead are active organs, releasing hormones and cytokines that interact with other parts of the body. Energy homeostasis is, without doubt, essential to protect us from starving to death. It is easy to forget, when we are thinking about trying to control our weight, that feeding is a vital process and that our energy balance needs to be very carefully regulated by our physiology.

Keeping things stable

Homeostasis is a way of keeping things *tickety-boo.* The literal definition of homeostasis is 'to remain the same' and it is essentially a resistance to change in a changing world. Homeostasis is one of the essential principles in all branches of science and we know that electronic and mechanical systems break down if their systems are not controlled.

For an example of homeostasis, think about the control of body temperature. Those of us in temperate countries with variable weather are familiar with having to cope with changing ambient temperatures. In one moment we might move from a temperature of 23°C indoors to an outdoor temperature that is below freezing, yet we keep our body at the same temperature. The temperature of the blood is monitored by an area of the brain called the hypothalamus and the external temperature is detected by thermoreceptors in the skin that are connected to the hypothalamus. When the temperature is too high measures are taken to lower it: we sweat, our body hair lays flat against our skin and blood is diverted to capillaries just below the skin's surface. Our metabolic rate is lowered so we generate less internal heat. We take off our jumpers, switch off the heating and eat ice creams. On the other hand, when the temperature is too low, we stop sweating and start shivering, our body hair stands upright and the blood capillaries close to our skin are closed down. We pull on our jumpers, turn up the heating and have some hot soup. These measures keep our temperature within a very narrow range between 35°C and 38°C.

For another example, think about breathing, which is normally controlled unconsciously so we don't have to think about it, but our conscious mind can take control if we want it to. You can easily control the depth of breathing and the rate. If you take the conscious control away, you will continue to breathe and the depth and rate of breathing will be precisely regulated according to your body's requirements. When you run up the stairs you will breathe a bit faster and a bit deeper; when you fall asleep you will breathe slowly and in shallow breaths. Conscious control of breathing is difficult to sustain for any great length of time – it's too much of an effort and your breathing won't necessarily be sufficient for your body's needs. If you try taking over control of your breathing with your conscious mind you will find that it is not easy, without training, to take regular, rhythmic breaths that are just right. Every so often you will have to take a big breath to catch up. At worst it can make you feel ill, and at best it gets rather boring and you just give up. At this point the master controller – your physiology – will take over to ensure that you get sufficient oxygen for your needs. It is as if your unconscious brain were thinking, 'if you want a job done properly, do it yourself'.

Leave it to the experts

Our conscious minds are, in fact, not very good at controlling our physiological processes. We might have the power to take control in an emergency but we just don't have the fine-tuning ability. Coaching for top-level sports often involves some mental training to let go of conscious control. Physiological management is best left to the expert subconscious and this includes management of eating, because our physiological mechanisms are best at controlling the amount of food we eat. When we try to take over using our conscious minds, as we do when we try to lose weight by dieting, we might be able to do it for a short time if we really try hard, but eventually our body has to take over.

If you have ever tried a diet, full of determination at the start only to give up and stuff yourself after a few days, you will know what I mean. You seem to be making up for all those calories you so valiantly resisted for the first few days. Where did that hunger come from? We find excuses for giving up – 'it's boring' – or blame difficulties in our lives, such as problem at work, but the truth is that our conscious mind was overpowered by our homeostatic control mechanisms. We see it as a weakness, but instead it is an indication of the *strength* of our physiological control. As far as our physiology is concerned, our being unable to do up our jeans or having a poor body image is a trivial matter compared to our survival – and we must eat to survive.

Since breathing and temperature are carefully controlled, as are, indeed, every function of our bodies, there must surely be regulation of body weight. The popular view is that we are overweight because we have a natural tendency to be greedy and lazy – tendencies that we must keep under control by using our conscious minds – but this view does not make biological sense. The fact is that there are mechanisms in place for controlling the amount we eat and the amount of fat we store in our bodies, and when we understand how the body controls energy we can appreciate just how powerful these mechanisms are.

The internal controls over body weight

In a system of energy homeostasis, what, exactly, can be controlled? There are three main points of control. These are energy intake, energy partitioning, and energy expenditure – and they all need to be in balance to maintain a stable weight. Energy intake can be controlled by managing how much we eat and by regulating the amount of food absorbed in our digestive system.

Control of appetite

If we wanted to design some appetite control, what, exactly, would we need to control? We eat our food, normally, in several sessions – meals – during the day. We don't eat at night because we need unbroken sleep and we can manage without food for at least eight hours at night. During the day, it would be inefficient to eat all the time as it would leave no time to do anything else, but it would mean that we could manage with smaller digestive systems. On the other hand, imagine if we could eat a day's supply of food in one meal – we would have more free time to do other things but our digestive systems would have to be enormous. Eating three meals a day, as most of us do, can be seen as a compromise between getting as much as a reasonably-sized digestive system can cope with in one meal and enough to allow us to forget about food for intervals in between. This freedom between meals allows us to spend our time and energy on education, industry, technology, leisure and all the other things we do. What signals do we need to make sure that we eat the right amount at the right times?

I'm hungry

Firstly, we need a signal that tells us when we need food. Whatever we happen to be doing at the time, our attention must be diverted to the need for food or else we could easily starve simply by forgetting to eat. Our brains must be stimulated into thinking about food and must motivate us to seek out food, so we need an appetite-initiating factor. If we try to ignore it and allow time to go by without eating, the appetite gets stronger. At first we might just think that we would like something to eat, gradually our appetite becomes stronger, and the need for food – and the energy that we are willing to put into finding food – increases. If time without food is prolonged, eventually we become obsessed about food. This is important to avoid starvation. If we had no appetite we would starve to death, so we need to ensure that the appetite is sustained until we start eating.

Mmmmm, this food looks delicious

Now that we have found our food we need a signal to start eating. This is what we are familiar with as the everyday meaning of the term appetite – the desire to eat the food in front of us. We need to start eating and then we need to continue until we have had enough. Food looks good and smells good when we are hungry. Taste and smell of course are very important, but the hungrier we are, the more delicious a meal seems to be. The food itself is not saying 'eat me' but our need for it makes it attractive. If we are hungry for a burger and chips but find the 'healthy' alternative, a sesame seed salad, unappetising, could it be because we need the burger and chips more than we need the salad? In other words, perhaps our hunger is related to our nutritional needs rather than a quality intrinsic to the food.

Please, Sir, can I have more?

We may perhaps need a signal to carry on eating until we have had an adequate amount. Taste, smell and satisfying feelings keep us eating.

I couldn't eat another morsel

Then we need a signal to stop. Given an endless supply of food, what makes us feel full and decide to stop eating? We need a signal that makes us satisfied once we have eaten sufficient to keep us going until the next meal. We need a satiety factor and it needs to come at the right point. If we stop eating too early, we will not get enough energy to last until the next meal and if we stop eating too late, we will not be able to digest the food.

I'm busy

Finally, we need a signal to suppress appetite so that we can forget all about food and are free to get on with other things in between meals.

In summary, we need appetite to be initiated, sustained, increased, decreased and suppressed. A complex hormonal and neuronal system can achieve all of this. We can see that a fault at any point will cause problems. People with anorexia cannot eat much because they lack appetite. They may either lack the appetite-initiation signal so that they simply forget about eating, they may have an interest in food but cannot bring themselves to start eating, or they eat very little at each meal. They would seem to have a faulty appetite control. So, too, would people with bulimia who cannot stop eating, even when they have eaten enough and consequently they eat far too much. They would seem to lack the satiety factor. Having then eaten too much for their digestive system to cope with the logical thing is to make themselves sick to reduce the amount of food in their stomachs and thereby reduce the load on their digestive systems. Without this, it is possible to eat so much that the stomach swells, pushes other organs aside and presses on the major veins causing circulatory problems – a condition called acute gastric dilatation. This can be fatal but usually the pain and discomfort of an extended abdomen limits the excess. (I once saw an explanation of bulimia that said it is a 'hunger for emotional attention'. Why not a hunger for *food*? Sometimes it seems that eating has become like the naked emperor in the story *The Emperor's New Clothes* – we are not seeing what is in front of our eyes.)

Some people are hungry all the time because their appetite-initiation signal seems to be switched on permanently, but the majority of people who are overweight experience a relatively moderate increase in appetite. The time between meals when they forget about food becomes shorter – leading to snacking – and they eat a little more (or perhaps a lot more) at each meal. It seems that the main problem in overweight is not that the appetite signals are faulty, since most people will stop eating for a while, but that they are working at a higher level – the volume has been turned up. It is as if they have been instructed to increase food intake.

Appetite signals

What are some examples of the signalling in appetite control? One of the signals that controls appetite is called cholecystokinin. It was one of the first such signals to be discovered – along with insulin, which is also known to affect appetite – in the 1920s. Cholecystokinin is released by the stomach in response to nutrients and levels remain high for about five hours after a meal.

The more fat there is in the meal the more cholecystokinin is produced. In the brain, it acts as a satiety factor. Cholecystokinin is also a coordinator of digestion: stimulating release of enzymes from the pancreas and gall bladder, increasing intestinal motility and inhibiting gastric emptying. In other words, it helps you to digest the meal you are eating, or have just eaten.

Like cholecystokinin, the level of another signal, called peptide YY (so called because it has the amino acid tyrosine at each end and Y is the abbreviation for tyrosine) goes up after a meal and stays up for about six hours. The higher the calories in the meal, the more peptide YY is produced, so the bigger the meal, the longer it takes to go back down again. Pancreatic polypeptide is another signal that is similar to peptide YY in that it goes up after a meal and stays high for about six hours.

These are just a few of the signals that are released when we eat. They help us to digest the food we have eaten and to feel satisfied, so that we stop eating when we have had enough and forget about food for a while between meals.

Whereas these three signals – cholecystokinin, pancreatic polypeptide and peptide YY – are low before a meal and go up after eating, a substance called ghrelin does the opposite. Ghrelin was discovered in 1999 and already it has been established that it has an important role in the control of eating and energy expenditure. It rises in the blood before a meal and seems to be a hunger signal. Once we have eaten, ghrelin levels fall but only after eating food – not if we just drink water. Drinking water is sometimes recommended in diets to increase the feeling of a full stomach, but it wouldn't fool ghrelin. Ghrelin is produced by the stomach (as well as the intestine and pituitary) and its production is suppressed after gastric banding surgery. This loss of ghrelin production persists for years after the surgery and it may be the key to the success of the technique, since patients feel less hungry after the surgery. Another substance that, like ghrelin, goes down after eating and then goes up again during fasting is called neuropeptide Y.

In summary, it seems that normally neuropeptide Y and ghrelin are high before a meal and these could be responsible, at least in part, for making us hungry and once we have eaten a meal they drop down again. While neuropeptide Y and ghrelin go down as we eat, cholecystokinin, pancreatic polypeptide and peptide YY, which were low before our meal, go up once we have eaten. These may be responsible for making us stop eating once we have had enough. There is cross talk between these signals – for example cholecystokinin influences the levels of peptide YY. It is still early days when it comes to understanding how all these signals interact. What is without doubt, however, is that these signals are part of a complex system and when we try to consciously control our eating we must override these powerful signals.

Control of absorption

We have so far only considered the control of appetite but this is only one point of control in energy homeostasis. Another is in the absorption of nutrients from our food by our digestive system. Not all of the food we eat becomes part of us – the nutrients contained in food need to be transported from inside the digestive system to the bloodstream, and it is possible that the brain can instruct the digestive system to absorb certain nutrients and not others according to the body's needs. If so, this could mean that one person might take in more calories than another person, even when they eat exactly the same meal.

Not much is known about the control of absorption but we do know of a few examples in which absorption can change. One familiar example is the use of phytosterols in products such as spreads to reduce the amount of cholesterol absorbed from the diet. Other examples are phytates, which are found in unrefined cereals, and oxalates, found in some foods such as rhubarb, sweet potato and spinach. Phytates and oxalates bind metal ions such as calcium, iron and zinc preventing their absorption. For example, spinach contains more magnesium than kale, but because it also contains more oxalates you will get more magnesium from eating kale than from spinach. People with a diet high in unrefined cereals and low in meat are at risk of mineral deficiencies because of this, and some people refer to phytates and oxalates as antinutrients for this reason. When people are put on a diet high in calcium they absorb less fat, although it is not known how or why this should be. It is certain that we do not absorb everything that we eat and it is likely that absorption is an active process – we absorb what we need, perhaps. The well-known saying *you are what you eat* should more accurately be *you are what you absorb.*

Control of energy expenditure

Energy expenditure is another thing that can be controlled, and the amount of energy we use can be restricted in three ways. Firstly, we can feel inclined to do less. If we eat too much just because plenty of food is available and we like it, and end up with an excess of energy, then why are we not bursting with energy like hyperactive children who are 'full of beans' and unable to sit still? Why don't we feel the need to use up this energy – desperate to run up the stairs instead of taking the lift, and to walk instead of drive? The fact is that when we are overweight most of us experience quite the opposite – we feel a need to conserve energy expenditure and prefer to drive instead of walk, and to take the lift rather than the stairs.

In addition to controlling our activity levels our metabolism can alter so that we use energy in a more efficient way. This means we can use less energy to perform the same task, for example, going for a walk. It is also possible for energy partitioning to be controlled. This is about the way that the body manages its resources. Energy can be obtained from fats, carbohydrates and proteins. As you read this book, energy is used to transmit impulses from your eyes to your brain and your hand uses energy to hold the book (or whatever device you are reading from). Why does your brain use glucose as a fuel for energy, while the muscles in your hand use mostly fat for fuel? Your body can control the amount of fat it stores. Think about a single molecule of fat that you eat in your lunch. What will happen to it? Will this molecule be broken down and used to power a muscle, will it be remade into another molecule, will it become part of a cell membrane, will it be removed from your body altogether, or will it be stored in a fat cell on your waist?

One way to understand energy homeostasis is to think of energy as money. Energy intake is like income and energy expenditure, like spending money. You can spend money on goods – as you spend energy on activity – or you can save money, just as you can store fat. If money is short, you might increase your income by getting an extra job, or taking in a lodger. Alternatively, or in addition, you control your spending. You might try to spend less by buying fewer things and you might spend more carefully, not paying more for an item than you need to. We need to conserve energy when it is in short supply, just like saving and counting the pennies or cents. Energy partitioning is like deciding whether to put a sum of money into a savings account, whether to spend it all on a luxury, spread it over several small purchases, or do a bit of each.

Energy circuits in the brain

Hormones and transmitters produced by the digestive system sometimes signal to other parts of the digestive system and also to the brain, keeping it informed at all times as to what is going on. This communication is essential to avoid system overload, especially when you consider that there can be several metres between one part of the digestive system and another. The communication pathway between the digestive system and the brain is called the gut–brain axis. In bariatric surgery the gut–brain axis is affected and, in essence, seems to work by letting the brain know that plenty of food has been eaten at an earlier stage in the meal than it did before surgery.

The signals controlling appetite described above are short-term signals. These go up and down during and between meals. The pattern might be determined by our behaviour – for example, our level of the signal peptide YY goes down after six hours because we usually eat after six hours, but if we changed our habit and ate every three hours it might go down after three hours. It might also go down quicker if we need to increase our food intake. But what about the long-term signals? How does the brain know how much fat we have stored in our bodies? We know that in any normal circumstances if we haven't eaten for days our hunger becomes very strong but is this just a consequence of the absence of food in the stomach, or is it related to fat mass? Does the brain know how much fat we have and how much we need?

The brain, of course, is the command and coordinating centre of energy homeostasis and the part of the brain involved is the hypothalamus. Early researchers thought that there was a hunger centre in one part of the hypothalamus and a satiety centre in another part, but it is now thought that one area of the hypothalamus integrates all the signals that regulate appetite. This centre is called the arcuate nucleus at the base of the hypothalamus and it is not protected by the blood–brain barrier, so substances in the blood that signal our energy status can get direct access to it. What was once thought to be two areas is now thought to be one, but it turns out that the connecting sets of neurons – the circuits – involved can by divided into two. One circuit increases the energy reserves in the body by stimulating appetite and reducing energy expenditure and it works by effectively blocking the first one, which has the opposite effect of reducing energy reserves.

There are two opposing forces in energy homeostasis: the first I call energy accrual – the careful, frugal force – and the second I call energy dissipation – the spending, squandering force. We can think of this as two sides of the balance of energy and when we need to increase energy – for example, if we experience a famine, certain steps are put into operation not only to conserve the energy we have, but also to obtain as much additional energy as we possibly can. Once the famine has ended the steps taken to conserve energy can be cancelled. Rather than having two separate pathways – one spending and the other saving – it makes sense to ensure that they cannot both operate at the same time in opposing directions by having one pathway which conserves energy and the other which blocks it.

The two pathways are reciprocal and this arrangement is typical in homeostatic systems. When we need to get rid of energy, the energy dissipation circuit is active and the energy accrual circuit is dormant. When we need to increase energy, the accrual circuit becomes active. The signals that activate the different circuits are produced in different parts of the body. Some signals are produced in the brain itself, others by fat cells and some by the stomach and the intestine, for example. But eventually they all converge on the brain and exert their influence via one particular system.

- *The energy dissipation* circuit that inhibits appetite is called the POMC circuit (POMC is an abbreviation for pro-opiomelanocortin).
- *The energy accrual* circuit – the one that makes us hungry – is the AgRP/NPY circuit (AgRP is an abbreviation for agouti-related protein and NPY for neuropeptide Y).

If the energy dissipation circuit is not working properly – as can happen in certain rare genetic conditions – overeating and overweight occurs. Both these circuits converge on the receptors for melanocortins called the melanocortin 3 receptor (MC3R) and the melanocortin-4 receptor (MC4R). It is the melanocortin system that seems to coordinate all the signals involved in weight control.

Melanocortins, discovered in the 1980s, are small molecules – peptides – that affect skin and hair pigmentation, inflammation and fertility as well as energy homeostasis. At the moment, it seems rather odd that the melanocortins, related by their molecular structures, have these different functions. But there is a possibility that the melanocortin system is the master controller of overweight and that pigmentation, fertility and weight gain are coordinated as part of a winter response system; this is discussed in the following chapters.

Weight loss by dieting is starvation

What happens when you try to lose weight? When we go on a diet or try to lose weight in any way it is easy to assume that, since we have some excess fat sitting around our bodies doing nothing, this excess fat will simply be used up to provide our energy in place of the food that we have cut out. But what do we know about what really happens when we lose weight?

When we lose weight there are changes in hormones, the nervous system and our metabolism that make energy expenditure more efficient. One of the key signals in weight control is leptin. Leptin provides the brain with information as to how much fat we have stored in our bodies. The main function of leptin seems to be to monitor fat mass and to initiate a starvation response when fat mass declines. When leptin levels are high our brains get the message that we don't need so much food and we can spend our energy. When we lose weight, our leptin levels fall and our brain puts into action an energy conservation plan. This involves increasing our appetite, lowering our metabolism and storing fat.

The Minnesota experiment and Biosphere 2

When energy intake is restricted there is an adaptive decrease in energy expenditure. How do we know? In the 1940s a group of volunteers were put on a restricted diet and were studied extensively to understand the effects of famine during and after the Second World War. These men were conscientious objectors – they refused military service because they had a strong conviction not to kill another human being but they were keen to put themselves 'on the line' for their country in a way that did not involve harming others. The experiment was called the Minnesota experiment. The volunteers had 3,200 kilocalories per day for 3 months, followed by 1,800 kilocalories per day for 6 months – this was comparable to the energy intake of populations in war-torn regions at the time. In the following 3 months their intake was increased by different amounts.

This severe energy restriction resulted in a marked reduction in energy expenditure; both as a reduction in physical activity and in the resting metabolic rate. (Incidentally, many of the psychological effects of starvation observed in the Minnesota experiment are seen in anorexia nervosa and bulimia nervosa). This metabolic adaptation is a way of conserving energy supplies to ensure survival when energy intake is low. In the Minnesota experiment the men lost about 25 per cent of their weight, so it was a pretty extreme experiment.

Later, in the 1990s, eight volunteers – four men and four women – were confined inside Biosphere 2, a glass and steel structure in Tucson, Arizona, constructed to provide seven biomes including a human habitat. The volunteers inside were completely isolated from the outside world for two years and had to grow and harvest their food. They were all on a healthy diet, took vitamin supplements and remained in good health – able to do the work they needed to provide their own food. The biomes were designed so that the food supply would be sufficient but unfortunately there was less food than expected and the volunteers lost about 15 per cent of weight in the first 6 months, which was then maintained for the remainder of the two years. At the end of the experiment, they were extensively studied and it was found that their 24-hour energy expenditure was significantly lower due to lower spontaneous physical activity and sleeping metabolic rate. Six months after returning to normal life, even when their body weight had returned to normal, their energy expenditure was still lower.

The body adapts to conserve energy

It is interesting that weight regain after energy restriction, as seen in patients with anorexia, cancer sepsis and AIDS is almost all in the form of fat. This is called post-starvation obesity. When 10 per cent or more of body weight (e.g. 7 kg from 70 kg, 1 stone from 10 stone, or 20 pounds from 200 pounds) is lost, leptin levels are lowered and the energy homeostatic system responds in such a way that results in a reduction in energy expenditure.

These changes take place when you lose weight, whether you were overweight or a normal weight to start with. These changes also persist for years after losing weight. The highest effect is seen in muscle, which becomes more energy efficient. With a 10 per cent loss of body weight comes a 20 to 30 per cent reduction in the amount of energy used up in physical activity.

What this reduction means is that after weight loss your body will use up less energy even when you put the same effort into a task. If you go for a walk with a friend, you can both walk the same distance, at the same speed, using the same effort, but one of you will use less energy than the other. We can make sense of this in terms of money again. If you have suffered a considerable drop in income – such as a redundancy – you are more likely to be careful when spending money, even when your income goes up again, than if you have never experienced such a dramatic loss of income. In a similar way, your energy homeostatic system is more careful to conserve energy once it has experienced a loss in energy intake and this safeguard can *last for life*.

This is undoubtedly what happens when you diet. Your body adjusts to conserve energy and regains the weight lost as fat. When you go on a diet you are instructing your body to *get fatter*. This is one reason why diets don't work in the long term and why the people who are most overweight might be those who have tried hardest to lose weight, in spite of appearances. It also explains why someone can remain overweight even though they eat less than a slimmer person.

Weight gain is no accident

Since we have this powerful system with its multitude of signals designed for keeping our weight stable, how did we become overweight in the first place? Surely the fact that so many people are overweight when they don't want to be is a sign that the energy homeostasis system has gone wrong – it must be out of control. What happens to energy homeostasis when we are overweight?

Every time a new signal involved in energy homeostasis is discovered there is the hope that the key to the problem of overweight has finally been discovered. We know that some people have a problem with the signals involved in energy homeostasis. A few people with a mutation in the gene that codes for leptin, for example, become overweight at an early age and can now be treated with leptin therapy. There are numerous other genes which have been found to cause overweight but these cases are rare and do not explain overweight in the majority of people. Most people who are overweight have plenty of leptin because their fat mass is large and the fat cells are producing it. So it seems that in overweight there is some kind of resistance to leptin. The leptin is telling the brain that there is plenty of fat but the brain does not seem to be listening. It is possible to raise the leptin concentration with an injection, which causes a reduction in food intake, increase in energy expenditure and weight loss. But when leptin is not deficient, large doses that produce 10 to 20 times the normal leptin concentrations in the blood are required to have any effect on weight loss. It also has no effect on energy expenditure and thyroid hormones. So far, it seems that energy homeostasis in overweight people is mostly normal and, where they have been found at all, the differences are only small.

We know that, in normal circumstances, weight is stable. When we become overweight has the control of appetite become uncoupled from the control of weight? This is the popular view of overweight – that there is no need to eat, we just eat because there is plenty of tasty food around and the tasty fattening food just happens to be more energy dense than the less appetising food. We seem to prefer a chocolate bar (300 kilocalories) to an apple (100 kilocalories) because it is more rewarding. But is it the other way around – is the chocolate bar more rewarding because we need it more than the apple? Is the system of energy homeostasis working just as well in overweight as it does when weight is normal? *Is weight gain deliberate*?

Energy homeostasis and overweight

There are essentially two theories that can explain weight gain. The first is that the energy homeostatic system is not working properly. In this case a biochemical disorder characterised by an abnormal resistance to homeostatic mechanisms, either acquired or genetic, must have become extremely common, extremely quickly. If the signalling pathways are not working properly, the brain doesn't get the message that fat mass is sufficient, or rather it gets the message that fat mass is lower than it should be even when in fact it is too high. As we have already seen, however, despite the accumulation of knowledge about the signals involved in energy homeostasis, there is no evidence of faulty signals that would fit in with this idea and trying to put any faulty signals right, by administering leptin for example, has little effect.

The second idea, the thrifty genotype hypothesis, is based on the assumption that the purpose of storing fat is to use it for energy when we need it at some later date. It has also been called the Absence of Protection model, since it does not protect us from weight gain, only from weight loss. It is thought that, because food scarcity has been the cause of starvation and death so often in the past, those people with genes favouring weight gain at times when there was plenty of food available were more likely to survive famines. Those people with thrifty genes had the best chance of survival during periods of of food scarcity. Most of us alive today are descended from the survivors of famines and so have these thrifty genes. All well and good until you get to our modern obesogenic environment and there is no food scarcity, no famine, just feast following feast, then you can hardly help but gain weight. It is assumed that the overabundance of food and the lack of physically demanding work that we now experience are new in the history of humans and consequently, while strategies have evolved to deal with food shortage and excess physical work, there are no similar strategies to deal with having lots of cheap chips and chilling out on the sofa.

The thrifty genotype hypothesis was first proposed in the 1960s by a geneticist, namely, James V. Neel of the University of Michigan, to explain why diabetes was common in urban–industrialised societies but rare in societies that followed an ancient, hunter–gatherer way of life. His hypothesis has not only survived for more than 40 years, it has also been extended and has become increasingly popular because it can explain why overweight has increased in the past few decades (because the environment has become more obesogenic), why some people gain weight while others do not (because some people have more thrifty genes than others) and why overweight is more prevalent in some countries than others (because some countries have more people with thrifty genes and/or a more obesogenic environment).

According to this model, our problem lies with the benefits of modern life. This model assumes that the majority of our ancestors were survivors of famines, i.e. that famines were selective events, which seems a reasonable assumption given that famines seem to have been recurring events throughout history. This assumption will be explored in a later chapter. It also suggests that it is healthier for us to be in a state of deprivation and hardship than comfort and wealth. I find this to be an unpleasant concept.

These theories assume that we are protected against energy restriction in case of food scarcity but that there is a complete absence of any protection against food excess. This thinking suggests that, to maintain a normal weight, we need an environment with exactly the right amount of food available. There are many problems with this idea and I will come back to it in the following chapters. One problem is that it doesn't account for the increase in weight at a point in an individual's lifetime. At the beginning of this chapter we met Ken. Ken's weight was a normal and steady 83 kg (13 stone or 182 pounds) until he gained weight in his forties. He gradually put on weight over the next 10 years and by the time he was 56 years old he weighed 102 kg (16 stone or 224 pounds). Emma had always been a size 12 until she was made redundant, then she put on 20 kg (3 stone or 42 pounds) in a year and went up to a size 18.

These two cases in which people of normal weight become overweight during adulthood are not unusual. Both Ken and Emma had maintained a normal weight without any effort throughout their childhood and part of their adulthood. They clearly didn't have any deficiency in their energy homeostatic system then, and they didn't experience a sudden change in genotype. Nor can an increase in food availability explain why Ken gained 20 kg (42 pounds) in weight slowly over ten years, while Emma gained 20 kg (42 pounds) in one year.

If the model were correct, we could predict that with increasing food availability there would be a gradual increase in weight throughout the population, but although there is a gradual increase in *average* weight it is obvious that some people are affected to a much greater extent than others. The difficulty many people experience in losing weight suggests that it is very tightly controlled. In people who are overweight, leptin levels are high because fat mass is high. The fact that feeding continues in spite of high leptin levels is referred to as leptin resistance. This is assumed to be because the function of leptin is in protecting against starvation. It is thought that the physiology of the system that enhances survival in the face of food shortage by conserving energy is not mirrored by a complementary system that prevents excess energy accumulation. But this suggests that energy homeostasis is not really homeostatic. The fact that energy homeostasis is controlled by reciprocal circuits in the brain, with the energy dissipation circuit being the one that stops us from eating when there is no need for it, does not fit in with this idea.

Suppose we assume that energy homeostasis really does 'what it says on the tin'. If we assume that the brain knows there is plenty of fat but overeating continues, then it is clear that the fat is still not enough and the brain is asking the body to increase the fat mass still further. When leptin is telling the brain there is plenty of fat, the brain is listening but it is saying: *it's still not enough – get more please.* In other words, there is no inherent bias in the system of energy homeostasis and there is no fault in the system. Instead, the energy control system is working perfectly and weight gain occurs because accumulation of fat is deemed necessary.

The fatstat

This book proposes that weight gain is an active process with a purpose. In normal circumstances, the controls that protect us against weight loss also operate to prevent the gain of weight even in the face of excess availability of calories. The concept of the adipostat (here I call it a fatstat) was developed in 1953 by Gordon Kennedy, who worked at the Department of Experimental Medicine at Cambridge University. Kennedy proposed that a factor circulates around the body and provides the brain with a report on the level of fat stores within the body. Such a factor was unknown at the time that Kennedy suggested it, and was not to be discovered until 40 years later – this was leptin. As predicted by Kennedy, leptin is produced by fat cells, circulates in the bloodstream and is proportional to the amount of fat – the more fat there is, the higher the concentration of leptin in the blood.

Since weight is normally stable, we can suppose that the body has a set point, like the set point of a thermostat. It follows that when weight is increased, it is because the set point has gone up. For example, if your normal weight is 80 kg (12.5 stone or 176 pounds) and your weight increases to 90 kg (14 stone or 198 pounds), your set point has gone up by 10 kg (22 pounds) for some reason (which we will come to later). To increase weight by 10 kg requires either an increase in food intake, or a reduction in energy expenditure, or both. The brain sends the necessary signals to make you hungrier than usual so that you eat more, and perhaps it slows you down a bit so you feel more like a couch potato than usual. Once the new set point has been reached, the weight becomes stable and there is no longer any need to overeat, so that at 90 kg you do not have to eat any more than you did when you were 80 kg to maintain your weight.

If you try to lose weight, and the fatstat remains set at 90 kg, you are battling against the homeostatic mechanisms that are trying to keep your weight at 90 kg. It is not surprising that this attempt often fails. Unless the fatstat is turned back down to 80 kg, the body thinks it is suffering from starvation and initiates even more ways of conserving energy. To lose weight in such circumstances requires nothing less than a heroic effort and it is no wonder that weight loss requires an individually tailored, multi-approach management project, or just a lot of grit and determination.

What happens after dieting is the starvation response has ensured that energy is better conserved but the set point has not lowered, so whether weight has been lost or not any subsequent attempt to lose weight will require even further decreases in calorie intake to achieve the same effect and you can remain overweight while eating relatively little. In those cases where people do manage to lose weight for the long term they may have unwittingly lowered their set point that enabled them to lose weight. They got lucky.

There is some debate over whether there is a set point but it is biologically inconceivable that there isn't. None of our physiological systems need to be consciously controlled, so why should energy be any different? If there were not a body weight set point we would surely see a huge variation in the sizes of animals and birds. The fact is that body weight is stable for most people for most of the time, whether overweight or not. The trouble is that evidence for a body weight set point will be more difficult to find as more people are affected by overweight and keep trying to control their weight. If we find a way to lower the set point, then we will be able to have real control of our weight. Then we can become a normal weight and stay that way for life even while eating as much as we like, with no need to worry about calories or exercise. First, we need to understand why and how our fatstat increased before we can understand how to turn it back down again. In the next chapter we ask: *What is the point of overweight?*

Chapter 6

Ice Age Endurance

YOU GET UP IN the morning and the scales show you've gained two kilograms this week. How do you feel? Do you punch the air with excitement or do you just feel a soft, warm glow of achievement? On the way to work you waddle along the street feeling smug that you are so big. At work, you proudly show off your rolls of fat to your colleagues. You are winning the race to be the first in the office to reach 100 kilos. One of your colleagues is thin and can't gain any weight even though she tries to eat as much as possible. As you try to hide your disgust at her flat stomach, you feel sorry for her but at the same time secretly pleased that you are so much fatter than her – you can't help feeling that you succeeded where she failed.

Is such a scenario possible? In what circumstances could being overweight be a good thing? In what kind of world would the fattest people be the most attractive? If we put aside the common assumption that fat is simply a store of some energy we had left over because we just happened to eat more energy than we used and there is nowhere else to put it, and if, instead, we accept that our set point – our fatstat – has gone up, that gaining weight is a deliberate strategy by the body, then we must assume that extra fat has a function, a purpose – it has a job to do. What is the point of overweight?

Being big

It is a general rule that the bigger you are the more fat you can carry before you become so restricted that you are unable to move or breathe. Among all living things mammals have the greatest capacity for fat and in humans the capacity for storing fat seems to be almost unlimited – ranging from no fat at all to hundreds of kilograms. According to the Guinness Book of World Records, the heaviest person recorded in medical history was Jon Brower Minnoch who lived in the USA from 1941 to 1973. At his heaviest he weighed 635 kg (100 stone or 1,400 pounds) – the equivalent of ten women of average weight.

Since fat is the best source of energy available to us, the obvious explanation for this massive capacity for fat is that it provides stores of energy. Without energy we die so we need to save any that we don't need immediately in case we need to survive a future period of food scarcity. When the hard times come we can rely on supplementing our meagre food intake by obtaining energy from this store cupboard. If you weigh 100 kg (16 stone or 220 pounds) you probably have enough stored energy to last four or five months without food. This explanation underlies the assumption that dieting is safe.

Protection against hunger is the most common evolutionary explanation for obesity, but there is a second, related explanation. The team at the Department of Human Biology in Maastricht University, led by Margriet Westerterp-Plantenga, Professor of Food Intake Regulation in Humans, study many aspects of eating and energy intake. Over the course of several studies they have shown that men and women exposed to low temperatures use more energy than those exposed to higher temperatures. Energy is used to keep us warm and the bigger you are, the easier it is to keep warm.

In 1984 five men were on a fishing boat when it capsized off the coast of Iceland. The air temperature was –2°C and the sea temperature was 6°C. As they were unable to release the emergency raft, three of the five men climbed onto the keel of the upturned boat, but the other two men disappeared within ten minutes. Forty-five minutes later the boat sank; one man died as soon as he entered the water and the other two started swimming. After a few minutes one man realised he was now alone. He was 23 years old. He swam for an incredible 6 hours until he reached land and, although his pulse was undetectable by the time he reached hospital, he survived and recovered in good health.

In water at 6°C most people would not survive for much longer than an hour, so it is a remarkable tale of survival – so remarkable that it was written up in the British Medical Journal by Bill Keatinge, Professor of Physiology at the London Hospital Medical College. If you've heard about wearing a hat because a quarter of your body's heat is lost through your head, you may have heard it from Bill Keatinge, who would often talk to the media about the dangers of the winter and how we are good at keeping our homes warm but then fail to dress appropriately when we go out.

Keatinge joined the London Hospital Medical College, Department of Physiology in 1969 and became its head in 1981. He kept a vast water tank in the laboratory to study how the body copes with different surrounding temperatures. When Keatinge heard about the survivor's tale he invited the young man into his cold water tank so that he could study his responses to cold water; these proved to be remarkably different to other people's. One of the reasons the fisherman had survived was because he was an unusually big man at 1.93 metres (6 ft 4 in) tall and weighing 125 kg (19.5 stone or 276 pounds). This big body enabled him to maintain his core temperature more easily and for much longer than would be possible for most people.

In winter the need to keep warm is just as vital as having an emergency food supply but this necessity has mostly escaped our notice. In this chapter I suggest that overweight is part of an adaptation to help us survive severe and prolonged exposure to cold.

Big bodies can be better

Some of the problems you experience when you become overweight are caused by the fact that your body gets bigger – you can't fit into your clothes and onto chairs so easily. Instead of thinking about the purpose of overweight as an increase in fat storage, what if the main purpose is to get bigger?

Weight depends on height, muscle and bone mass as well as fat mass. All these components of weight can change, but we know that fat mass is the main problem when it comes to overweight and obesity. If you are 1.83 metres (6 ft) tall and weigh 70 kg (11 stone or 154 pounds) at the age of 30, you know for certain that you will still be 6 ft tall at the age of 40 but you cannot be so sure that you will still be 70 kg. We grow in height only during our childhood and once we reach adulthood we expect to stay the same height, except for a bit of shrinking in old age. It is generally thought that inherited genes determine height – if you have tall parents you will be taller in adulthood than if you have short parents. But actually only a few genes have been identified that determine height and it appears that there are environmental influences on height, such as socioeconomic factors.

Humans have increased in height since the late eighteenth century and this is thought to be due to improved nutrition and to better healthcare for pregnant women and children. Several studies comparing the lives of tall and short people find that tall people tend to be more successful. For example, a study conducted at Princeton University showed that tall people earn 10 per cent more than people who are four inches shorter. So we tend to think that an increase in height is good, in complete contrast to the situation with fat, which we think of as wholly bad when it increases. To adapt a slogan from George Orwell, we think in terms of *height increase good; fat increase bad.*

Once you reach adult height you cannot get taller because the cartilage of the growth plates at the end of the long bones change to bone at the end of puberty, so if your body needs to get bigger increasing fat mass is one way is to do it and overweight can be seen as a useful way of changing body size. You could also change size by increasing muscle and bone mass, but fat mass is easier to alter and has the greatest capacity for change. Increasing fat is reversible – you can increase it when you need to get bigger and then lose it when you no longer need it. All in all, it seems that increasing fat is a good way to bring about a temporary increase in body size. It can be achieved fairly quickly once the set point has gone up – in a matter of weeks – and it can be removed when the set point goes back down.

What would be the advantage of having a bigger body? Animals come in different sizes, of course, but what do we know about what determines body size in animals? The smallest mammal is Kitti's hog-nosed bat, weighing 2 grams, while the largest is a whale, which weighs over 190,000 kg.

The largest land animal is the elephant – the African elephant can weigh as much as 7,000 kg – but the largest land creatures ever to have existed are the dinosaurs. As far as we know, the blue whale is the largest creature to have lived – and is even larger than the dinosaurs. Nobody knows how the dinosaurs and whales got so big or why a mouse is smaller than a cow. Humans are intermediate in the range of mammals' sizes, but we are among the largest primates with more subcutaneous fat than other primates. We are also unlike other primates in that we have relatively little hair and we share this feature with other large mammals such as elephants and rhinoceroses. The question of whether large size and hairlessness are related will be considered in the next chapter when the role of vitamin D in evolution is explored.

Size rules

There are no clear evolutionary or ecological *laws* that govern how big an animal must be and it is thought there may be many different determinants of body size, but there are ecological *rules* about body size resulting from observations of patterns in nature. A rule in biology is a general trend – it is what we most commonly find but is not a law such as the laws of physics that are strictly observed. There are no laws in biology because none has yet been formulated that can account for all the variation in living things – there are always exceptions to the rules.

The two rules concerning body size are called Cope's rule and Bergmann's rule and are both named after the individuals who first published work on these observations. These nineteenth-century biologists were interested in how geography affected the physical characteristics of different organisms and how the environment could account for variations in the distributions of species. Their rules were mostly descriptive, but there has recently been renewed interest in this subject of biogeography in the context of the increased awareness of the importance of biodiversity and the effects of climate.

Cope's rule describes the tendency of size to increase over geological time. It is named after a palaeontologist, Edwin Drinker Cope, who made this observation in 1887. Cope went on expeditions across America looking for fossils and discovered more than a thousand species including many dinosaurs. He was not just a fossil hunter but also a theorist and still, it is said, holds the record for producing the greatest number of publications. Cope did not suggest any reason or mechanism for his observation and, although widely accepted to be true, it is still the subject of academic discussion. It is a general rule that animals start small and, through successive generations, they get bigger, so the most ancient animals are the smallest and the most recently evolved are the largest.

Bergmann's rule is that animals of the same species tend to be bigger when they live in cold climates. Karl Bergmann was born in 1814 in Göttingen; he trained in medicine and became a Professor of Anatomy and Physiology at Rostock, Germany. Bergmann's rule has received considerable attention in the past ten years or so and recent work has found that the majority of birds and mammals follow this rule. Mammals show greater differences in size than birds, and large mammals show greater differences in size than small mammals. Polar bears are a good example as they are much bigger, at 400 to 680 kg, than the Asian black bears, 100 to 200 kg, or the sun bears, at 40 to 60 kg, both of which live in warmer climates at lower latitudes than the polar bears. Bergmann's rule has been generally accepted as true, although there is still some debate about it, particularly as there is some evidence for Bergmann's rule and some against. Unlike Cope, he did propose a reason for his rule – bigger sized animals reduce their heat loss because their surface area to volume ratio is decreased as their size increases. The mechanism by which colder climates result in bigger sized animals, though, is as much a mystery today as it was when he first published his observation.

While we are on the subject of ecological rules, here are two more: Allen's rule and Gloger's rule. Allen's rule states that extremities, such as arms, legs, ears and nose, are relatively shorter in cold environments. This was observed by Joel Allen, an American zoologist, in 1877 and it complements Bergmann's rule. The geometric shape with the lowest surface area to volume ratio is the sphere, so in a cold environment it is better to be short and thick than tall and thin. This is why it is common for animals to curl up into a shape that resembles a sphere when cold. It also explains why protruding parts of the body such as arms, legs and ears tend to be shorter in cold climates. An example is the black-tailed Jackrabbit (really a hare in spite of its name) that lives in a hot climate in Mexico and southern USA and has a long head with long ears and very long front and rear legs. The arctic hare, on the other hand, has a rounded head with short ears and shorter legs and lives in the cold climate of Canada, Greenland and Alaska. With regard to humans, Allen's rule has been used to explain why Maasai, who live in equatorial Kenya and Tanzania, have longer legs than Inuit, who live in the Arctic Circle.

Gloger's rule is that dark pigments increase in animals in warm and humid habitats. In 1833 Constantin Gloger, a natural scientist at the German Academy of Sciences, Leopoldina, published a review of climate and plumage colour in birds. He noted that birds in warm, humid climates tend to be darker in colour than those in cooler, dryer climates. Those in hot and humid climates tend to have more of the black melanin whereas those in hot and dry climates tend to have more of the red melanin. This rule also holds for insects such as butterflies and wasps. Recent migration aside, humans generally follow Gloger's rule. This rule can at least partly be explained by the effect of pigmentation on vitamin D production (this will be explored in the next chapter).

Going back to Cope's rule, one explanation of the increase in size over evolutionary time is that body size increased with colder temperatures – in other words, Bergmann's rule can explain Cope's rule. Evidence for this comes from a study of the evolution of a tiny sea creature called ostracode (pronounced 'ostracod') – a type of shellfish. The ostracodes are still living today, and fossils of ostracodes suggest they have been around for 40 million years (which makes our human existence of around 4 million years seem like not very much time at all). The oldest ostracodes are the smallest – less than 500 micrometres – whereas modern ostracodes are much larger – more than 800 micrometres – which fits nicely with Cope's rule. When the body size of ostracodes was compared to global ocean temperatures, it was found that for every degree Celsius of climatic cooling, the length of the ostracode increased by 29 micrometres. The ostracodes living in deeper water in the ocean, and therefore living in colder habitats, tend to be larger than those from shallower sites.

This study provides more evidence for Bergmann's rule, and that climate is the major determinant of body size with cold temperatures resulting in bigger bodies. Allen's, Bergmann's, Gloger's and – it now seems – Cope's rules postulate a relationship between physical characteristics and the environmental temperature.

By now you may be wondering what ostracodes have to do with overweight. We will come back to the mechanism later, but if, for the time being, we accept that there is a relationship between body size and cold we can begin to understand the point of overweight. Just before returning our attention to humans, we shall consider life in a cold climate for birds and mammals.

Coping with the cold

Polar bears are not just the largest bears but also the largest land carnivores. They live in the Arctic in temperatures of 0°C in summer and -34°C in winter. To survive the cold they have a layer of fur up to 5 centimetres thick made up of colourless hairs that allow more sunlight to penetrate the skin. Polar bears eat seals, which are high in fat, and as a result they put on a lot of fat – up to half their body mass – making them obese by our standards. In winter, polar bears catch seals as they come through holes in the ice, but in summer, when the ice breaks up, they cannot reach seals and have to survive on the little food they can find – berries, seaweed and perhaps, if they are lucky, carrion. This means that in winter they need to eat enough seals to survive a food scarcity, or even a total fast, in summer. It is particularly important for pregnant polar bears to gain fat as they do not feed for several months at the end of the pregnancy and the beginning of lactation and, of course, they need enough stored energy to nourish their cubs as well as to survive themselves.

Also living in the Arctic, on Svalbard, a group of islands between Norway and the North Pole, are reindeer that are shorter and fatter than reindeer that live on the mainland – in accordance with Bergmann's and Allen's rules. Males weigh around 65 kg in spring and 90 kg in autumn.

At the other side of the globe, Antarctica is the coldest and windiest place on Earth, where winter temperatures can be as low as -80°C (at which the bare hand of a human would freeze within three minutes) and is mostly uninhabited except for penguins and seals that live on the coast and humans who occupy research stations. Emperor penguins are the largest of all penguins; they weigh around 30 to 40 kg, which is at least ten times bigger than African penguins of 3 kg, which live in the temperate climate of South Africa, or the Galapagos penguins of 2.5 kg, which live in the equatorial Galapagos Islands off Ecuador. In spite of the low ambient temperatures, the Emperor penguins' internal temperature is maintained at around 38°C. They can keep warm because of their size and shape, the density of their feathers (penguins have more feathers than other birds – around 70 per square inch), their thick layer of fat and by huddling together.

We can marvel at the Emperor penguin for its ability to survive the cold of the Antarctic, but to a migratory bird, such as the tiny storm petrel, the penguin surely must be seen as a useless bird. I can imagine the storm petrel wondering, what use is a bird that cannot fly at all and cannot even walk properly? It is so fat it can only waddle and swim. The storm petrel weighs just 30 grams and flies all around the globe after breeding in the Antarctic so that it can spend almost its whole life in summer, while the penguin, weighing 30 kg, can only waddle to its breeding ground a few miles away. But, from the point of view of the penguins, the storm petrel cannot tolerate the year-round low temperatures of the Antarctic, which are normal for penguins, and has to leave. When the going gets tough, the storm petrel gets going, while the penguins can stay and tough it out.

Emperor penguins, polar bears, Svalbard reindeer and other fat birds and mammals are regarded by biologists as naturally obese, whereas human obesity is regarded as unnatural. Imagine if the African penguin and the brown bear looked down their noses (or beaks and snouts) at their fatter counterparts and considered their appetite for so much fish as disgusting. Should we be encouraging polar bears to eat healthily, to make the right choices, to eat more fruit and vegetables, to eat a more varied diet and cut back on the saturated fat? Should we encourage polar bears to be careful not to gain too much weight in pregnancy? Of course not, we accept that polar bears need fat to survive cold temperatures and periods of fasting. They need to eat fat to survive.

These animals don't suffer diabetes and other the associated health problems that we do, in fact the fatter they are, the more likely they are to live longer, whereas for us, it seems, the fatter we are, the shorter our lives will be. So we think in terms of *fat animals good; fat humans bad.*

An exception to this rule applies to those animals that live with us – our domesticated cats and dogs that we keep as pets – these animals suffer the same health problems as we do, such as diabetes and heart disease, when they gain weight. Since they share our way of living we may modify this slogan as follows: *fat animals in a natural environment good; fat animals in a human environment bad.*

What if the reason for getting fat in humans and pets is *exactly the same* as in those cold-adapted animals, like polar bears, living in a natural environment? The *cause* of overweight is the same but the *consequences* are different because we don't live in the cold. For the moment imagine that we do live in a cold environment like the polar bears, and imagine that you were storing up energy for the winter and the more fat you have, the more likely it is that you will see the next spring. Can you see that in this situation you might feel proud of your fat? In our world, the overweight are pressured to lose weight while the thin can be scornful. But in the polar bear world, the opposite would be true. Of course, most of us – even those of us who are severely overweight – are not living in below-zero temperatures and don't suffer from food scarcity in the winter. There are overweight people all over the world, including the parts of the world with the hottest and the coldest climates. But, remember, although we can understand the reason for Bergmann's rule we don't yet have any idea of the mechanism. This we will come back to later, but in the meantime, if we can accept that big bodies do better in cold climates we can think about how overweight, and its associated health problems, can be understood as an adaptation to the cold. The next section will consider how we can adapt to the cold and, finally, we will see if we can make biological sense of overweight.

Keeping warm

Hypothermia is defined as a body temperature below 35°C and death is almost certain to occur if our body temperature either falls below 30°C or rises above 43°C. We produce heat all the time and can lose heat as long as we are in surroundings at a lower temperature but in surroundings of the same temperature, i.e. at 37°C or higher, there is nowhere for the heat to go and we may not lose enough heat to maintain our body temperature. In those circumstances we are in danger of suffering from overheating. On the other hand, when the ambient temperature is low, for example if we go outdoors in the winter without enough clothing, we may lose heat faster than we can make it. Without doing anything and wearing clothes, we can be comfortable at 23°C because the heat which is given off from basal metabolism is sufficient to keep us at 37°C. This is the reason why normal room temperature ranges from 20 to 25°C, although of course we may be comfortable at lower temperatures if we are wearing plenty of clothing or covered with a quilt. Without clothing we need to be in a tropical temperature to be comfortable.

What happens if we get too cold?

Why is it so important to maintain a constant temperature? Any biological activity has an optimum temperature above and below which the activity declines, and many cellular processes depend on fatty membranes that change state with temperature. If they get too cold, they become more solid, preventing molecules from moving through them, and if they get too hot, they become more fluid, allowing molecules to move through them without any regulation or control. The electrical impulses in the nervous system, the muscles and the heart depend upon movement of ions across such fatty membranes. The nervous system is one of the first of the body systems to be affected in the cold, leading to problems with decision-making and alertness, poor coordination and reduced fine motor control. Eventually the rhythm of the heart is disturbed, leading to cardiac arrest. Frostbite – when ice crystals forming inside the cells and kill them – affects the extremities: hands and feet first, then the arms and legs.

Tragically, deaths from hypothermia occur every winter, even in our modern, centrally-heated world. Elderly people who do not feel the cold as well as they did when younger and do not take measures necessary to keep warm, climbers and walkers who are unprepared for sudden drops in temperature, drunks and anyone who finds themselves outdoors at night for longer than planned, are particularly susceptible to death by hypothermia.

In addition to frank hypothermia, we can die of the effects of cold on our cardiovascular and respiratory physiology. In spite of all the effort we have put into the creation of artificial summer in the winter and in spite of a plentiful supply of food throughout the winter, thousands more people die in the winter than in the summer. Each year in the UK, for example, there are approximately 50,000 excess deaths thought to be related to cold, mainly due to circulatory and respiratory diseases. The increases in deaths due to these diseases can be related to temperatures of up to two weeks earlier. Changes in the circulation, induced by cold, appear to affect the heart and lungs. Blood pressure increases in the cold and constriction of the peripheral blood vessels may increase the work that the heart and lungs have to do. In addition, the concentration of clotting factors in the blood increase and the volume of blood lowers, resulting in 'thicker' blood, which is more prone to clotting.

Adjusting to cold temperatures

In the cold, thermoregulation is a matter of life or death and maintaining the right temperature takes priority over everything else. To prevent hypothermia, all those other things that are vital to life – feeding, reproduction and growth – may come to a standstill while we divert all our resources into keeping warm. Consciously and unconsciously, we go to great lengths to keep warm. Keeping a constant temperature requires constant vigilance and maintenance by our bodies. Every time we do any exercise, or indeed any activity, our heat production goes up and we need to lose more heat to avoid overheating. This is why, when we do vigorous exercise, we sweat, go red as the blood flow to the skin increases and we lose heat from our mouths as we breathe faster.

In cold conditions the reverse happens and we start to lose heat faster than we are making it. To prevent this we can either increase the amount of heat we produce or try to stop losing so much heat. When physical mechanisms for reducing heat loss are unable to prevent temperature lowering, the 'lower critical temperature' is reached and heat production is stepped up. This temperature varies from one species to another and, in some animals, is seasonally adjusted. The lower it is, the better the mechanisms of reducing heat loss are. It can therefore be used as a test for how cold-adapted an animal is.

The coati is a tropical animal and will start to shiver at any temperature below 20°C, whereas the red fox adjusts its lower critical temperature from 8°C in summer to -13°C in winter and the porcupine from 7°C to -12°C. The arctic fox is particularly well equipped to survive the cold, as it can tolerate temperatures as low as -40°C without increasing its metabolic rate. In these animals the thickness of the underfur varies between summer and winter, but the harbour seal shifts its lower critical temperature from 22°C to 13°C in water and from 9°C to -9°C in air almost entirely by an increase in fat thickness.

Smaller animals, of course, have a limit on how much they can vary their fur or fat so, for example, the red squirrel has the same lower critical temperature in winter and summer. These small animals rely on warming their microclimate by making nests or increasing food consumption to raise their metabolism. In general, the bigger or furrier (or bigger *and* furrier) the animal, the easier it is to lower its winter lower critical temperature by increasing its insulation thickness.

What about humans? Just like the coati, our lower critical temperature is above 20°C – in fact it is around 27°C. In terms of thermoregulation, we are tropical animals and we do not generally adjust our lower critical temperature. As we have so little hair, to lower our critical temperature we would be less like the arctic fox and more like the harbour seal – we would increase our insulation by gaining fat.

On the face of it, humans don't demonstrate much in the way of physiological adaptation to the cold. It would seem that we are not adapted to winter in temperate climates, let alone the cold temperatures of the circumpolar regions. In fact we are not even physically adapted to the spring or autumn, let alone the winter. Even in summer, if we go out in the evening or on a cool day without a jacket, we might shiver and complain that it is chilly. We can easily die of hypothermia if we stay outdoors all night without clothes on, even at a relatively high temperature.

The reason we have not adapted – despite occupying cold climates all over the world – is that we manage to survive mainly by controlling our microclimate; indeed, it would be fair to say we have *mastered* control of our microclimate. We have shelters with doors, insulated walls and roofs, and windows – often with double-glazing or triple-glazing. Inside our shelters, we have artificial sources of heat – blankets, quilts, hot water bottles, central heating, hot drinks and hot food. When we need to leave our artificial tropical climate and venture outdoors into the natural climate, we have patio burners and heated vehicles, and use artificial insulation. We wear several layers – with hats, scarves and gloves, and padded trousers, fleeces, thermal underwear, and fur-lined boots if necessary. What better form of insulation is there than clothing that can be adjusted from day to day – even minute-to-minute if necessary? Who needs fur or feathers stuck on our skin all year round?

A winter response

Many of us live in temperate climates with seasonal changes in temperature as well as daily changes. We know we should always be able to maintain our temperature in fluctuating conditions and in the same day we can go from shivering to sweating if necessary. But it would be helpful to be able to adjust our body so that it can cope with a severe or prolonged winter. Do we have a winter setting and a summer setting – just like a combi boiler? It makes biological sense that we need to have a winter response – a system of short-term adjustments in our anatomy, physiology and metabolism ensuring that, when the temperature drops and food is scarce, we can survive through the winter. When summer comes, these adjustments can be reversed, as we might need to protect ourselves against overheating instead.

If we wanted to design a winter response, what changes should we need to make? If we compare our bodies to our homes we can think about how we keep a constant temperature even when the outside temperature is falling. In our homes we may have a central heating system, which heats water by burning a fuel, usually gas or electricity, pumps it around the building and controls the internal temperature by means of a thermostat. We try to minimise loss of this heat to the outside by insulating our homes with double-glazing, loft insulation, wall insulation, radiator reflector panels, pipe lagging and draught proofing. Thanks to central heating, it may be freezing outside but we can be surrounded by temperatures as high as a warm summer's day.

Inside our bodies, too, we can produce more heat and we can reduce the amount of heat lost to the outside air. In our bodies, the central heating system consists of our metabolism (our boiler), food (our fuel supply), the circulation of the blood (our piping system), and skin, with a little hair on top and sometimes lots of fat beneath (our insulation).

Our winter metabolism

I think overweight could be a way of protecting ourselves from cold. The medical conditions that are strongly associated with overweight – insulin resistance, high blood pressure, and so on, are collectively known as the metabolic syndrome. The risks associated with the metabolic syndrome can be divided into the risk of atherosclerosis, which is a risk for coronary heart disease, and the risk of diabetes, which in turn is a risk for heart disease, kidney disease and stroke. It is these medical consequences that cause concern and it is with the medical perspective that the metabolic syndrome has been described and studied. The metabolic syndrome is not an illness – you may have no symptoms – but it is a condition that has arisen out of the ability of medicine to take certain measurements of metabolism and physiology. These measurements suggest something has gone wrong – or, at least, something is different – inside the body. It is well established that the different features are all connected, but it is a puzzle as to how and why they are related. What does high blood pressure have to do with glucose tolerance, for instance? There is no central unifying mechanism that can explain all the features of the syndrome. Could all the different changes in metabolism and physiology be part of a winter response?

Fat as insulation

Physiologists distinguish between the core temperature and the shell temperature. The shell is our outer layer comprising our outer tissues including the skin, subcutaneous tissue fat, muscle and blood vessels. This shell becomes thicker in the cold and thinner in the warm. In the warm, we can make the shell thinner by dilating the peripheral blood vessels. In the cold, we can increase the size of our shell very quickly by constricting peripheral blood vessels. This means a thicker layer of our outer tissues is allowed to fall in temperature, so that we can concentrate on keeping the rest of our body at core temperature. Our core temperature may stay at 37°C even though our skin temperature may fall below 30°C. For example, when volunteers were in a chamber kept at 11°C, their internal temperature remained at normal 36.4°C even though their skin temperature had dropped to 27°C. In the longer term we can increase our shell by increasing insulation, either by increasing the thickness of fat underneath the skin, or by covering the skin.

The best way to improve insulation is to grow some thick fur or down and feathers because to keep warm, fur is better than fat. Many animals increase their hair density in winter, so why don't we go hairy? One possible reason is that hair or fur shields our skin from the sun and although this is a good way of protecting our skin from sunlight damage, it also makes it harder for ultraviolet to get to the skin. Another is that in hot weather it is not so easy to lose heat by sweating when skin is covered in hair. It might be a good idea for a polar bear to have 6 centimetres of thick hair when it lives in the Arctic but not for us mid-latitude animals who have seasons to deal with. For us, the best form of insulation outside of our skin is clothing, which we can put on and take off as the weather changes. But if we need to adapt to cold for a long winter, increasing fat thickness is probably the best option for us.

Increasing fat actually has two useful properties. It allows the shell to be thicker by providing an extra layer between the skin and the blood flow, and it makes the body surface bigger. Subcutaneous fat provides an all-round extra layer between the skin and the circulation – much like putting some insulation between the radiators and outside walls of our homes. Making our body size bigger reduces our surface area relative to our size, in accordance with Bergmann's rule. This means there is effectively less area in contact with the outside air, so less heat will be transferred to the air. An explanation of the change in surface area to volume ratio with size can be found in the notes.

To understand the effects of size on heat loss (and heat absorption), think about cooking potatoes. Potatoes that are cut into small pieces will cook faster than exactly the same amount of potatoes cut into large chunks. When it comes to eating them, the smaller pieces of potato will cool the fastest. Similarly, thin fries, of the kind you get at burger chains, take around 6 minutes to cook, whereas thick cut chips, of the kind you get from the fish and chip shop, take at least 10 minutes to cook. Children and babies are more susceptible to hypothermia than adults because they have less body mass to generate heat and they have a larger surface area from which to lose heat. So in low temperatures they get cold quicker than adults. This is why we must ensure that babies are kept well wrapped up in clothing in cold weather. Unfortunately, for the same reason they also overheat faster. Because they have a higher surface area to volume ratio, they have a greater surface exposed to absorb heat in a hot environment faster and, as they have a small mass, they heat up faster. For example, a child who weighs 10 kg could die of heatstroke in 15 minutes if left in a hot car. It is easy to see why adults cannot rely on their own degree of discomfort to judge when a child might be too hot or too cold.

Subcutaneous fat is distributed through most of the body but is thicker around the trunk. The trunk is the main source of heat loss and thicker fat around the middle is a good strategy for minimising heat loss. This agrees with Allen's rule – it makes us a more rounded shape to help to minimise heat loss. In addition, we have fat around our organs, called visceral fat, which can provide a source of energy as well as insulation for organs. The presence of abdominal fat is associated more strongly with the metabolic syndrome than body mass index measurements and it is generally agreed that waist to hip ratio is a better measure of weight with regard to health than weight or body mass index. Perhaps waist to hip ratio is also associated with our winter metabolism and could be a measure of how well adapted to cold we are.

Metabolism – turning up the boiler

Our metabolism is the equivalent of a central heating boiler and our food is its fuel. The energy our body uses is largely in the form of adenosine triphosphate – ATP for short. Energy from food is released into the electron transfer chain and passes along to another process called oxidative phosphorylation where the energy is captured as ATP. Like cash as a currency of money, ATP is the currency of energy – it is in a form that can easily be exchanged. It is used for many different processes by many different molecules for many different chemical reactions. We 'earn' ATP by a process called oxidative phosphorylation, in which oxygen is used to break down proteins, fats and carbohydrates and we 'spend' ATP on all the different activities that go on in our bodies, for example, making new proteins, moving stuff from one cell to another and making our muscles contract.

We say that oxidative phosphorylation is *coupled* to the electron transport chain – as if the electron transport chain were like a car's engine and oxidative phosphorylation the wheels. If you disengage the engine from the wheels (as you do when you are in neutral), the energy produced by the engine is not being used to move the wheels. Likewise, if the electron transport chain is uncoupled from oxidative phosphorylation, the energy is produced but is not used in making ATP. Instead the energy is released as heat.

A certain amount of energy is released as heat even when the two processes are coupled, so making ATP gives off heat just as heat is produced by a car engine, a computer, or any machine that gets hot when it is used. The more ATP you make the more heat you generate – or to put it another way – the greater the rate of metabolism, the greater the heat produced. The heat production of a person at rest is about 0.07 kilojoules per kilogram per minute but rises by approximately 15 times that value – to about 1.1 kilojoules per kilogram per minute – during a marathon, for example. The marathon runner must lose this heat otherwise he or she will suffer from hyperthermia because without losing the heat in 30 minutes their body temperature would rise to a lethal 45°C.

When it is cold outside, how can we turn up the boiler? Since we generate more heat every time we make ATP, one way of increasing heat is simply to make more ATP. We can produce more ATP to contract muscles and using these muscle contractions for doing exercise is one way of turning up the boiler, but another way is to use the muscles without increasing activity – this is what happens when we shiver. Since ATP is used for other things, such as moving molecules about inside a cell, we can also produce more ATP for moving stuff around and between cells for no reason, in a kind of cellular fitness exercise class. This is called futile cycling and, as with shivering, it is a way of doing some extra work that is not really necessary – like switching on a computer just for the heat but not actually using it.

Brown fat

Instead of making more ATP, it is possible to produce more heat, even when we make the same amount of ATP, by making adjustments to our metabolism. We can produce more heat by causing the two processes – oxidative phosphorylation and electron transfer – to be separated, making the processes less efficient. In some animals, this uncoupling takes place in a specialised tissue called brown fat. Brown fat produces a lot of heat and is generally found in small hibernating animals, such as bats and rats. What about humans? Until recently, there were a few isolated reports of findings of brown fat in adults, but they weren't terribly convincing and it was thought that, in general, adult humans don't have brown fat, although it had been found in newborn babies. It may be present in babies because they are not sufficiently developed to be able to shiver, and because they are more prone to heat loss as they are small and have a high surface area relative to their size. Recently, researchers have found some brown fat activity in adults when exposed to cold but not when they were at a comfortable room temperature. Overweight adults also had brown fat but it was less active than in the lean individuals. This makes sense because being overweight means you have better insulation and wouldn't need to increase heat production until you reach very low temperatures.

There is a hope that if it is possible to increase brown fat or increase uncoupling in any tissue, you could reduce weight by simply burning off extra calories, even without exercise. This is one target for the development of drugs to treat overweight. If a drug can increase uncoupling, more energy will be used to produce heat and that will tip the energy balance in favour of weight loss. In fact, one such drug was tried in the past but it has been banned since the 1930s because it turned out to be too effective and caused death by hyperthermia. Nevertheless, it remains possible for a safe drug of this type to be developed and much research is going on with this aim.

The trouble is that we don't yet know much about how the activity of brown fat is normally increased in the cold. Small animals have uncoupling proteins that control the process, but although a number of uncoupling proteins have been found in humans, it is not clear whether or not they are involved in increasing heat production. Thyroid hormones affect the expression of uncoupling proteins. The role of thyroid hormones in cold adaptation in humans is not yet understood, but people with an overactive thyroid (hyperthyroidism) tend to feel hot (and lose weight) because there is more uncoupling, while people with an underactive thyroid (hypothyroidism) tend to feel cold (and gain weight) because there is less uncoupling. Weight loss by dieting can result in increased energy efficiency by reducing thyroid hormones, so I wonder if it is possible that dieting might sometimes lead to hypothyroidism. It's been known for 100 years that thyroid hormone affects metabolism but only recently has there been research into its role in cold adaptation. In summary, uncoupling and brown fat in humans is a relatively new area for scientific research. Nevertheless, it is conceivable that changes in uncoupling could accompany weight gain and be part of an adaptation to the cold.

Shivering

Whether or not we have brown fat or uncoupling anywhere else, shivering is without doubt the main way we turn up our boilers and increase heat production when we get really cold. Normally, when we use our muscles, the energy is required for work and the heat produced is a wasted by-product that must be disposed of to our surroundings. When we shiver, the opposite is true. We shiver in order to produce heat and it is the work in contracting our muscles that is the wasted by-product.

Shivering is very effective at warming us up. Skeletal muscle makes up about half of body mass in a lean person and contributes about a fifth of total heat production at rest. Being relatively big animals with such a huge amount of muscle, we can produce a lot of heat by shivering (so perhaps we simply don't have much need for brown fat). Vigorous exercise can increase heat output by ten times and shivering can increase heat output by five times, so if you want to keep warm in the freezing cold, wouldn't it be better to run around a lot rather fast than to lie still and shiver? The trouble is that exercise demands more oxygen and increases blood flow to and from the muscles, so while you will be increasing heat production, you will also be increasing heat loss at the same time. Shivering can be done at the same time as adjusting the circulation to reduce heat loss but exercise cannot. Furthermore, shivering is involuntary – it is hard to consciously control shivering (and impossible at very cold temperatures). It is fine-tuned so that we shiver at the rate and intensity necessary to maintain a stable temperature. It may also be that shivering is a more efficient way of using fuel reserves and oxygen than exercise.

Red and white muscle fibres

Muscle is made up of bundles of fibres. These fibres can be divided into different types, depending on characteristics such as the fuels that they use for energy. In the past they were called red and white (like wine) because muscles which contained a predominance of one type of fibre appear red as they contain more of the oxygen-carrying protein, myoglobin. This protein, like haemoglobin in blood, contains iron and gives the muscle a red appearance.

You can see the difference in meat – think of steak as red fibres and chicken breast meat as white fibres. Today, biologists call the red and white fibres type I and type II, and the white fibres can be divided into three subtypes: type IIa, type IIb and type IIx. Type IIb fibres are the most unlike type I and type IIa and IIx are in between (so perhaps they should be called *rosé*). For simplicity, I will mainly refer to red and white fibres. Getting back to meat, the red meat of beef and lamb is made up of mostly red fibres. In fish, most of the meat is white fibre, except close to the skin where the meat appears darker, and the dark meat on a chicken drumstick contains red fibres. More details about muscle fibres can be found in the notes.

All muscles contain these fibres in different proportions. On average, about half our muscle fibres are red and the other half white, but there is a huge range with some people having almost all red and others having almost all white. The fibre types affect how muscles contract and what activities they are best for. Back muscles, needed to maintain posture, have a higher proportion of red fibres than arm muscles, needed to make fast movements like catching. The differences in muscle fibres have been studied mostly in relation to exercise. If you want to be a long-distance runner, it would help if you have a high proportion of red fibres, which are best for strength and endurance. On the other hand, if you want to be a sprinter, then it would be best to have mostly white fibres, which are best for power and speed.

The different proportions in different people were thought to be genetic, but the proportions can change with development – for example, babies and young children have less type IIb than adults. Recent studies suggest that the proportions can be altered by giving insulin or by exercise, so that effectively one muscle fibre type can change into another. Endurance training, for example, can increase the proportion of red fibres.

What muscle types are best for shivering? Muscle has mostly been studied in relation to exercise rather than shivering. This is hardly surprising as it is easier to ask a volunteer to do some exercise than to suffer temperatures low enough to induce shivering. Nevertheless, there are some heroic volunteers who have been willing to do exactly that for François Haman, an Associate Professor at the School of Human Kinetics at the University of Ottawa. His work is concerned with the way that humans use different fuels in different situations and he has published several studies on shivering in humans. Haman and his colleagues have been able to show that there are two types of shivering. In one type, called low intensity shivering, the shivering is continuous and uses mainly red fibres fuelled by fats. In the other type, called high intensity shivering, the shivering occurs in bursts and uses mainly white fibres fuelled by carbohydrates.

It is possible that, in extremely low temperatures, survival may depend upon the intensity of shivering, with high intensity shivering producing the most heat, but to survive a prolonged exposure to cold in a long winter, shivering endurance may be more important. At 30°C, shivering ceases as the nervous and muscular systems become too cold to function. Once a body reaches this temperature it cannot produce heat and will cool until it reaches the temperature of its surroundings. It is therefore vital in low temperatures that heat production is sufficient to keep the temperature above 30°C. Imagine a long period of cold exposure with no access to food and you can see how important it would be to ensure fuel reserves are optimised to keep shivering continuously. We know that birds can increase their capacity for shivering in the cold. Some birds shiver almost continuously during the winter, except when they are flying when they generate heat in the muscle activity involved in flapping wings. Can we humans increase our capacity for shivering? One of the things that would help would be a change in the composition of muscle.

We know that the capacity of different fibres can be altered by exercise, so it is reasonable to assume it could be altered to increase shivering capacity. White fibres are responsible for the high intensity shivering and it is possible that having more of these fibres could increase the amount of heat we could produce with limited fuel reserves. Low levels of red fibres (type I) and higher levels of white fibres have been found in overweight people, patients with insulin resistance and patients with high blood pressure. In other words, they are a feature of the metabolic syndrome. Men in Finland who were healthy and of normal weight at age 20 were more likely to put on weight over the next 19 years if their proportion of red fibres was low. They were also more likely to develop cardiovascular risk factors, such as high blood pressure. In another study, when black and white women in the USA were compared, there was no difference in muscle fibre type between black and white in the lean women, but among obese women, the black women had more white fibres (type IIb) and fewer red than the white women, and women who lost weight after a gastric bypass lost more when their red fibre percentage was higher than those whose red fibre percentage was lower. The more red fibres they had, the more weight they lost. In confirmation, one study found a difference in gene activity in muscle when comparing people with metabolic syndrome and people with 'normal' metabolism. The study found that genes mostly used in white fibres (in glycolytic metabolism) were more active, whereas genes mostly used in red fibres (in oxidative metabolism) were less active.

Fuels

Shivering requires plenty of fuel to provide the energy to enable the continuous contraction of the muscles. This energy can come from fats, carbohydrates or proteins. Proteins make a relatively small contribution to fuel for shivering. Carbohydrates used as fuel are derived from muscle glycogen stores and from glucose in the circulation, which can be topped up from glycogen stores in the liver. Glucose uptake into the muscle is usually controlled by insulin. This role of insulin is well understood, having been much studied with the aim of understanding diabetes. Fats come as triglyceride stored in the muscle and adipose tissue. Comparisons suggest shivering and exercise use fuels in a different way. In both exercise and shivering there is a gradual change in the fuels used from mostly carbohydrate to mostly fats, but in shivering the changeover takes place much earlier. It seems we use less glucose for shivering than for exercise of similar metabolic rate. Which fuels are used must depend partly on the fibre composition, with red fibres using mainly fat while white fibres use mainly glucose.

For a winter metabolism we would need to increase our fuel reserves and ensure we have the right fuels available for the muscle. It is plain that fuel reserves and availability have changed in people with the metabolic syndrome. In the blood, there is an increase in the levels of glucose and fats (as triglyceride and free fatty acids) and a reduction in HDL cholesterol, while in the muscle there is an increase in triglyceride and a decrease in stored glucose (glycogen). There is also a decrease in glucose in the liver.

Insulin resistance is a key feature of the metabolic syndrome and is thought to underlie many of these alterations in metabolism. One of the effects of insulin is to mop up glucose from the blood. After eating a meal, fatty molecules and glucose are released into our bloodstream by the digestive system and if they stay in the circulation they can stick to proteins in a random manner, rendering the proteins unable to function properly. To prevent this, there is a clearing up process, so while we are clearing the plates from the table, insulin and chylomicrons are tidying away the excess glucose and fatty molecules from our blood. After a meal the pancreas releases insulin until the concentration in the blood is five times its normal level.

In type 1 diabetes, the amount of glucose in the blood becomes too high because there is not enough insulin produced. In type 2 diabetes, glucose in the blood remains high even though there is plenty of insulin – the level of glucose has become insulin resistant. Normally, the majority of the glucose removed by insulin is used by muscle. If the muscle doesn't take it up – if the doors are closed – it hangs around in the bloodstream and more insulin is released to deal with it. This resistance to insulin could conceivably be due to changes in muscle composition and metabolism. During shivering, the uptake of glucose by muscle would need to be much higher than normal and there would, perhaps, be a need to get glucose into the muscle in a way that is independent of insulin so that other tissues are not affected.

In fact, white fibres, when compared to red fibres, appear to have their own form of transport of glucose independent of insulin. In addition, it may be advantageous to have a higher than normal concentration of glucose in the blood to cope with a higher demand for shivering. Certainly, there would be less storage of glucose and fatty molecules. Insulin resistance is also high in starvation and so is muscle triglyceride, whereas athletes have high muscle triglyceride but not insulin resistance. So muscle triglyceride is high, not surprisingly, when demands for fuel for muscle are high (for shivering or exercise) and insulin resistance is high when the body is conserving energy. Since coping with food shortages and cold exposure is necessary to survive winter, the winter metabolism may adapt us for both challenges. In essence, insulin resistance can be understood as a change to the normal pattern of energy storage, which is exactly what we would expect in a winter metabolism.

Circulation – the piping system

Once you have turned up the boiler and are producing more heat you need to ensure the heat is circulated around your whole body. The circulation of the blood is understood mostly as a transport system but we often forget that it is also an important system of thermal regulation. The circulation means that, even though the different parts of our body are producing different amounts of heat at any point in time, the temperature is evened out throughout our body and if you have poor circulation you will suffer from poor thermal regulation.

Any increase in metabolism – by exercising a muscle, for example – will generate more heat, but it also requires more blood flow to provide more oxygen. The increased blood flow helps to remove the extra heat from the muscle. Appendages, such as legs and feet, are susceptible to the cold because they have a large surface area exposed to the cold through which heat can be lost, and feet (or paws) might come into contact with ice or snow on the ground where the temperature difference between the outside and the inside of the body is even higher than elsewhere. Fingers and toes don't generate much heat. If you've ever experienced a temporary loss of blood flow in the fingers or toes due to Raynaud's disease, you will know how cold they become without blood – it is blood that provides the warmth.

Preventing legs and feet from freezing in winter conditions requires a blood supply but the constant heat loss from the blood lowers the temperature in the rest of the body. To counter this, the legs and feet are kept at a lower temperature from the rest of the body. The blood in the surface veins can be seen in the back of the hand and the forearm in many people. When the temperature lowers, some of the blood flow is switched from these surface veins to the deep veins that run alongside the deep arteries. The cold venous blood flowing back from the hand is warmed a little by the warmer arterial blood coming from inside the body. You can read more about this in the notes. Vasodilation opens up the blood vessels and vasoconstriction closes them down. By controlling these processes, heat can be moved towards or away from the skin. If we want to be cold adapted we need to be able to constrict or dilate different blood vessels in a rapid response to cold exposure. In severe and prolonged cold, constriction of all the peripheral blood vessels could be vital for maintaining our core temperature.

Re-setting our vascular system could improve our ability to constrict and dilate blood vessels in response to cold exposure. Being able to increase our blood viscosity would also help. There is little understanding of the changes in circulation in both human cold adaptation and the metabolic syndrome.

However, high blood pressure is very common (in the UK about 16 million people – that is one in three adults – have hypertension defined as blood pressure above 140/90 mmHg) and is strongly associated with overweight.

Blood pressure refers to the force of blood as it flows through the blood vessels and it is measured on the pushing against the walls of blood vessels in the arm. It depends on the rate of blood flow produced by the heart – termed cardiac output – and how strong the walls of the blood vessels are – termed the peripheral resistance. In general, people who are overweight tend to have lower cardiac output and higher peripheral resistance than people of normal weight. This peripheral resistance can be increased by constriction of the blood vessels. The antihypertensive drugs used to treat high blood pressure (calcium-channel blockers, thiazide diuretics, angiotensin converting enzyme inhibitors) all work by either preventing this constriction or the opposite, by promoting dilation of the blood vessels. Hypertension, endothelial dysfunction and blood viscosity have all been associated with overweight. It is conceivable that these three things are altered to improve the capacity of the circulation, so it can be adjusted in response to cold exposure.

The winter response and ice age endurance

In summary, there are three things we can do to if we want to survive the cold:

- 1. Increase our fat thickness.
- 2. Improve our ability to constrict our blood vessels.
- 3. Adjust our metabolism to produce more heat.

Overweight and the metabolic syndrome could collectively be understood as an adaptation that enables us to survive in cold climates.

It is possible that there are two stages to cold adaptation – the first stage is a winter response, preparing us for a few months of moderately cold weather, and the second stage is for ice age endurance, and prepares us for many months of severe cold. In the first stage, we increase our subcutaneous fat and become overweight, but not obese. This small amount of additional fat may be enough to give us a little extra insulation and a more energy reserves to cope with reduced food availability in the winter. This slightly increases our surface area to volume ratio and thickens our layer of subcutaneous fat but perhaps more importantly, provides us with extra energy reserves to sustain us through a mild winter. The second stage is for more severe and prolonged winter conditions. In addition to increasing our fat mass even more, our muscle composition alters, the fat begins to release adipokines, which alter our metabolism and our circulation, and we become suitably prepared for coping with severe and prolonged exposure to cold. In this stage we become obese and our winter metabolism is set up – in other words there is a switch in our metabolism from a summer setting to a winter setting.

Take two people – one adapted to the winter (a winter person) and another who isn't (a tropical person). How would they differ in their responses to two environments, the first being our normal, artificially tropical climate with occasional exposure to cold and the second, our ancestor's ice age climate of low temperatures all year round? The tropical person has what we regard as a 'normal' metabolism and blood pressure, with muscles optimised for exercise, and is highly active and lean. Compared to the tropical person, the winter person has more fat, conserves energy, is less active, has fewer red fibres, is insulin resistant, has higher levels of fats and glucose in their blood, higher levels of fat in the muscle and liver, and their blood vessels constrict more easily. In a 'normal' environment, which is warm, the tropical person is very active but the winter person is not. In hot weather, the winter person suffers from the heat and becomes even less active, while the tropical person cools easily and remains active. The tropical person has the advantage over the winter person in a warm or hot climate.

But in the cold, the situation is reversed. At low temperatures, the tropical person soon starts shivering and becomes less active, while the winter person can keep warm and stay active without shivering. When the winter person does shiver, the muscles are optimised for shivering and produce more heat than the tropical person. Our tropical person is fine in our artificially warm microclimate but suffers from hypothermia and dies quickly if exposed to cold. Imagine you are living in the next ice age and know that the more overweight you are, the more likely it is that you will survive the winter. Perhaps you'd feel pity for the thin people because you know they'll be lucky to see the next spring.

One important point to be made is that a winter metabolism prepares us for exposure to cold by improving insulation and by increasing our capacity to respond to cold, but mechanisms for increasing heat production and changes in circulation will not be started up until we are actually exposed to cold. We will not start to shiver until our cold receptors detect a fall in temperature, but we may change the fibre type and the fuel reserves in readiness. Coupling of oxidative phosphorylation and the electron transport chain may be even tighter to conserve energy while we are in the warm, but could be equipped for rapid and extensive uncoupling as soon as we are exposed to cold. With thicker fat giving us better insulation, the mechanisms for high-output heat production will not be switched on until a later stage than in lean people who do not have a winter metabolism. Counter-intuitively, then, the winter person may not respond to cold exposure as quickly as the tropical person.

This idea is rather speculative with little evidence for it. To take one example, I am suggesting that the fibre composition of muscle changes to optimise shivering, but there is little evidence that fibre composition can change in humans and no understanding as to how it might be changed. Furthermore, nobody really knows which type of fibre composition is best for shivering and, indeed, there is precious little understanding of the physiology and metabolism of shivering at all. Muscle metabolism is understood mainly in respect to exercise. Adaptation to the cold in humans is not particularly well understood because the small animals that are often used in research – usually rats and mice – are not suitable for understanding thermoregulation in humans. While many processes, such as the production of ATP, are the same in any living creature, the study of small animals will never provide us with a complete understanding of the control of temperature in humans because size is an important factor. Compared with mice and rats, humans are big animals with a huge potential resource of heat production in massive amounts of muscle

This idea I am suggesting needs a lot of further investigation but in the meantime, I am not aware of any other idea that can explain why overweight can lead to insulin resistance, nor why hypertension, high cholesterol and insulin resistance are associated. For now, I think it is reasonable to accept this winter response hypothesis and see if it makes biological sense of what we experience when we are overweight.

Living with a winter metabolism

If we think of the metabolic syndrome as a winter metabolism, we can understand what links high blood pressure, insulin resistance, high cholesterol and all the different alterations in metabolism found in association with overweight. We can also have a better understanding of the effects of being overweight on our health.

Overweight is seen as a positive energy balance but we don't feel like we have lots of energy when we are overweight. Since we have so much excess energy, why are we not bouncing around, like activated, energetic toddlers, working the calories off by doing lots of exercise? Why do we drive to the corner shop when we could walk? Why did we join a sports and fitness club, thinking that paying a monthly membership fee would motivate us to go at least several times a week, but then find we couldn't drag ourselves away from the sofa after the first enthusiastic few weeks? Why will our muscles tell us they don't want to work today, but maybe tomorrow, or definitely next week, but actually never?

Perhaps the answer lies partly in our muscle metabolism. It could be that it is because our muscles are not using fat as energy but are tending to use glucose instead. We have fewer of the red fibres that are powered by fat oxidation and can keep going for longer, like a battery-powered bunny. Instead we have more white fibres that tire easily. It wouldn't be surprising that if you have a low proportion of red fibres, you are more likely to gain weight (and less likely to lose it), since these are the fibres that use up fat.

Imagine two people with different proportions of red and white fibres doing the same exercise. The one with fewer red fibres uses up less fat than the other and their fat is more likely to be stored either as triglyceride in the muscle or fat. This means exercise may not be so beneficial for the person with fewer red fibres and it may make endurance exercise a much tougher experience. This is one aspect of overweight that needs to be better understood before pressurising people to do exercise to lose weight. It is well known that regular exercise can prevent or reverse the metabolic syndrome. This might be because exercise is a substitute for shivering, using up the fuel reserves put aside for shivering and it may also stave off the metabolic syndrome by increasing the proportion of red fibres. But we might have to recognise that for some people, particularly those who have been overweight for some time, endurance exercise could be much more difficult or even impossible because their muscle composition and metabolism are adapted to heat production and not suitable for exercise.

Since we are adapted to the cold of winter it would not be surprising if we feel uncomfortable in the heat of summer. Could this explain why there has been a massive increase in the demand for air conditioning where the prevalence of overweight is high? What if we expose ourselves to the cold like the polar bears? In a study that compared Inuit to Canadians, the Inuit had lower blood pressures and lipid levels in relation to their body mass or waist measurements than the Canadians. Perhaps they do not suffer so much from the metabolic syndrome because, in spite of their warm microclimate, they are exposed to colder temperatures when they go outdoors.

What are the consequences of living in a perpetual summer with a winter metabolism? Here we are with our winter metabolism, with our shivering muscles set up, with extra fat and glucose at the ready, but we don't actually need them because we are keeping ourselves warm, thanks to central heating, warm clothing, and so on. What happens? The increase in glucose made available for shivering is not being used, so it hangs around in the blood. We then produce more insulin to deal with it, so our insulin goes up and we have impaired glucose tolerance, insulin resistance and hyperinsulinaemia. Eventually, perhaps after years of this, the pancreas can't make enough insulin to keep the glucose concentration normal and diabetes develops.

The target tissues of insulin are the liver, muscle and fatty tissues. When there is insulin resistance, these tissues end up with higher levels of fat and lower levels of glycogen. In diabetes, the rate of glycogen synthesis is only about half that normally made because less glucose is transported into the muscle and the liver in the first place.

It is generally thought to be fat that causes insulin resistance, which in turn causes the metabolic syndrome, and it seems to be visceral fat (the fat around the organs such as the heart and liver) that causes the metabolic syndrome. This can explain why people who do not appear to be overweight can develop the metabolic syndrome, since visceral fat cannot be seen or measured from the outside, except by internal scanning such as with magnetic resonance imaging. People of normal weight with the metabolic syndrome are described as 'thin on the outside but fat on the inside'. It may be that it is, in fact, changes in the muscle fibre composition that occur first, followed by increases in fat and then changes in metabolism. But since taking muscle biopsies is more difficult than measuring fat or testing blood concentrations, it would be difficult to find out. It may even be that instead of fat causing the metabolic syndrome, it is the other way around and the winter metabolism causes overweight, although this does seem unlikely at the moment. So far I have suggested that the winter metabolism protects us from cold, but of course it must also protect us from food shortages, just as extra fat can both keep us warm and provide extra energy reserves, since food scarcity is an inevitable consequence of low temperatures.

Overweight is a survival issue

The previous chapter showed that weight is very tightly controlled and when we gain weight it is because our homeostatic mechanisms are working perfectly well, but they are working to a different setting; the body weight set point – or fatstat – has been turned up to a higher position on the scale. Once the fatstat has gone up, the energy accrual circuit in our brain becomes more active, while the energy dissipation circuit becomes less active. We then have a bigger appetite and a more careful control of energy expenditure. We eat a little more before we are satisfied and perhaps we eat a little more often. The production of leptin increases because we have more fat but we still need to gain more weight so we continue to increase our appetite until the set point is reached. The body is being prepared for winter and it is vital that energy is conserved as much as possible. Overweight is about warmth, not food.

As far as our bodies are concerned, keeping the fat that we might think is excessive is a matter of survival and this is why losing weight can be difficult. If we try extremely hard to reduce our calorie intake and we do manage to lose weight because we are so determined to control our weight, the body cannot increase energy intake and will therefore switch to decreasing energy output, so it lowers the metabolic rate. Subsequently, it becomes even harder to lose weight next time. This explains why dieting seems sometimes to make us gain more weight in the long term – we are in a state of energy accrual that can only be overcome by starvation. If the increased fat sends signals to convert our metabolism to a winter setting, it is not surprising that losing weight can prevent or reverse the metabolic syndrome. The problem is that losing weight is almost always temporary because the cause of overweight has not gone away and the benefits of losing weight do not improve health in the long term.

We are tropical animals

From the point of view of thermoregulation, we are tropical animals – our high critical temperature, our lack of hair, and our control of our microclimate show we are suited to a warm ambient temperature. This is not surprising given that humans lived in the tropics for a few million years and only migrated to colder regions a few hundred thousand years ago. How then, did humans survive the ice ages, when average temperatures in Europe were at least 10°C lower than present day temperatures? Perhaps you can imagine yourself in Palaeolithic times, sitting by a warm fire inside a cave, covered with the skins of musk oxen, whose wool is eight times warmer than sheep's wool, cooking a piece of reindeer carcass you'd stored in the natural deep freeze of the snow-covered ground outside. But would this be enough to survive an exceptionally cold winter, with temperatures below -10°C for weeks at a time, and what happens when you need to go outside?

The thrifty genotype hypothesis assumes that we are descended from humans who had the best characteristics for surviving famines, and that famines were selective events. It is a theoretically strong explanation for overweight, but the evidence that it underlies overweight and the metabolic syndrome is weak and conflicting. Also, if famine killed the contemporaries of our ancestors, it was most likely to occur in winter conditions when cold kills off the plants and animals we eat, so it is perhaps not unreasonable to assume that many of us alive today may have inherited a predisposition to protection against the cold from our ancestors. Perhaps we have winter genes as well as thrifty genes or perhaps they are all the same.

I think warmth, not food, is the driving force behind overweight. The importance of thermoregulation cannot be overstated – it goes on for every moment of our lives. When thermoregulation ends, death begins. It goes on largely without any of us noticing it, because of the extensive engineering of our environment. Even this, we tend to put down to civilisation without really appreciating its importance in keeping us at the right temperature. Life expectancy has increased by more than 30 years since 1900 and it is logical to attribute it to better health. Several factors have been considered – public health reforms, personal hygiene, nutrition, increased calorie intake and advances in medical knowledge and practice. Improved protection from cold has rarely been considered as a possible contributor to increased life expectancy.

The winter response is not triggered by cold

This chapter has suggested that overweight is an anatomical, physiological and metabolic adaptation to a cold environment. How do our bodies know winter is on its way and preparations need to be made? How is the onset of winter communicated from our environment to our brain? We can feel the warmth and see the light of sunshine in the summer and in the winter we can feel and see the cold and the dark. But early organisms with no vision or cold receptors could only tell whether it was day or night, summer or winter, whether they were underground or overground, or whether they were in the depths of the ocean or close to the surface, by detection of the ultraviolet radiation from the sun that interacted with a compound to form vitamin D. The next chapter will show why I think our bodies use vitamin D as a signal to tell us that the sun is shining. When there is no sun, there is no vitamin D and we need to prepare for the cold.

PART III

UNDERSTANDING AND TACKLING OVERWEIGHT

Chapter 7

An Evolutionary Exploration

THERE IS SOMETHING QUIRKY about vitamin D. Its function is enigmatic, its production eccentric and its origin exotic. It appears to be the only essential nutrient that we can make using sunlight. That is not to say light-sensitive compounds are unusual in biology. Our vision depends on retinal, which absorbs photons of visible radiation and is obtained from the vitamin A we get from our diet. Another example is the plant pigment chlorophyll, which absorbs solar radiation in the visible spectrum and uses it for photosynthesis. There are other photoreceptor molecules in nature – flavins, carotenoids, porphyrins, phytochromes and phycobilins – but vitamin D appears to be the only essential nutrient that we are able to produce ourselves and is dependent on light.

The origin of vitamin D

Of all the solar radiation available to us, why is it *ultraviolet* radiation that is necessary to make vitamin D? A physicist would say this is the only wavelength that can interact with 7-dehydrocholesterol, but a biologist would ask why, in the first place, should we have a compound dependent on ultraviolet radiation for its synthesis? This particular band of radiation is weak at the Earth's surface; it is subject to global and local variability and there are a multitude of factors that influence the intensity of ultraviolet radiation falling on our skin. In short, it is extraordinarily unreliable. There is no doubt that vitamin D is essential for good health, so why is its production dependent on such an inconsistent resource?

Ultraviolet-B is a small percentage of the solar radiation reaching us on the Earth's surface – just 1.5 per cent, compared to 6.3 per cent of ultraviolet-A, 52.8 per cent of infrared and 38.9 per cent of visible light. If we must have a compound that is dependent on solar radiation, then why not the more abundant visible or infrared radiation, rather than ultraviolet? It makes biological sense for living things to take advantage of the strongest band of radiation available, so we can understand why chlorophyll and retinal evolved with sensitivity to radiation in the visible spectrum, but why did vitamin D evolve with an absolute requirement for ultraviolet?

We talk about vitamin D as if it were just one thing – one chemical entity – as scientists thought when it was first discovered, but it actually has different forms and there are several names for each form. It is a type of steroid that can be modified to change what it can do – to turn it from inactive to active, from the vitamin calciferol to the hormone calcitriol. We know that one of these metabolites, calcitriol, is essential and we know that calcidiol is an intermediate between calciferol and calcitriol, but we have no idea what many of the other 30 metabolites do. A chemist would say vitamin D can easily be modified by hydroxylation. But how can we make biological sense of the need for so many metabolites, and why does the metabolite calcitriol, which clearly is essential, have such diverse functions as immune cell activation, calcium absorption and skin cell differentiation? To understand vitamin D a little better, we need to understand its origin.

Vitamin D in living things

Vitamin D was first discovered as a treatment for bone disease and because of this connection to bone, vitamin D was (and still is) widely thought to be associated with the skeleton. As a result, it has been mainly studied in vertebrates – fish, birds, mammals, reptiles and amphibians. There has been little interest in studying vitamin D in invertebrates, which by definition do not have an internal skeleton. Nevertheless, vitamin D has been found in land snails and goliath birdeater spiders as well as plants, fungi and algae.

Insects do not appear to have vitamin D. Many texts say that invertebrates have ergocalciferol (vitamin D_2) but the academic texts I have seen show that invertebrates have cholecalciferol (vitamin D_3) and none show ergocalciferol, so this appears to be a misconception. We now know that mammals, birds, reptiles, amphibians, fungi and algae need vitamin D.

Fungi

Fungi are not plants – they do not make their own food. They are either saprophytic, which means they live on dead or decaying material, or parasitic, which means they live on other living organisms without killing them. In fungi, the equivalent of 7-dehydrocholesterol is ergosterol, which is a component of the cell membrane (the skin of the cell) and in response to ultraviolet radiation, ergosterol changes to ergocalciferol (the equivalent of 7-dehydrocholesterol changing to cholecalciferol – the difference is in one small bit of the molecule). Fungi can live underground without sunlight. So why do they need ergocalciferol?

Plants

Very little is known about vitamin D in plants. Early research found that irradiating plant products (cottonseed oil or mixtures of wheat and corn) did not produce any vitamin D-like activity while irradiating animal products (meat and butter) did. It has generally been thought ever since that there is no vitamin D in plants. Some texts say that cholecalciferol (vitamin D_3) is found in animals and ergocalciferol (vitamin D_2) is found in plants but this is incorrect. In fact, recent research has found cholecalciferol in a few flowering plants including those from the potato family, the gourd family, the legume family and the grass family. In the waxyleaf nightshade, 7-dehydrocholesterol, cholecalciferol, calcidiol and calcitriol have all been identified and calcitriol is present both as a free steroid and as a glycoside derivative.

Does vitamin D have the same function in plants, and is it made in the same way as in animals? Fruits and vegetables are not regarded as a source of dietary vitamin D, but if vitamin D is as important for plants as it is for animals, it is most likely to be present in the leaves and the vascular system and since most plant foods consist of fruits or roots, it is possible that there is no vitamin D – or very little – in the parts of the plant we eat. It is also possible that the concentration of vitamin D in leaves is just too low to be detected when analysing plants for their nutrient content.

It is well known that plants respond to light and there is evidence they can respond specifically to ultraviolet-B; for example, the development of seedlings can be inhibited by ultraviolet-B exposure. There is thought to be a specific ultraviolet-B photoreceptor but it has not been identified. Could it be vitamin D? Most research into the effects of ultraviolet radiation on plants has been done with the aim of studying the damaging effects of excessive exposure to ultraviolet. It is therefore difficult to be sure whether vitamin D is common in plants and whether, when it is present, it is the only ultraviolet-B receptor or just one of several. In both plants and fungi, the effect of ultraviolet-B, whether it acts via vitamin D or not, is generally to inhibit growth. In experiments with fungi it also, in some cases, increases the concentration of melanin and it is known to stimulate sporulation.

Fish

Any dietician will tell you that fish are a good source of vitamin D. Vitamin D was originally discovered in the 1930s as the component of cod-liver oil that treated rickets. One of the mysteries to be solved was where the vitamin D in cod-liver oil came from.

Cod is a deep-water fish. The ultraviolet radiation penetrating the sea below one metre is only a hundredth of the intensity at the surface, and below two metres it is reduced to only a thousandth, so it was unlikely that cod are exposed to sufficient ultraviolet-B to make their own vitamin D as we do. A large proportion of the cod's diet is a kind of zooplankton called copepods – tiny crustaceans (relatives of crabs and lobsters) that float at the top of the ocean. Testing done as early as 1934 discovered that copepods contain vitamin D in sufficient quantity to promote bone healing.

It is now apparent that phytoplankton and zooplankton floating at the surface of the sea with plenty of exposure to sunlight can make abundant vitamin D, which then passes along the food chain into fish. With such a rich supply of vitamin D in their diet, fish have no need to make their own vitamin D, even if they are exposed to ultraviolet-B. In the cod, the vitamin D is mostly stored in the liver, while in oily fish such as mackerel and sardine, the vitamin D is mainly stored in the muscle.

Birds and animals

As mentioned above, fish do not make their own vitamin D but obtain it by eating plankton – the beginning of the marine food chain. What about land animals? Animals and birds can make vitamin D in the skin in the same way described for humans. It is well known that reptiles need sunlight. Gary Ferguson of Texas Christian University observed that panther chameleons bask in sunlight to maintain their vitamin D levels. When given high amounts of vitamin D in their diet they spent more time in the shade, but on a diet low in vitamin D they chose to spend more time in sunlight. Reptiles kept as pets are at risk of vitamin D deficiency and often develop osteoporosis and osteomalacia because they lack sunlight exposure and they do not get enough vitamin D from their diet. Most owners are aware of this problem and install lamps that emit ultraviolet radiation for their pets.

How does a bird get its vitamin D? Like us, it produces 7-dehydrocholesterol and needs ultraviolet-B to convert it to vitamin D. Most birds have an oil-secreting gland under their tail called a preen gland (also called the uropygial gland). The bird rubs its bill against the gland and then spreads the oil over the surface of the feathers, stroking along the barbs of each feather from quill to tip. This is called preening and may be done every day. The oil is thought to keep the feathers flexible and waterproof, but it also contains the 7-dehydrocholesterol stored in the uropygial gland. Preening spreads the 7-dehydrocholesterol over the feathers, enabling it to be exposed to sunlight and converted to cholecalciferol. With the next preening, some of the oil containing the newly synthesised cholecalciferol is ingested. Male great bustards have been observed lifting and pointing their bottoms towards the sun – thought to be a curious mating display but I wonder if they are making vitamin D.

Some birds, such as blackbirds and hens, can often be seen sunbathing – lying down with wings outstretched. Indeed, I have seen birds apparently sunbathing in my garden. Birds kept as indoor pets are known to suffer poor health if they lack a source of vitamin D. Owners of African Grey parrots, for example, are advised to provide egg yolks and fish liver oil to prevent seizures caused by vitamin D deficiency. All mammals can make vitamin D in their skin even though their skin is covered by hair – even sheep with their heavy pelage – and, like birds, can ingest vitamin D by licking their fur. I wonder if this is one reason cats seem to spend hours licking their fur?

Animals lacking sunlight exposure

Most animals can make vitamin D, but those that cannot must instead rely on obtaining vitamin D from their diet. Most species of land animals live in the tropical regions where there is plenty of sunshine. Animals that live at high latitudes may be capable of synthesising vitamin D but are dependent on being able to obtain vitamin D from food, at least in the winter when the intensity of ultraviolet-B is too low to produce adequate amounts of vitamin D.

Most animals and birds living at or near the Poles, such as polar bears and penguins, eat fish and sea mammals. These contain vitamin D originally produced by plankton and may provide plenty of vitamin D in the diet. Reindeer and musk oxen eat lichens, a symbiosis of fungi and algae rich in vitamin D.

Some animals, though, do not have any obvious sources of vitamin D. Nocturnal animals and those that live underground are not much exposed to sunlight and there are some that do not appear to have any dietary source of vitamin D either. The Egyptian fruit bat is nocturnal and roosts in trees or caves during the daytime, eats only fruit, and consequently has very low levels of vitamin D. In these bats, calcidiol levels are undetectable and it appears that any calcidiol provided is immediately converted to calcitriol. Similarly, the Damara mole rat, which lives in underground burrows, has a herbivorous diet but can use cholecalciferol when given as a supplement and can synthesise vitamin D when exposed to sunlight. It is possible that there are sources of vitamin D that have not yet been identified – in plant fruits and roots, for example, but it is also possible that these animals are living in a permanent state of vitamin D deficiency. For most animals, vitamin D is a conditionally essential nutrient – meaning it is essential in the diet when conditions (lack of sunlight exposure) prevent production in the skin.

Vitamin D is a sunlight sensor

Lars Olof Björn, Professor Emeritus at Lund University, has spent many years studying the effects of ultraviolet radiation on living things. His first publication, in 1958, was on the influence of red light on the growth of pea seedlings. Since then he has published more than 200 papers on the effects of light on plant growth and has written numerous books. With his colleague Ting Wang, he proposed that the original function of vitamin D was as a sunlight detector. How do you know whether the sun is shining or not? With no access to a clock, calendar or any sense of time, how would you know whether it is night or day, winter or summer? We can see the light radiating from the sun and we can feel its heat. We have a nervous system with eyes that are sensitive to light and skin receptors that are sensitive to heat. When there is no heat or light we know that there is no sun. But what of species that don't have a brain or a nervous system?

Imagine you are such a primitive thing – a fungus living on a dead tree root underground, or a planktonic creature floating in the sea with no means of resisting the water movement. As a simple creature you have no eyes, no skin receptors, no brain and no nervous system and you cannot see the sunlight or feel the heat of the sun. How do you know whether it is day or night, winter or summer, whether you are overground or underground, on the surface of the ocean or down in the depths? Could vitamin D be just the thing you need? Björn and Wang proposed that the change from ergosterol to ergocalciferol tells algae and fungi that they are in daylight. When there is no ergocalciferol, there is no ultraviolet radiation and therefore no sun. It could be that vitamin D originated as photoreceptor sensitive to sunlight in primitive organisms.

As we saw above, vitamin D is found in mammals, birds, reptiles, amphibians, fish, some plants, fungi and algae. In mammals, birds, reptiles and amphibians, 7-dehydrocholesterol converts to cholecalciferol (vitamin D_3) when it absorbs ultraviolet-B. In fungi and algae, the earliest life forms, ergosterol converts to ergocalciferol (vitamin D_2) in response to ultraviolet-B. Some of the simplest life forms – the sponges and diatoms *Skeletonema menzelii* and *Emiliania huxlei*, for example – have ergosterol. And in these organisms ergosterol might act as a sunscreen – like melanin – it absorbs ultraviolet-B to protect other molecules, such as DNA, from its harmful effects.

Suppose, then, that vitamin D evolved as a sunlight detector? We come back to the question of why it developed the ability to absorb ultraviolet-B and not the stronger wavelengths of sunlight reaching the Earth. Is it possible that in earlier times, the intensity of ultraviolet radiation was higher than visible radiation? Life is thought to have begun in the Archaean Eon, which occurred between 4 billion and 2.5 billion years ago. What was the spectrum of solar radiation reaching the Earth's surface when life began? We can only make an educated guess, but we can be sure that the atmosphere of the Earth was very different then. The ozone layer, which absorbs most of the ultraviolet-B reaching the stratosphere today, is thought to have formed around 540 million years ago (i.e. almost 2 billion years after the Archaean Eon), so it is reasonable to assume that before then, with less absorption by ozone, the amount of ultraviolet radiation reaching the Earth's surface would have been far higher. In addition, the amount of ultraviolet radiation emitted by the sun was probably higher. The Sun was formed nearly 5 billion years ago and, by comparing it with the evolution of other stars, astronomers believe it is halfway through its life as a star and in another 5 billion years it will enter its red giant phase. Our Sun, then, is a middle-aged star. The study of young stars has indicated that the intensity of ultraviolet radiation from the Sun in the past may have been much higher than it is today, even though the *total* intensity of the radiation emitted by the sun was lower. The spectrum of solar radiation was different in those Archaean days when life began. This could explain why an early photoreceptor was sensitive to ultraviolet radiation.

Vitamin D and size

You may remember the discussion about Bergmann's rule in the previous chapter. Karl Bergmann said that animals tend to be bigger when they inhabit cold climates. Bergmann's rule has been contended throughout the hundred or so years since he published his work. It is found to be generally true of birds and mammals, although there are many exceptions. Every so often a paper is published showing good evidence for Bergmann's rule and every so often a paper is published which shows the opposite. The problem with Bergmann's rule is that nobody knows how it works. If Bergmann's rule is correct, what is the stimulus? Since cold is associated with larger size, it is quite reasonably assumed that low temperature is the direct cause of the increase in size. Although there is a general correlation with temperature that fits in with Bergmann's rule, the exceptions cannot be explained by temperature. If the mechanism is natural selection with cold as a selective pressure, so that larger size is advantageous and bigger animals more likely to survive, then the exceptions could be explained by other factors that are not yet understood. But here I would like to suggest the possibility that ultraviolet-B, acting via vitamin D, has a direct effect on size.

In general, when sunlight is strong, temperatures are high and ultraviolet-B is intense. And when ultraviolet-B is strong, vitamin D is plentiful. At the other extreme, when sunlight is weak, temperatures are low, ultraviolet-B is weak and vitamin D becomes scarce. Suppose we accept that vitamin D originated as a photoreceptor specific for ultraviolet radiation because this was the strongest band of solar radiation at the time and vitamin D really was a sunlight sensor in primitive organisms. Could it have been the signal that tells a body how big it needs to be to keep warm in the ambient temperature? Does a fall in vitamin D result in bigger size?

In the sea

Life began in water. As you go down the water column in the ocean, the pressure increases and light decreases. The water column is divided into layers. At the top is the epipelagic or photic zone, which extends down to around 200 metres (650 ft). In this layer, occupied by many fish, sharks and jellyfish, there is sufficient penetration of sunlight for photosynthesis to take place. Next is the mesopelagic, or twilight zone, down to 1,000 metres (3,300 ft) where there is little sunlight. Swordfish, squids and cuttlefish live in this zone. Then there is the bathypelagic or dark zone, down to 4,000 metres (13,000 ft), where the only light comes from luminescent creatures such as the lantern fish. Giant squid live at this depth. Finally, from 4,000 metres to the ocean floor is the abyssopelagic or abyssal zone.

Ultraviolet-B can penetrate the photic zone at the top of the ocean but the intensity is sufficient for vitamin D synthesis to take place only at the very top of this layer. The food chain in the sea is roughly aligned with the water column. Creatures floating at the surface are eaten by creatures just below them, which in turn are eaten by creatures just below them, and so on. There is a gradient of sunlight and aligned with it, there is a gradient of size. As you go down the water column, the temperature goes down and, in general, the body sizes of the inhabitants go up. At the same time, the amount of vitamin D available goes down. Large creatures are said to display abyssal gigantism or deep-sea gigantism, because they are much larger at these depths than their counterparts at shallower depths. Examples are the oarfish, which can be up to 11 metres long and is recorded as the largest fish in the world, the giant squid can be up to 13 metres in length, and even bigger is the colossal squid that can be up to 14 metres in length. I am not aware of any study of vitamin D in these creatures, but as these deep-sea dwelling creatures are at the end of the food chain they are likely to have the lowest concentration of vitamin D. Bergmann's rule was originally described in warm-blooded animals and, as far as I know, nobody has looked at the possibility that Bergmann's rule applies to sea creatures. But could his rule explain why the largest sea creatures are those in the deepest and coldest parts of the sea? The principle that larger size reduces heat loss to the environment by reducing the relative surface area would also apply in the ocean.

On land

What happened when living things evolved on land? In terms of ultraviolet-B exposure, living in cold environments is equivalent to living at the bottom of the ocean. We have seen that animals either get their vitamin D in their diet – mainly from fish and sea creatures or eggs and milk – or they make their own vitamin D by exposure to ultraviolet-B. And we have seen that on land some of the big animals and birds live in the cold polar regions – termed polar gigantism – where ultraviolet-B is at its lowest.

In the marine environment, the vast majority of animals live in water that is below 5°C all the time. Heat is rapidly dissipated from the surface of the body, but on land, dealing with the heat becomes a greater problem and maintaining body temperature gets more complicated. The relationship between cold, vitamin D and body size is more complex on land. By getting vitamin D from food, life is possible in environments with low ultraviolet radiation. In a sense, animals that eat vitamin D are cheating – their bodies are fooled into believing that they are living in a tropical environment or, perhaps, floating on the surface of the ocean. Without a dietary source of vitamin D, polar animals, for example, would naturally be much larger but they would then need more food than is perhaps available. On the other hand, they need to be large enough to survive the cold of the winter. In fact, many animals in the polar regions do not survive the winter. Reindeer for example, gain weight in winter and survive when the weather is mild, but in a harsh winter many die.

There must be a trade-off between getting sufficient vitamin D to maintain health and being deficient *enough* to be to survive the cold by getting bigger, and getting the right balance is not easy. Getting bigger is, of course, only one way of coping with the cold. Some animals survive the cold by manipulating the microclimate or by going into hibernation. We believe humans survive mostly by manipulating the microclimate, but of course we are also relatively big animals and have the capacity to get even bigger. It is worth remembering that only a few animals and birds survive cold temperatures and those that do are mostly large, such as the Emperor penguins, polar bears and giant squid.

Prehistoric giants

Although animals generally increased in size over evolutionary time, in accordance with Cope's rule, with the exception of blue whales the biggest giants of all time existed in the past and are long extinct. The biggest land animals were the dinosaurs that first appeared 230 million years ago. Both the reason for their large size and the reason for their extinction 65 million years ago are not understood and are matters ripe for speculation. One can idly speculate that their massive sizes could have been caused by lower levels of ultraviolet-B at the Earth's surface resulting from a change in the atmosphere, perhaps caused by either volcanic activity or asteroid impact (both of which have been hypothesised as the cause of the mass extinction).

The giant penguins of Peru are another example of extinct giants. In 2005 on the southern coast of Peru, Peruvian palaeontologists found the fossils of two species of penguins never seen before. One species, called *Icadyptes salasi*, was dated to 36 million years ago and was more than 1.5 metres (5 ft) tall. The other, called *Perudyptes devriesi*, was dated to 42 million years ago and was around 0.9 metres (3 ft) tall, the same size as modern, extant King Penguins. Palaeontologist Julia Clarke, of the North Carolina Museum of Natural Sciences and the American Museum of Natural History and her colleagues reported the discovery. Previously, it had been thought that penguins had evolved in high latitudes in Antarctica and New Zealand and later, around 10 million years ago, moved into lower latitudes after a cooling period, but these new finds suggest otherwise. What were huge, cold-adapted birds doing in a tropical region at a time when the Earth was in a relatively warm period and tropical temperatures were similar to those of today? If temperature cannot explain it, could this mystery be solved if we knew something about ultraviolet radiation at this time? Ultraviolet radiation and vitamin D could potentially explain inconsistencies like this between body size and climate and could be the unifying explanation for Bergmann's rule. If this were true, the study of body sizes from fossils could help us to learn more about the ultraviolet environment and the composition of the atmosphere of the past.

The winter response

Even if we accept that vitamin D originated as a sunlight sensor, does it still work like that in our human bodies today? In this chapter we have strayed quite far, it seems, from the human problem of overweight into an exploration of the ancient origin of vitamin D. Returning to present day reality, the vitamin D winter that we experience outside of the tropics is preceded by a vitamin D autumn in which ultraviolet radiation, having peaked in the summer, gradually falls as the Earth moves around the Sun. It reaches its lowest point in the winter and gradually rises again in the spring. Not surprisingly, vitamin D synthesis follows this seasonal pattern. Regular measurements of calcidiol in individuals always exhibit a seasonal effect, with their highest levels at the end of the summer and the lowest at the end of the winter.

Vitamin D could be understood as a sunlight monitor, signalling the season. I think it is possible that falling vitamin D in the autumn is a signal to our brains that winter is on the way and is responsible for switching our physiology to its winter setting. The trouble is that – rather like measuring a person's wealth by how much cash they carry in their wallet or purse – this signal is no longer direct. There are now so many variables that there is no longer a direct relationship between the intensity of the sunlight and vitamin D levels. But assuming, for a moment, that vitamin D does act as a sunlight monitor, how would it work? In the first step, your body detects how much vitamin D is coming in, like the balance in your bank current account – is it going up or down? Is it low or high? If it is getting low, then we need to prepare for the winter, if it is above a certain level, it must be summer and we don't need to get bigger. If it falls and stays low there must be an ice age out there. Vitamin D can conceivably act like the barometer, or weather station, we might have at home. It is located inside us and tells us what the weather is like outside. How does the body monitor its vitamin D status? Where is the meter?

It seems reasonable to guess that the hypothalamus is the part of the brain that coordinates the winter response since the hypothalamus is the sensing organ of the brain. It is the centre of homeostasis – the part of the brain that checks everything is just right and organises adjustments when there is any disturbance, to maintain the *status quo*. The blood–brain barrier protects the brain from harmful substances and refers to the tight junctions between cells of the capillaries that can stop many substances from crossing from the blood into the brain and spinal cord. But it is thought that in parts of the hypothalamus this barrier is thinner to allow it to detect what is circulating about in your blood. One part of the hypothalamus controls body temperature by sensing the temperature of the blood and getting information about the temperature of the skin from thermoreceptors, then adjusting heat production or heat loss. Perhaps in the same way it senses body fat by getting information from leptin and makes adjustments to ensure our body weight is maintained at the set point. If necessary, the set point can be reset. For example when we have a fever, the temperature set point (or thermostat) may be increased (from, say, 37°C to 39°C) in response to substances called pyrogens acting on the hypothalamus. In the same way, the body weight set point (or fatstat) may also be increased (from, say, 60 kg to 65 kg) and perhaps the body weight set point is raised when the hypothalamus detects low vitamin D.

The signal

Which form of vitamin D is the signal? When vitamin D is produced in the sunlight it is in the form of calciferol. Calciferol is then converted to calcidiol that, in turn, is converted to calcitriol. All these forms are present in the blood, so the signal could be any one, or all, of the three. The first form, calciferol, is rapidly converted to calcidiol and is the form stored in muscle and fat, so it doesn't hang around in the blood. The third form, calcitriol is the active form of vitamin D. Although calcitriol is also found in the blood, it is present in concentrations of a thousand times lower than calcidiol (it is measured in *picomoles* whereas calcidiol is measured in *nanomoles*). Furthermore, the amount of calcitriol in the bloodstream seems to be tightly regulated. If the concentration lowers, more is made, and if it goes up, more is removed so that there is always the same amount of calcitriol in the blood, give or take a few picomoles.

This leaves the second form, calcidiol, which is only found in the blood – it is not found much anywhere else except for milk. The concentration of calcidiol is much more variable than calcitriol and it rises in a dose-dependent manner. If we spend a bit more time in the sun, calcidiol goes up. If we start taking a vitamin D supplement, calcidiol goes up. We know this because there have been numerous trials in which people were given supplements or exposed to ultraviolet radiation and their calcidiol levels measured. Of these three forms, calcidiol would seem to be the best candidate to act as the sunlight sensor. It is quite possible that one of the other forms of vitamin D, about which very little is known, acts as the sensor, but for now I will assume it is calcidiol.

I suggest, then, that the purpose of calcidiol is to act as a barometer of our vitamin D status. It is used as a measure of vitamin D status in the clinic and perhaps it is also used as a measure of vitamin D status by the brain. The hypothalamus uses the amount of calcidiol to assess what the weather is like, and when necessary it initiates a winter response. When calcidiol falls, the body weight set point goes up and fat is increased. The metabolic changes that help to protect us against the cold and result in insulin resistance, high blood pressure and dyslipidaemia, might precede or accompany weight gain, but it is more likely that they occur once the gain in weight – perhaps in the form of visceral fat – has reached a threshold. Perhaps moderate weight gain prepares us for a winter, while obesity and the metabolic syndrome prepare us for an ice age. In any case, I will refer to the whole process of gaining weight and adjusting our metabolism to help us to survive the cold as our winter response.

The functions of vitamin D

If we accept that vitamin D is basically a sunlight sensor how did it get involved in calcium regulation, differentiation and all the other things it seems to do? The active form, calcitriol, acts by binding to a receptor and regulating gene activity. This receptor is present in just about every type of cell, where calcidiol can be converted into calcitriol as and when is needed. It is evident that vitamin D has many functions, only a few of which have been studied in any depth.

Recycling

How would a photoreceptor have evolved to function as a gene regulator? Once you have converted ergosterol to ergocalciferol, or 7-dehydrocholesterol to cholecalciferol, and you have noted that the sun is out from your increase in vitamin D, you need to remove the vitamin D product to ensure that the signal is not permanently switched on. The pathway of vitamin D once it has been made in the skin – being transported in a vehicle (vitamin D-binding protein) in the blood, and then being taken off to the liver for hydroxylation, followed by a trip to the kidney – is reminiscent of a detoxification process. The enzymes that process vitamin D belong to a group called the P450 enzymes, many of which are detoxificating enzymes. The resulting metabolites of vitamin D may have started as inactivated by-products and found a useful role later (i.e. millions of years later) – a bit like recycling rubbish.

The control of calcium

When it comes to the physiological function of vitamin D in fish, researchers were puzzled to find that it is not essential for calcium metabolism. Both elasmobranchs (e.g. sharks and lampreys that do not have a calcified skeleton) and teleosts (that do have a calcified skeleton) have extremely high concentrations of vitamin D. One advantage of living in the oceans is that there is plenty of calcium around, which is probably why it came to be used for such a variety of things in the body, from forming the skeleton to muscle contraction. When a fish needs more calcium it can simply take some from its surroundings. But on land, although calcium is abundant, is not so easily accessible. This means an active process of absorbing calcium is required to ensure there is enough for all the body's needs. So perhaps calcitriol adapted into a useful role to ensure that plenty of calcium was obtained from the diet in land-dwelling organisms. Vitamin D existed before the calcium homeostatic system, but the perception that vitamin D is simply a calcium regulator persists, even among scientists. Indeed, our view of the function of vitamin D as just a bone vitamin seems to have much more to do with the history of its discovery than with science.

Skin adaptation

Some of the earliest functions of calcitriol may have been concerned with controlling the amount of vitamin D synthesis. Skin changes in relation to the amount of sun exposure it gets – it tends to become thicker and darker with increased exposure. This photoadaptation can also occur to some extent in response to vitamin D supplementation, so it appears that when vitamin D is in short supply the skin increases its sensitivity to the sun to allow more vitamin D to be made, and when we have plenty of vitamin D, the skin allows less ultraviolet radiation in. When the skin is thin and pale, the chances of making vitamin D are increased but so are the chances of DNA being damaged by ultraviolet radiation. If DNA is damaged, there is a need to repair it. Similarly, if the skin is damaged, it needs to be repaired. Calcitriol has the potential to do both these things. It is known to influence the immune system and to increase skin cell production as well as melanin production. Indeed, vitamin D is used as a treatment for the skin conditions psoriasis and vitiligo and a lot of studies are investigating the potential of using calcitriol as therapy for different diseases. The functions of calcitriol may have originated to maintain the integrity of the skin because it is essential for the manufacture of vitamin D, and to control the penetration of ultraviolet-B into the skin.

It seems quite possible, then, that vitamin D changed into different useful forms – it evolved, just as living things evolved, and by the time humans came along it had become essential for many different processes, although it still did its original job as a sunlight detector.

This is speculation and doesn't get us very far in making biological sense of all the different forms of vitamin D and their different functions. Vitamin D remains biologically mysterious. Perhaps it would help, when we think about the function of vitamin D, if we can divide up its roles into two. The first is its original role as a sunlight detector and the second is its role in the development of cells – a role that ultimately keeps us healthy by defending and protecting us from damage, including protecting us from infections and cancer. It follows then that vitamin D deficiency must also be dichotomous and to understand its effects we may need to separate calcidiol deficiency (which causes overweight) from calcitriol deficiency (which increases susceptibility to infectious and other types of disease).

Revisiting the thrifty genotype

The main scientific explanation for overweight, as discussed previously, is the thrifty genotype hypothesis. It makes good biological sense but the evidence for it is contradictory and confusing. So should we throw out the idea of the thrifty genotype? The hypothesis – that those genes which were an advantage to our ancestors in an environment of undernutrition are now disadvantageous in our modern environment – arose from Neel's observation that diabetes, although relatively frequent in urban-industrial societies (even in the 1960s), did not occur in societies which followed an ancient way of life, such as the Amazonian tribe Yanomama on the Brazilian–Venezuelan border. He also noted that the children of parents with diabetes tend to be bigger at birth and reach puberty earlier, both features that can be regarded as advantageous in evolutionary terms. Bigger babies are more likely to survive a famine and in famine conditions, when life expectancy is shorter, earlier puberty allows reproduction to start earlier.

Neel spent 30 years working with the Yanomama to put his hypothesis to the test, finding, for example, that blood pressure and glucose levels of the indigenous people living ancient lifestyles were lower than those of urban people. Many of Neel's assumptions are now regarded as wrong – not because he made mistakes, but because we now know much more about diabetes as a result of the research that has been done in the period of over 40 years since he wrote his paper. (I have no doubt that similarly, many assumptions in this book will prove to be wrong in 40 years' time.) Nevertheless, his main thesis persists. It was particularly attractive for explaining the high rates of diabetes in certain populations, such as the Pima Indians of the USA and Pacific Islanders and could explain the relatively high rates of diabetes in western Europe and the USA in comparison to the low rates in developing countries.

How would the thrifty genotype work? Theoretically, those individuals who, at the start of a famine, have the most fat stored on their body will survive the longest. If a person has a gene variant – suppose it is called XA – which gives him or her a propensity to gain weight, he or she is more likely to survive a famine than a lean person who has a variant called XB. If, after successive famines, the people with XA survive and the people with XB die, there will eventually be few people left with the XB variant and those with the XA variant are said to have a 'fat gene'. Successive famines can wipe out a particular gene variant and famine is then called a selective event or selective pressure.

The thrifty part refers to energy expenditure. If you expect to have a low income in the future, you will be more careful with how you spend your money today and will make sure that any excess is saved in a high-interest account to ensure that, when hard times come along, you will have a nest egg to draw on to supplement your low income. Similarly it is thought that genes that promote the saving of energy, which can involve many different processes of metabolism, helped our ancestors to survive periods of food scarcity. Neel's original interest was in the metabolic and physiological processes that respond to food intake, specifically the insulin response to glucose, but it has since been extrapolated and extended by others to encompass all aspects of energy balance including things such as behaviour.

So those of us with thrifty genotypes are thought to have a super-efficient metabolism, with all non-essential processes switched off, as well as a tendency to overeat when food is available and to avoid exercise whenever possible. The thinking is that we are genetically predisposed to get fat when there is food available and we have adapted to oscillate, metabolically speaking, between periods of feast and famine and between periods of physical activity and rest. My overwhelming difficulty with this idea is that it suggests that for us all to be a normal weight, we need to suffer from prolonged and intense hunger in between periods of eating a lot. This is, of course, is exactly what some people do in order to keep control of their weight – 'yo-yo' dieting re-creates the feast–famine cycle. This doesn't seem normal to me, but what do the experts say?

Human ancestors

Is the popular image of our ancestors realistic? We imagine our ancient ancestors to have been like the Yanomama in the rain forests of the Amazon, or the Suri living on the savannah in the south-west of Ethiopia, or the nomadic Darhad of northern Mongolia. Ancient humans are thought to have experienced extreme changes in food supply – feast or famine. The idea is that a successful hunt produced a large beast, which needed to be eaten quickly (assuming there were no means of food preservation) and in between successful hunts there were times of food scarcity. But Jared Diamond, Professor of Geography and Physiology at University of California, Los Angeles, challenged this view. In truth, he says, the food supply may have been more consistent, with frequent hunting of small animals and gathering of plant food on a daily basis.

Andrew Prentice is Professor of International Nutrition at the London School of Tropical Hygiene and is often invited by the media to comment on news about overweight. He was born and grew up in Uganda, a country that straddles the equator, and he has spent much time working in Africa, studying nutrition. He says famine has probably only been an important factor for the past 6,000 years. He has pointed out that pre-Neolithic hunter–gatherers were less likely to experience famine than post-agricultural societies, because the small populations had the mobility to find new sources of food when necessary. People in agricultural societies, on the other hand, become dependent on a limited range of food and cannot easily relocate.

There are records of famine that can be dated to within the past 5,000 years and some believe that famines may have occurred throughout the period of 50,000 years. Certainly in recent history famine has occurred frequently. For example, in the great famine in Finland in 1696 it is estimated that more than a quarter of the population died and, in Italy in 1376, two thirds of the population are thought to have died. When bad weather or disease ruins a crop the result can be devastating. John Speakman is a Professor at the University of Aberdeen where he leads the Energetics Research Group. He has identified several flaws in the thrifty genotype idea. He points out that famines are rare events and that, in any case, starvation is not the main cause of death in famines. A more important cause of death in famine is not so much a shortage of food but the effects of inequality of wealth that results in shortages for a proportion of the population. Some of John Speakman's arguments against the thrifty genotype hypothesis are set out below.

1. People with plenty of food don't always get fat

Modern hunter–gatherers do not become overweight even when there is plenty of food available. The body mass index of modern hunter–gatherers tends to be the range of 17.5 to 21, which is at the lean end of normal category even though there is plenty of food. However, they become overweight when they leave their traditional lifestyle behind.

2. Deaths in famines are not all due to starvation

In the Irish potato famine of 1845–1850 the blight fungus ruined the potato crop. The population reduced from 8.17 million in 1841 to 6.55 million in 1851. Almost 1 million people died and almost 1 million emigrated. It is estimated that of 985,000 deaths, 23 per cent were caused by fever (probably typhoid), and 35 per cent by diarrhoea and dysentery. Only about 0.6 per cent of deaths were due to starvation.

Most deaths in famines are not caused by simply running out of energy, as can occur in hunger strikers, and cannot be simply avoided by being overweight at the start. Most deaths are caused by infections because the immune system is impaired due to lack of micronutrients. The impairment of the immune system due to lack of vitamins and minerals would affect those who were overweight just as much as those of normal weight. Other deaths are caused by poor quality and unsuitable foods – for example, eating rotting food and poisonous plants – which would also affect overweight and lean people equally.

3. Children are more likely to die in famines

For genes to be selected, the survivors of famines need to be those who will go on to reproduce – young adults and children. Although young adults are the most likely to survive, children, along with the elderly, are the most susceptible to death from infectious disease.

Thrifty or winter genotype?

Where does cold fit in? Could the thrifty genotype, if it exists, really be the *winter* genotype? It seems almost inconceivable that any of us could trace a descent through generation after generation that entirely escaped hunger. Perhaps all of us who are alive today have inherited our genes from people who survived the vicissitudes of food scarcity. But in any kind of society food is most likely to become scarce in the winter, when deaths in famine may be due to food shortage, disease and cold, since heat production requires a healthy nutritional status.

We have documented records of famines and plagues so we are familiar with the horrors and reality of hunger and disease and how it ravages populations and challenges survival. We can understand clearly that we are descendants of those who survived these horrific challenges to the human existence, but we are less familiar with the challenge of cold. Perhaps a more powerful and ancient selective pressure than post-agricultural famines was the ability to survive the cold of the ice ages.

Cold

Was cold a selective pressure? It is vital that we are able to keep warm, yet prehistoric humans lived at the times of ice ages. Could the challenge of living in winter conditions be an underestimated force in human evolution? After years of relative stability in the Earth's climate, we are now facing the reality of a changeable climate and are beginning to recognise the effects of the climate on our history. Climate is increasingly thought to have been a major influence on the existence of humans at different times in different regions. There is now abundant evidence from palaeontology, archaeology and genetics to indicate that early human species evolved around 2.5 million years ago in Africa and modern humans originated in the tropics between 200 thousand and 100 thousand years ago. All of us humans living today are thought to be descended from the humans who lived in East Africa around 200 thousand years ago. The question of when, how and, to a lesser extent, why humans migrated to places all around the globe has been a matter of much study and speculation.

Human migration

The oldest fossil evidence for human existence outside of Africa is some skeletal remains found in Israel dated to between 120,000 and 90,000 years ago. After that, there is no further evidence of humans living outside Africa until around 50,000 years ago, leading to speculation that there was a short (at least in evolutionary terms) period of occupation outside Africa followed by a period of little or no migration out of Africa for the next 40,000 to 50,000 years, although migration *within* Africa did take place.

Genetic analysis (of mitochondrial DNA lineages) has shown that all non-Africans are descended from one small group and, not surprisingly, the earliest lineages remain in Africa. This suggests that those people outside of sub-Saharan Africa are either descended from one group that migrated out, or that other humans left Africa but only those with this particular genotype (called the L3 lineage) survived, while those with the earliest lineages only survived in Africa.

It is possible, therefore, that those people whose recent ancestors lived outside of sub-Saharan Africa are descended from the only population of humans to survive the conditions in those regions. Climatic conditions are now commonly used to explain the times and routes of prehistoric human settlements throughout the world. Sea level changes that exposed land bridges are one of the results of climate change and these are thought to have allowed migration across land now covered by sea – from Asia to America, for example. Cold is also thought to have caused extinction of populations in the northern latitudes.

Evolutionary biologists sometimes talk about humans being driven out or pushed back from one region to another. What I think they mean is that there is evidence for humans inhabiting in a certain place at a certain time whereas there is no evidence that they were in that same place a bit later ('a bit later' being perhaps some tens of thousands of years later). In northern Europe, for example, sites of collections of artefacts suggest that small populations occupied the sites infrequently. In contrast, southern sites in the Mediterranean regions suggest larger populations and almost continuous occupation. Thus there was an ebb and flow of populations in northern regions where the climate was colder.

The settlement of Britain has been studied by the Ancient Human Occupation of Britain Project, a collaboration between specialists at different institutes and universities headed by Chris Stringer, Professor of Palaeontology. Humans have been in Britain continuously for around 12,000 years. But the work of the project has found there were six previous occupations, the first dated to 500,000 years ago, and it appears that Britain had no human population in between these occupations. Comparing the dates of the occupations with climatic conditions, there is a clear correlation between the occupations and warm periods.

It is conceivable that some of us have inherited genes making it more likely that we gain weight and switch to our winter metabolism sooner than others. If there are any thrifty genes, perhaps they are really winter genes, or perhaps there are both. But overweight is not confined to any population group. Neel first put the thrifty genotype hypothesis forward in the 1960s when overweight and diabetes affected population groups mainly in the developed world. Forty years on, overweight and diabetes are affecting many more population groups, all around the world. Although several genes have been associated with overweight and the metabolic syndrome, not one has been explicitly demonstrated to be a thrifty gene, despite advances in genetic techniques and expertise and despite the increasing population available to study. It appears that no population group is protected from overweight by their genes. In fact, when it comes to overweight, genes, whether they are thrifty or winter, pale into insignificance against the influence of the environment. But before we move on from the thrifty genotype idea, we will consider what recent genetic changes can tell us about the environment in which our ancestors coped. Cold and hunger in the winter were not the only selective pressures to be faced by humans when they left Africa and moved to regions with more extreme seasonal variations.

The ancestral diet

Loren Cordain, a Professor in the Department of Health and Exercise Science at Colorado State University, is one of the many proponents of the Palaeolithic diet. In keeping with the thrifty genotype hypothesis, the principle is that genetically we are the same as our Palaeolithic ancestors but our diet has changed drastically in the past 10,000 years. In this period only a few small changes have occurred in our genes, yet agriculture and industrialisation has changed our diets almost beyond recognition. Palaeolithic hunter-gatherers survived on diets high in meat and fat in the winter when plants were not available, yet they did not suffer from atherosclerosis. There is evidence that they suffered from ill health when they changed from the traditional diet to a post-agricultural diet based on grains. Furthermore, modern hunter-gatherers become overweight and suffer from the metabolic syndrome when they adopt a modern diet of processed food.

The Palaeolithic diet (other versions are called the stone-age diet, the caveman diet and the evolution diet) includes meat, fish, eggs, fruits, vegetables and nuts and excludes the post-agricultural foods – sugar, cereals including wheat, refined fats, potatoes and dairy foods – which make up much of our modern diet. Trials of this diet in diabetic patients have shown an improvement in the risk factors for cardiovascular disease. One possibility to consider is that this diet may contain more vitamin D than the grain-based diet as it contains higher proportions of fish, meat and eggs. But what can we learn from the people alive *today* who follow traditional ways of living and do not suffer from overweight? It is estimated that around 300 million people around the world follow ancient ways of living that have not been altered by industrialisation or technological advances, or if they have, only slightly. Some examples are described below.

- *People who live in rain forests,* such as the Sanema (part of the Yanomama), who live on the banks of the Cuara River in southern Venezuela, wear little or no clothing. Abundant water and tropical heat leads to a diversity of plant and animal life, which means there is plenty of food.

- *In Papua,* there are about 1,000 indigenous groups including the Kombai. Again, they wear little or no clothing. They hunt wild pig and keep domestic pigs.

- *The Suri* in the south–west of Ethiopia are semi-nomadic. They wear no clothing. Cattle are important for their milk and their blood; the cows are bled once a month and the blood is drunk straight from the wound before it congeals.

- *Outside the tropics,* the Darhad live in northern Mongolia, which is on the border with Siberia. It is remote, with lakes, forests and wide open grasslands. They live there in the summer but before winter they migrate over the mountain to spend the winter by Lake Khövsgöl. They keep animals – horses, yaks, sheep and goats – that are herded out to graze on pastures and milked every day. Milk and dairy products are very important part of the diet. They wear clothes and hats because it is cold – the temperature is low, often below –20°C in winter.

One of the things that is always overlooked when comparing the modern and hunter–gatherer way of living is the exposure to sunlight. People who follow traditional ways of living mostly live in tropical regions and tend to wear little or no clothing. This means they are exposed to relatively high amounts of sunlight and we would expect them to have high levels of calcidiol all year round. In addition to their exposure to sunlight, the drinking of milk and blood and eating meat would provide a dietary source of vitamin D. Those like the Darhad who live at higher latitudes, drink milk and eat mostly dairy products and meat. Is the real reason why they have low body weight and do not gain weight or suffer from the metabolic syndrome, diabetes and cardiovascular disease, that they have greater access to vitamin D?

Lactase

One of the supporting lines of evidence for the Palaeolithic diet is the idea that our food supply has changed so fast that our genes just could not keep up. It is thought that our ancient genome is not suited to the modern diet. This is based on the assumption that adaptation to environment takes place over hundreds of thousands of years. But is this assumption correct? It is true that there have been only few changes in our genome in the past few thousand years, but these changes may shed light on our ancestors' diet. One of the best studied is the gene that codes for the lactase enzyme.

Lact*ase* is produced in the digestive system where it breaks down the sugar lact*ose*. Lactose is the only sugar in milk and it is only found in milk, so the lactase enzyme is only found in mammals. As a north-west European I took it for granted that I would be able to digest milk and dairy foods throughout life, but what I thought was normal actually turns out to be abnormal. In fact, in most humans and other mammals, lactase is only produced during infancy and gradually disappears after weaning, so that by adulthood lactase is no longer produced. Without lactase, milk and dairy products cannot be digested properly. Lactase deficiency can occur in gastrointestinal disease, when it is called lactose intolerance. But even without such disease it is quite common to be unable to digest milk as an adult.

The ability to produce lactase throughout life is called lactase persistence and in the 1970s a genetic variant was found which associated with this trait. This genetic variant is very common in people of European descent. More recently, other variants have been found which also associate with lactase persistence. It is not known how these variants cause lactase persistence – exactly how the gene is switched on after birth and switched off again after weaning is still a mystery – but there is a very strong association between the genetic variants and lactase persistence.

Since lactose is only found in milk and dairy foods, it is not surprising that those regions where milk and dairy products form a large part of the diet have the highest rates of lactase persistence. It is most common in north-west Europe, but is also found in the north-west of the Indian subcontinent and in nomadic tribes that keep cattle for dairying in Africa and the Middle East, while their immediate, non-dairying neighbours do not have lactase persistence. So there is an apparent correlation with dairying.

Dairy farming is widely thought to have started in the Neolithic age. Archaeological evidence, such as the presence of milk proteins preserved in ceramic vessels, suggests dairying was present in south-eastern Europe at the onset of the Neolithic in Romania and Hungary 7,900 to 7,450 years ago and in England 6,100 years ago.

The most common genetic variant for lactase persistence became widespread between 12,000 and 7,000 years ago, a period that encompasses the onset of dairying, according to archaeological evidence. Mark Thomas is Professor of Evolutionary Genetics at University College London where he heads the Molecular and Cultural Evolution Laboratory. He and his colleagues found that this variant was not present in Neolithic humans in Europe, suggesting that it was rare in early European farmers. Furthermore, using a computer simulation, he calculated that the variant first spread from the central Balkan region. In fact, the genetic analysis of lactase persistence has been used as a marker for the spread of dairy farming in the Neolithic period. It is generally believed – and makes biological sense – that, first, milk-drinking persisted into adulthood and then the genes changed as a result, although of course it is possible that it happened the other way around – perhaps the gene was altered by a chance mutation which enabled people to continue to digest milk.

Either way, all the evidence suggests lactase persistence was not present in early humans, but became common during the Neolithic because it was positively selected. This means it may have had an advantage – those who adapted to the lifelong digestion of milk were more likely to survive than those who did not. The positive selection of any particular gene could be a coincidence – it might be a hitch-hiker that just happens to be on the same bit of chromosome as some other selected gene, for example – but in this case, the evidence of the history of farming and the fact that lactose is only present in milk, together with the geographical distribution of the gene variants, mean it is reasonable to assume the gene was *vital* to the survival of European populations in the Neolithic period. It remains non-selected and therefore non-essential in other populations, including most of the African and Chinese populations.

The survival advantage of drinking milk

What is it about milk and dairy foods that became vital to Europeans in the Neolithic? Gebhard Flatz of the Hannover Medical School and his colleagues first suggested in the 1970s that drinking milk was advantageous because of the vitamin D and calcium content. While working in Saudi Arabia in 1975, Gordon Cook, with his colleague M.T. al-Torki, suggested the arid-climate hypothesis – that in dry, desert conditions milk provides a clean source of fluid as well as nourishing food, especially from camels who can survive up to two weeks without food and water. However this does not explain why lactase persistence became so common in northern Europe and continues to be common to the present day. Could it be related to latitude? It is not unreasonable to suppose that, because milk contains vitamin D, it was advantageous in the relatively low ultraviolet environment of northern latitudes and in the absence of other sources of vitamin D. It is possible that survival outside the tropics was enhanced by drinking milk throughout life, and perhaps it is just as important today.

Low ultraviolet-B

We are fascinated by the question of what makes us human. In truth, we are not hugely different from other animals, but what are the small differences making us – the third chimpanzee, as Jared Diamond describes us – different to other primates? What are the characteristics unique to humans, if there are any at all?

The three essential traits distinguishing us from our nearest relative, the chimpanzee, are an upright stance, a big brain, and sparse hair. Recent work has studied the human genes that differ from those in chimpanzees (or, rather, *other* chimpanzees), as well as genes that have been selected for recently in humans, like the gene associated with lactase persistence. Some of the genes that have undergone recent positive selection are involved in skin pigmentation and metabolism.

Biologically speaking, humans are tropical animals. We have little hair and the temperature at which we start producing heat is high – much higher than other mammals living at high latitudes, such as the arctic fox. But those of us with thin, pale skin do not have the skin resilience suitable for tropical sunlight, indeed some of us burn easily even at high latitudes. When humans migrated out of tropical regions they had to survive the unfamiliar challenges of seasons, cold and low ultraviolet. We have so far considered the difficulties of surviving hunger and cold and we now turn to the question of whether low ultraviolet-B was also a selective pressure.

Lack of hair

One of the intriguing questions that the winter response idea brings to mind is that, if we are adapting to winter conditions, why don't we just grow fur? There is no doubt that hair can increase the size of the shell and help to reduce heat loss to the outside environment. The lower critical temperatures of animals that live in the cold can be astonishingly low – as low as -30°C in the moose, -40°C in the arctic fox and possibly -50°C in the caribou – and this cold tolerance is due largely to seasonal changes in fur. But hair has many functions in addition to acting as an insulator.

Hair can protect the skin from insects such as mosquitoes. Hair extends the sensory field of the skin – clearly understood in the whiskers of a cat – but even we humans can recognise an insect like an ant crawling on us as it displaces the hairs on our skin. Hair can also be used as a warning to attackers to signal defence. For example, the hairs stand up when we are threatened – hence the term 'our hackles rise' – hackles being the hair on the neck. Again this is more obvious in animals other than humans, such as dogs, cats and particularly porcupines. Hair acts as a dry lubricant, which perhaps is why we still have underarm hair and in the groin, where it stops the skin from rubbing uncomfortably. Hair can work as a trap for dirt and dust and can keep skin from getting wet in light rain.

No one knows how or why hair developed in the first place. Only mammals have it and it is not clear whether hair evolved from scales or whether it evolved separately. All primates are covered with hair and in general, the larger the primate, the fewer hairs per unit area of body surface. The earliest humans are thought to have had dense hair covering the body but in modern humans, although we have a covering of body hair, it is sparse, fine and is mostly invisible, with the exception of the top of our heads, underarms, pubic regions, and chests in men. We are naked compared to most mammals. Almost all mammals have more hair than we do and the exceptions can mostly be divided into two groups – large animals, including elephants, rhinoceroses and hippopotamuses, and aquatic animals, including walruses, dolphins, whales and manatees.

Since one of the groups of hairless mammals is aquatic, one theory is that there was an aquatic phase in our ancestral history. The aquatic ape hypothesis was proposed by Alister Hardy and written up by Elaine Morgan. This theory has not been widely accepted due to lack of evidence. For example, some aquatic mammals such as otters have hair. But it is the larger aquatic mammals (such as the whale) that lost their hair, while the smaller ones (such as the otter) remain hairy. So is it really all about size?

Why should large size mean less body hair? One reason is that large size means that body surface area is smaller in relation to body size and heat loss is lower. This means there is less need for body hair to keep warm. In the tropics, in contrast, there is a greater need to keep cool and cooling by losing heat from blood diverted to the capillaries close to the skin and, in the case of humans, to cool by evaporation of sweat, is made easier when you have less hair.

Having a smaller body surface in relation to volume also means of course, there is relatively less skin in which to make vitamin D, so increasing the amount of naked skin exposed to sunlight will also increase the amount of vitamin D made. One big difference between humans and most other mammals is that we are bipedal and have less body surface exposed to the sunlight. As quadrupeds go about their daily business, the whole of their back and the back of their heads are exposed to sunlight but we bipeds normally expose just the top of our head and shoulders. So perhaps we lost our hair so that we could make more vitamin D in the upright stance, retaining it on the top of our heads as only the scalp needs to be protected from the sunlight.

Skin colour

It is clear that our skin can become a little darker when exposed to sunlight but the range of colour within which our skin can change is very limited and is determined by inherited genes that cannot be changed. Within a lifetime, a white person cannot become black and a black person cannot become white. However, it appears we are all descended from black Africans and some of us lost much of our pigmentation at some point in our history. The question of why humans have different skin and hair colours has been the matter of some considerable theoretical discussion.

In *The Descent of Man*, Darwin considered the colour of skin as an adaptation to different degrees of sunlight. It is interesting to read that his viewpoint was of the skin going darker on increased exposure to sunlight, whereas today's scholars approach the question from the opposite point of view of skin going lighter with reduced exposure to sunlight. Many experts believe sexual selection played an important role in the evolution of skin and hair because they are visible features, which can be used to select a sexual partner and because, although sunlight must have played some role, it cannot fully account for all the differences. Darwin dismissed the influence of sunlight because the Dutch settlers of Africa (the Boers) had not become dark even though they had been in Africa for 300 years. But we now know that 300 years is not very long in evolutionary terms. Jared Diamond considers a longer settlement in his book *The Third Chimpanzee*, and points out that sunlight cannot account for the dark skin of Tasmanian natives. They lived in Tasmania for at least 10 thousand years (and possibly up to 35 thousand years) until they died out in the nineteenth century after the island was colonised by the British. After 10 thousand years of living in Tasmania, which lies at latitude 42° S with a cool temperate climate (similar to Rome, Italy and Chicago, USA), they remained black.

These arguments, however, are based solely on the effect of latitude on sunlight and fail to take into account the many factors that affect vitamin D status outlined in Chapter 1 Helpful Radiation. If, for example, the Tasmanians had a good source of vitamin D – oily fish in their diet, say – there would be no need to increase sensitivity to ultraviolet-B by losing pigmentation. Similarly, Inuit tend to have darker skin than northern Europeans, even though they live at more northern latitudes where ultraviolet radiation is lower, and the traditional vitamin D-rich diet of fish and sea mammals can explain this. And perhaps the Boers in South Africa kept their light coloured skin because they did not spend much of their time naked and outdoors.

Nina Jablonski, Professor of Anthropology at the Pennsylvania State University, has spent many years studying primate evolution. In the year 2000, she tested the relationship between sunlight and skin colour, when she and her colleague (and husband) George Chaplin related skin colours worldwide with actual measurements of ultraviolet radiation obtained by NASA's Total Ozone Mapping Spectrometer on a satellite. They found there was a strong correlation between skin colour and ultraviolet radiation throughout the world. Jablonski believes that the earliest humans had light coloured skin covered with dark black hair, similar to the chimpanzee. The hair was lost soon after humans evolved and the skin then darkened because it was no longer protected from the sun by hair. When humans moved away from tropical regions into regions with varying ultraviolet irradiance, the pigmentation of the skin was lost to optimise the synthesis of vitamin D.

Dark skin has been thought to protect the skin from sunburn and skin cancer; however, Nina Jablonski points out that these are unlikely to have been factors in the evolution of dark skin, since they have little effect on reproductive success. She believes, instead, that dark skin protected against the degradation of folate by sunlight, an important vitamin vital for reproduction. So, in a nutshell, dark skin protects folate, while light skin allows vitamin D synthesis. As is often the case in nature, there is a delicate balance between the two.

Jablonski points out that the importance of vitamin D to general health has largely been overlooked in the debate and there is now evidence that vitamin D deficiency can have many effects. It reduces fertility, meaning fewer babies are born; increases bone deformities and infections in the young, meaning fewer of those babies reach adulthood; increases infections, cancers, bone disease, cardiovascular disease, lung disease, autoimmune disease in adults, all of which can reduce longevity. She believes that vitamin D deficiency in low ultraviolet conditions was a selective pressure.

Another omission in the debate, in my opinion, is recognition of the many factors other than latitude and climate, which can influence vitamin D status. In short, the arguments against the idea that sunlight exposure has influenced skin pigmentation ignore the mechanism by which sunlight is detected i.e. vitamin D production.

Hair colour

If we accept that skin pigmentation was lost in order to increase the amount of vitamin D we can produce in low ultraviolet conditions, could the same be true of hair colour? Many animals lose hair in a seasonal pattern with two moulting periods when hair is lost in the autumn and replaced with a winter coat, which moults in the spring. Some animals also change colour – it is thought that animals, such as the arctic fox, the ermine, the collared lemming and the snowshoe rabbit, turn white in the winter for camouflage. In the summer their coat is a brown colour to blend in with the colour of the earth and in winter the coat turns white to blend in with snow; this camouflage probably helps them to avoid predation. But could it be instead (or at least in addition) that the white winter coats help to maximise absorption of ultraviolet-B by the skin, while the darker summer coats help to absorb the heat of the sun? White hair results from an absence of melanin. When lacking melanin the hair is hollow and light is scattered and reflected rather than being absorbed. This means more ultraviolet-B can get into the skin. Temperature appears to control the seasonal change in colour in some species and day length in others, but I wonder if it could be controlled by ultraviolet-B via vitamin D.

What about humans? Perhaps blond, straight hair occurred in northern populations to help to increase the penetration of ultraviolet-B into the scalp. The colour of the hair, whether blond, brown, black or red, is genetically determined by a gene called *MC1R* – the melanocortin-1 receptor – and cannot be changed. What can be changed, however, is the amount of melanin in the hair. Whatever the colour of the hair, the pigmentation is lost with age, perhaps as vitamin D reserves decline. Reduction in pigment leads to grey hair first and then to white hair. If hair is dark to start with it is perhaps more likely to go grey sooner because it blocks the ultraviolet radiation more efficiently than blond hair, which is perhaps why people with dark hair tend to go grey at an earlier age, or more quickly than blonds.

Hair loss occurs in ageing – even those of us without obvious hair loss experience some thinning of the hair in old age – and it also occurs in captive animals. Baldness may also be a way of increasing penetration of ultraviolet into the scalp. Whether you go grey or bald depends partly on whether you are male or female and may also depend on other factors, including genetic factors, but falling vitamin D with age could potentially explain the phenomenon of both hair loss and greying.

It may be no coincidence that the gene that determines our hair colour (*MC1R)* is a member of the melanocortin family. The most common genetic defect causing obesity is in another member of this family – the gene for the melanocortin-4 receptor (*MC4R*), which is part of the circuit in the brain responsible for energy dissipation, described in Chapter 5 Fatstat Facts. Melanocortins are small molecules – peptides – discovered in the 1980s, which affect skin and hair pigmentation, inflammation and fertility, as well as energy homeostasis. I wonder if the melanocortin system may have developed as some kind of master controller of the winter response.

Being human is to be vulnerable in a low ultraviolet environment

You may remember a mention of Gloger's rule in the previous chapter. Gloger's rule is that pigmentation in animals tends to be reduced towards the Poles and northern animals tend to be lighter in colour than southern animals. It seems reasonable to suppose that in relatively recent evolutionary history, we humans lived in Africa with little hair and black skin and when we subsequently migrated to middle and high latitudes we lost some of our pigmentation. Where humans originated within the tropics ultraviolet-B is relatively high throughout the year, with two strong peaks at the equinoxes. Outside of the tropics, ultraviolet-B is not only lower all year round but also highly seasonal.

It makes biological sense that skin and hair lightened because of low ultraviolet-B, since the lighter and thinner your skin is, the more vitamin D you can make in a given time when exposed to sunlight. So perhaps we could regard all white people, or perhaps all people without dark, black skin, as having inherited vitamin D deficiency, or rather, descended from ancestors who at some point suffered from severe vitamin D deficiency.

If we accept that skin colour changed to allow vitamin D synthesis to take place at low levels of ultraviolet irradiance, we must accept that living in an environment of low ultraviolet radiation is a possible survival pressure and if so, then vitamin D is important to our survival.

It is certain that ultraviolet radiation has been overlooked when it comes to its influences on evolution and biogeography, which is not at all surprising when we consider how complex are the many influences on ultraviolet irradiance at the Earth's surface and the many ways in which vitamin D is obtained.

For a relatively simple living thing, like an alga floating on the surface of the open ocean, there may be a direct relationship between vitamin D and intensity of sunlight, but for humans and other animals the complexities of vitamin D mean the interaction with the environment cannot easily be observed. Even for the alga, there is not, perhaps, the direct relationship between sunlight and ultraviolet radiation there once was millions of years ago.

It is too easy to propose evolutionary explanations for our observations based on strands of evidence, which are few and far between – like constructing a biography from just a few snapshots taken years apart and using one's imagination to fill in the gaps. When it comes to human evolutionary history we are not so much improving our understanding but, as Bernard Wood, Professor of Human Origins at George Washington University, puts it, 'reducing our ignorance'. But if we are to make biological sense of overweight and the metabolic syndrome, we need to put it into context and consider all the possible corroborations. We can only speculate about whether, for example, depigmentation occurred as a gradual process in humans who lived at higher latitudes and who did not keep up their calcidiol levels through their diet, or whether a single cataclysmic event caused depigmentation. Either way, it is possible that the pressure of living in low ultraviolet and cold climates has been underestimated.

The survival challenges of seasons

The evidence suggests that humans have been naked and living in the tropics for most of their existence. When humans moved out of the tropics, getting enough vitamin D to survive was a survival challenge. Survival was not just a matter of getting enough food. It seems that our ancestors survived three interconnected challenges: cold, hunger, and low ultraviolet, all of which became greater after migration away from the tropics.

It makes biological sense that outside the tropics, depigmentation to increase vitamin D synthesis and the development of dairy farming and fishing to increase dietary vitamin D intake, improved the survival chances of humans. In some low latitudes the loss of pigmentation was limited, while in high latitudes the cold climate meant the skin had to be covered by animal skins and shelters, reducing sunlight exposure still further. Thus depigmentation was necessary to increase penetration of ultraviolet radiation into the skin and make sufficient vitamin D. The Inuit may have undergone less depigmentation, for example, because they maintained vitamin D levels by eating fish and sea mammals. Those northern Europeans who lived in cold climates and didn't get their vitamin D through their diet, survived by developing skin that was extremely sensitive to ultraviolet radiation.

In addition to low ultraviolet, those who migrated out of the tropics had other challenges to deal with. The fluctuations of temperatures with the seasons requires an ability to produce more heat in winter *and* lose heat in summer, and the low and fluctuating ultraviolet-B environment requires the ability to produce vitamin D in conditions of low ultraviolet-B and to obtain vitamin D from food in the winter when ultraviolet-B is absent. As we humans are essentially tropical animals, both clothing and shelter, which block ultraviolet from the skin, are essential for keeping warm in temperate and polar climates. In today's urban-industrial environment, even those of us who live in sunny tropical climates are shielded from the sunlight, covering most of our skin with clothing and spending much time indoors.

As it is for the polar bear and the reindeer, there must have been a trade-off in humans between being vitamin D deficient enough to gain weight (if there was enough food available) and survive the cold and not so vitamin D deficient that poor health resulted. A warm microclimate had to be sufficiently warm to survive the cold but, shielded from sunlight, there would have to be another source of vitamin D. I think this is a problem that our ancestors battled with and it remains a challenge today, whether we realise it or not.

We will always have the problem of seasons. If we have plenty of vitamin D we become tropical and able to tolerate the heat of the summer but find it hard to cope with the cold of winter. On the other hand, if we have less vitamin D, we become winter-adapted and cope better with the cold of the winter but suffer in the heat of the summer. Perhaps we need to find the right balance and accept that we should be a little bit deficient and perhaps a little bit overweight, to help us survive the winter, but not so deficient that we suffer from obesity and disease. As always in nature, it is a delicate balancing act.

Revisiting the obesogenic environment

We started looking at genes in this chapter, addressing the question of whether there may be genes that were advantageous in the past but today only make us overweight. We considered whether some of us might have inherited genes that helped our ancestors to survive famine or to survive cold, or both, particularly during the ice ages. But what we find is that an exploration of genes tells us more about the environment of our ancestors. It is clear that the environment has a far greater influence on overweight than genes, so we now turn to the matter of how the environment makes us gain weight.

We think about overweight as if it is a new phenomenon and if we look back through history, overweight seems to be rare, but it certainly existed in both historic and prehistoric times. There is no question that our modern, urban-industrial life is an obesogenic environment. To be obesogenic it needs to have plenty of food – you cannot become overweight if you only have 500 kilocalories per day, for example. But that is not enough; an obesogenic environment also needs to be short on vitamin D. For overweight to occur, there are therefore two environmental determinants:

- Low vitamin D
- High food supply.

With rare exceptions, one without the other is not sufficient to result in obesity, but the occurrence of both together has become more common in the urban–industrial environment of the developed world. Industrialisation increases the food supply, while both urbanisation and industrialisation reduce our exposure to sunlight and specifically reduces the ultraviolet-B component of sunlight reaching us.

The studies of overweight have so far been concerned mainly with the food supply – caloric excess, energy density, preferences for certain foods, the glycaemic index, the types and proportion of fat in foods, access to restaurants, and so on. The evidence gathered for the role of the obesogenic environment in overweight is contradictory and confusing because it has only been looking at one of the determinants of overweight. The second determinant, vitamin D deficiency, was not considered for a long time. Many of the contradictions and complexities can be explained when we take both determinants into account and these will be considered in the next chapter.

While it is not surprising that vitamin D has been overlooked because of its multifactorial nature, it is surprising that nutrient deficiencies in general, have been given little attention. As long ago as 1984, David McCarron – who was (at the time) Head of Nephrology at the University of Oregon and has published hundreds of studies about high blood pressure – noted that nutrient deficiencies were more common in people who were overweight than in those of normal weight. Yet it has generally been assumed that overweight people eat a lot and must get plenty of nutrients – indeed it has sometimes been described as 'over-nutrition'.

Overweight in the past

It is easy to forget, when overweight is constantly blamed on our modern way of living, that overweight is not a new phenomenon. Overweight has certainly existed throughout history and there is evidence that overweight existed in prehistory too – long before the Industrial Revolution and even before agriculture was developed. We have considered the evidence that getting enough vitamin D may have been a challenge for humans throughout prehistory, at least for those outside the tropical regions, but did it ever result in overweight?

Within my lifetime, a few decades ago, there were overweight middle-aged women and middle-aged men with 'beer-bellies', there were a few overweight children and young people and there were overweight families. Those few who were overweight from a young age were thought to have a genetic predisposition to overweight, and so they may have had, but perhaps instead (or in addition) they had vitamin D deficiency. The overweight in older people was put down to age – to a comfortable life with less exercise and more eating – but we can now see that overweight will occur as vitamin D reserves become depleted with age.

If we go back a few more decades, the situation is distorted by the war-induced food shortages. The rationing of food may have prevented any vitamin D deficiency-induced overweight. However, dietary vitamin D intakes were probably at their highest in the 1930s and 1940s as these were the decades after vitamin D was discovered and the importance of milk and vitamins in the diet became widely appreciated. Children were given school milk, orange juice and cod-liver oil, even during the Second World War.

Earlier, there were the prosperous Victorians, portrayed in figures such as Mr Bumble, the Beadle in Charles Dickens' Oliver Twist, and real Victorians such as Queen Victoria herself, who became overweight in later life. Benjamin Franklin, Winston Churchill, Alfred Hitchcock, Louis Armstrong, (and even Santa Claus) are other notable figures who were overweight. Mostly they appeared after the Industrial Revolution, when ultraviolet was probably lowered by pollution from industry.

Overweight is absent from early art; first beginning to appear in Renaissance art. Henry the VIII became overweight after he suffered a leg wound in a jousting accident in 1536. When Queen Anne succeeded to the throne in 1702 at the age of 37, she had to be carried to the throne in a sedan chair as her gouty legs could not carry her and when she died at the age of 49 she was buried in a vast, almost square coffin. She had 18 pregnancies but only 5 children (the rest ending in miscarriage or stillbirth), 4 of which died before the age of 2 and one at the age of 11. Many have speculated on the medical conditions she may have suffered but none, to my knowledge, has considered vitamin D deficiency. Earlier, there were reports of a Roman senator who needed two slaves to carry his belly for him when he walked and an Egyptian pharaoh whose belly was bigger than a man's outstretched arms.

Overweight in the past was often associated with upper classes of society. We can only speculate whether this is because only the lives of upper classes were recorded, or because it was more prevalent in upper classes.

Prehistoric overweight

The earliest known example of overweight is from the Venus figurines. The first to be discovered was found in 1908 by an archaeologist called Josef Szombathy in Willendorf, a small village in Austria. The statuette is 11 cm high and made from limestone. It portrays a nude woman with large breasts, belly and hips and was made about 25,000 years ago. The shape is plainly based on a real woman complete with fat thighs and wrinkles. More than 100 Venus figurines have been found since, mostly in Europe, from France to Russia (but not the Iberian Peninsula) and mostly dated to the Gravettian period, between 30,000 and 22,000 years ago. All are small enough to be held in the hand and depict women who are either obese or pregnant. The immense interest in these figurines, with shared similarities, which have been found over such a widespread region and over a long period, has led to much speculative interpretation of their meaning, often related to fertility and sexuality.

The figurines date to the upper Palaeolithic, during the last glacial period. From 25,000 years ago the climate got colder and by 18,000 years ago most of Europe became uninhabitable, as ice sheets covered northern Europe and the rest of Europe was covered by permafrost. Average temperatures in Europe would have been at least 10°C lower than present-day temperatures, with a greater contrast between summer and winter temperatures. The figurines are pre-agricultural – archaeological evidence suggests that clubs, stones and nets were used to capture animals and meat was the main food source. We can only guess what the figurines were meant to represent, but they provide clear evidence that human obesity existed before agriculture became widespread, at least in Ice Age Europe. The Venus figurines certainly present a contrast with the romantic view of the lean and athletic hunter ancestor.

We can only speculate on the vitamin D status of the women on whom the Venus figurines were based. Were the Venus figurines representative of the normal female figure at the time, or did they portray queens, or at least women from the upper echelons of Gravettian societies? Do they provide evidence for a traditional view of our ancestors – that the women spent all their time in a cave while their men went hunting? We do not know the cause of the ice ages. Greater snow or ice on the ground would increase the amount of ultraviolet at ground level because of reflectance, but cold prevents the exposure of much of the skin. In cold climates, sunbathing is rarely possible.

The pre-industrial, agricultural environment

In the pre-industrial, agricultural society where families cultivate small plots of land and keep small herds of livestock, all members of the family work outdoors. As long as enough time is spent outdoors, vitamin D status will not drop below the threshold at which the set point is raised, so even with an abundance of food availability, overweight will not occur. Weight is kept in balance by homeostasis – if there is a shortage of food, the body will make adjustments to manage on less and when there is plenty of food, the body will control the amount eaten by careful management of the appetite. However, those who do not need to work outdoors, such as landowners with tenant farmers and members of the ruling class, may experience both plentiful food and lack of vitamin D, in which case they will gain weight.

In agricultural societies, overweight tends to be found in the upper echelons of society and is associated with prosperity. This can explain why in pre-industrial societies, overweight was regarded as a sign of status – the rich gained weight because they had the advantage of having plenty of food available in an unequal society. It is assumed that the less advantaged members of society lacked sufficient food to get overweight, but perhaps the real reason is that the poor had better vitamin D levels. Those who had low vitamin D levels *and* lacked sufficient food to gain weight suffered a double misery of hunger and disease.

The urban-industrial environment

We know that our environment is obesogenic – there is a direct link between modern urban-industrial living and overweight. It can be seen particularly in countries undergoing transition. The globalisation of the urban-industrial environment results in the globalisation of obesity – this has been termed globesity.

The Industrial Revolution started in the UK and subsequently spread throughout the more developed regions in the second half of the twentieth century. It was during this period that overweight really shot up in the mid-latitude USA and UK and it has now spread to other countries.

In the developed world, urbanisation took off during the Industrial Revolution. The mechanisation of agriculture and growth of industry pulled people from rural areas into urban areas. The cities that grew in the eighteenth and nineteenth centuries are no longer growing, but in the developing world urbanisation is increasing and it is not always underpinned by economic wealth but by failing crops and conflicts. In Europe and North America about 80 per cent of people live in urban areas. Urbanisation was a major transition in the twentieth century and continues to take place in the present century. In 1900, for example, only 14 per cent of people worldwide lived in cities, but, by 2000, half of us lived in cities. The rate at which we are moving to cities and, not surprisingly the size of the cities, is accelerating. Megacities such as Tokyo, Mexico City, Sao Paulo and Bombay have more than 10 million inhabitants.

At the same time as industry reduced the intensity of ultraviolet-B reaching us, we moved from rural to urban areas, stopped working on the land and started working in factories and offices. Our air became polluted, first with the emissions from factories, power stations and home heating and then with the emissions from transport. At the same time, the industrialisation of agriculture and food processing reduced the amount of vitamin D we obtained from our diet. Is it any wonder that we are now suffering from vitamin D deficiency? Is it coincidence that overweight has spread at the same time? Is the obesogenic environment not so much about food availability and the type of food we eat, but more about ultraviolet-B?

It is clear to me that vitamin D deficiency is not the result of individual 'poor diet and inadequate sunlight exposure' and it won't be reversed by telling people to get a little bit more sun. It is an evolutionary pressure – it is a profound, continuous famine that has lasted for thousands of years and one of which we have had no awareness, other than an instinct that fresh air and sunlight are healthy.

The first step in dealing with it is to recognise the problem of getting sufficient vitamin D – just as we recognise the need for food security for an increasing global population, we also need to recognise the need for vitamin D security as industrialisation and urbanisation continues to spread. Once we understand the extent of vitamin D poverty we can begin to tackle it.

Chapter 8

Weightonomics

NO THEORY ABOUT HEALTH is plausible unless it makes sense to the people affected. The aim of this book is to make biological sense of overweight but it should also make sense of our experience of overweight in the real world. Earlier chapters have considered how and why vitamin D deficiency increased in the past few decades and how it is associated with urbanisation and industrialisation, but we need to understand how vitamin D deficiency can explain individual cases of overweight as well as the epidemiology of overweight. This chapter considers how we can use this new perspective to explain why some people are overweight while others are not, why people gain weight when they do, and why some people are more overweight than others. I think the idea that overweight is an adaptation to cold caused by vitamin D deficiency can provide us with a better understanding of overweight than we have ever had before.

Why gaining weight is easy

What happens in your body when vitamin D falls? This is a possible scenario. Remember, it is largely conjecture and may prove to be incorrect, but see if it makes sense to you. We will assume there is a sensing circuit in the hypothalamus that somehow measures the amount of vitamin D in the blood, perhaps by having receptors for calcidiol. When it detects a fall in calcidiol – which may need to fall for a certain time or to below a certain level – the body weight set point goes up and the brain coordinates an increase in appetite and a reduction in energy expenditure so that you gain weight.

Imagine your set point rises from 60 kg to 65 kg. You need to gain 5 kg, so you enter an energy accrual phase. The energy dissipation circuit goes into sleep mode while the energy accrual circuit fires up. The signals that control your appetite get a little stronger. Hormones such as ghrelin and neuropeptide Y, which make you feel hungry, stay high for longer and others such as cholecystokinin and peptide YY, which normally make you feel full, go down. As a result, food becomes more attractive and delicious and you enjoy your food a little more than usual. You can continue to eat for longer at a meal before you feel full and you start thinking about food sooner after your last meal. All these changes mean that you eat more than usual. You may also prefer food that will help you to store fat – fatty and starchy foods that are energy-rich – so you prefer a chocolate bar to an apple and would rather have a bacon sandwich than a chicken salad. As well as making you hungry, it is possible that you absorb more of the food you eat, particularly the fat.

Your body conserves energy by making you feel less active and you become more inclined to sit on the sofa and less inclined to do exercise. Your metabolism changes so you store more of the energy you have, rather than using it and losing it. And when you do perform exercise, you may actually use less energy even when you put the same amount of effort into it. As you accumulate fat you produce more leptin, but although the leptin is telling the brain you have plenty of fat it is not yet enough to reach the higher set point, so you go on eating and gaining weight. You may even feel that you have become addicted to food.

Once you have reached your new set point of 65 kg, you stop gaining weight and you no longer need to eat more than usual. At this point the energy accrual phase has ended and your weight becomes stable. You may go back to eating just the same as you did when you were 60 kg, but your weight remains at the higher set point of 65 kg. If you do nothing, and your set point remains the same, your weight will remain at 65 kg.

Why losing weight is hard

But what if you're not happy about being five kilos overweight? You feel a bit pudgy and notice your clothes are slightly more close-fitting and you don't want to end up like one of those huge obese people; you think it's important to keep control of your weight. You only need to lose the 5 kilos that seems to you and everyone around you, to be an excess, surplus to requirements and should therefore be easy to lose. So you go on a diet, but with your set point still at 65 kg your body will cling on to the extra 5 kilos, and the only way to lose it is for your body to go into a state of starvation. Your body then does all it can to conserve energy even more, just as much as if you were trying to lose 5 kg from your normal body weight of 60 kg. To make matters worse, you go on a low fat diet that reduces your vitamin D level even further and perhaps drives your set point even higher, say to 70 kg.

With a bit of determination, willpower and motivation, you may be able to lose the 5 kg. But with the set point still at 65 kg (or even higher now), sooner or later you will regain the 5 kg you lost and try to lose it again. Each time you might be lowering your vitamin D levels and raising your set point even higher. Eventually you need an enormous amount of determination, willpower and motivation to lose weight. Not only that, but you are teaching your body to cope with food scarcity. While you are in the midst of a feast, your body thinks there is a famine and does all it can to conserve energy.

If you have successfully lost weight, you may well have done so because your set point went back down. Perhaps you took up walking or cycling and without realising it, you increased your exposure to sunlight, improved your calcidiol level and your set point went back down to 60 kg. You congratulated yourself on losing weight, putting down to your personal attributes, such as motivation and willpower.

Or you may have lost weight in spite of your set point remaining high. This is like having a shortfall between your income and expenditure. The best way to deal with it is to either increase your income (take in a lodger, get a better-paid job or get a second job) or to reduce your expenditure (buy fewer new clothes, cut out the holidays, or move to a home with a lower rent). An alternative solution, and one which has been commonly used in recent years, is to borrow money. In the short term, this can solve the problem but it increases expenditure without increasing income (you need to pay back the money you borrowed, *plus* the interest) and therefore in the long term only exacerbates the problem. Losing weight by resisting your set point does this. It's hard work but the reward is that you lose weight and maybe you look good and you feel great for a while. The trouble is that in the long term, you will either regain the weight and find it even harder to lose it again, or you will have to fight for the rest of your life to keep your weight below the set point.

Slow weight gain

Sometimes your set point creeps up slowly, perhaps over a period of several years. When your set point goes up and you go into the energy accrual phase, you find your clothes are a bit tight and you are eating more than usual. You may put it down to feeling depressed, being self-indulgent, or having too much temptation put in your way, or even that your clothes have shrunk in the wash. If your set point stabilises you stop gaining weight.

This could happen a little each winter and you may gain a few hundred grams or a kilo each winter over a period of decades and call it middle-aged spread. But you didn't notice that you only gained weight at the end of the winter (or perhaps you did). In the autumn, calcidiol goes down, you become more hungry than usual and gain weight, so by the end of the winter you feel a bit like a pudding and your trousers are tight. In the spring your calcidiol rises and your set point goes back to normal and perhaps you lose that little winter fat – but not all of it. In this way, our weight can creep up slowly, year after year.

Rapid weight gain

Some people gain a lot of weight fairly rapidly. This can happen when your calcidiol level has dropped suddenly. One example is when you have a baby, because the demands for vitamin D by the baby lower your calcidiol levels during pregnancy. Suddenly you find that you are gaining weight fast. You think it's because you're putting the baby's needs before your own, as you are too busy to control what you are eating. By the time the baby is a year old, you are several kilos heavier. Once you start taking the baby out every day to nursery, or go back to work and get some sunlight every day you may recover and find it easy to lose weight. But a couple of years later you have another baby and you gain even more weight. If you have several children, you are more likely to be overweight than if you have one.

Another situation in which your vitamin D status can fall quite suddenly is if you have an acute illness, accident or surgery. With a change to your usual routine you are no longer exposed to daily sunlight, particularly if you have a spell in hospital or are housebound by your injury or illness. Your calcidiol falls, your set point goes up and you gain weight. If you recover from the illness or injury, you may lose the weight again once you get back into your usual routine and your vitamin D status goes up again. Other situations in which your vitamin D status may fall rapidly include moving to a different region, starting at university, starting a new job, or even bad weather which keeps you indoors and covered up.

Summer loss and winter gain

If your vitamin D status improves, you will find it easy to lose weight. If you have ever tried to lose weight in the winter and found it much harder than to lose weight in the summer or autumn, this is probably because it is easier to lose weight when your calcidiol is increasing and your set point is going down. It means the best time to lose weight is in the summer when your calcidiol level has already started to rise and will continue to do so for the next few weeks while you are dieting. But people often want to lose weight in the winter, especially after Christmas. It is at this time that you are most likely to want to try to lose weight and it is also the time you will find it hardest because by then your calcidiol levels will have been falling for several weeks and will be at their lowest point.

It is certain that in many different cultures the winter solstice – the point at which the Sun starts to 'return to the Earth' – was a point of celebration and winter festivals like Christmas predate Christianity. It is perhaps no coincidence that the major feast of the year is at a time when calcidiol levels have been falling for several weeks.

When you lose weight you feel great

One of the reasons you feel good after losing weight might be because calciferol is stored in fat, so when some of your fat is broken down, some of your stored calciferol is released and converted to calcidiol. Temporarily, you have more calcidiol available in your bloodstream and your brain thinks the sun must be shining. This helps you to keep losing weight in a virtuous cycle. The trouble comes in the long term because you have lowered your calciferol stores. It is a bit like getting money from your savings account and putting it into your current account – your bank balance is healthier and you have more to spend, but there will be less to fall back on at a later date when you need some money for a rainy day.

The winter metabolism phase

When you are overweight you may at some point enter the winter metabolism phase. Exactly when this happens is unclear. It might depend on how long your calcidiol has been continuously low, but it appears to be related to how much fat you have accumulated.

Having extra fat increases the size of your shell and your lower critical temperature – the lowest temperature at which you start to increase heat production – goes down. You become less like the tropical coati and more like the red fox, although you still probably have a long way to go before you can be comfortable at winter temperatures. Nevertheless, you become comfortable at colder temperatures than before, which means, at the other extreme, you suffer more in hot temperatures. You deposit more fat around your organs – perhaps to provide a local energy supply to the organs, as well as helping to reduce heat loss from them – and around the middle so you become not just bigger, but a more rounded shape.

The winter metabolism will ensure that you are prepared for surviving the cold temperatures of winter. Changes take place in your metabolism, fuel supply and circulation. These changes could include increasing the amount of brown fat you have (if that is possible) and/or increasing your potential to produce heat by uncoupling in other tissues, such as muscle. They also include increasing your potential to produce heat by shivering with the aim of producing heat as efficiently as possible.

The proportions of your muscle fibres change so you have fewer of the red and more of the white fibres. Your body changes the way it organises energy storage, resulting in higher amounts of triglyceride in your blood and muscles, higher amounts of glucose and fats (triglyceride, free fatty acids) in your blood and lower amounts of stored glucose (glycogen) in both your liver and muscle. As well as preparing for a rapid metabolic response to cold you also need to prepare for a rapid response to cold in your circulation, so that constriction and dilation of blood vessels can be altered as necessary to reduce heat loss and to control heat distribution around the body, and your blood pressure goes up.

Now you become switched to your ice age setting. If you were living in an ice age you would be more likely to survive because of these changes. The trouble is you are not living in an ice age and even in the winter you can keep warm thanks to central heating, double-glazing, warm clothing and heated transport and you have plenty of food. When you are not exposed to a winter environment of food shortage and prolonged cold temperatures, these preparations and changes in metabolism do not confer any advantage. In tropical conditions, whether artificial or natural, these changes cause problems.

Imagine the discomfort you would experience if you were to wear thick winter clothing to sunbathe on a Mediterranean beach, or if you wore a bikini to go out on a winter's night. It is not quite the same, since in some respects we may be *prepared* for cold conditions, but do not *respond* until the temperature actually drops. So it is more like we are sitting on the sunny beach in warm indoor clothing and have taken a thick winter coat and a hot water bottle just in case.

Personal stories

On the next pages, there are some personal stories of overweight and two interpretations of what happens – the first using the old way of thinking and the second using the new way of thinking.

Helen

Helen, 36, first gained weight when she was a student at Manchester University and took the opportunity of being away from the scrutiny of her parents to eat as much fast food as she wanted. She ate a lot of kebabs, pizzas and Chinese takeaways and gained 25 kg (4 stone or 56 pounds), which took her weight from 64 kg (10 stone or 140 pounds) to 89 kg (14 stone or 196 pounds). After graduation she worked in an office on an industrial estate with no canteen and ate sandwiches and burgers from a mobile van. But she and her colleagues were always talking about food and weight and frequently went on diets together, supporting each other in their efforts to lose weight. At one time, they also started weight training at a local gym. In the ten years she worked there, her weight went up and down and she was 100 kg (16 stone or 220 pounds) when she left her job after having a baby. When her daughter was a toddler, she started going to a slimming club and is now 64 kg (10 stone or 140 pounds) again. She has now maintained her weight for over two years by writing down everything that she eats and counting how many points she has had each day.

Old way of thinking: Helen gained weight at university because she drank alcohol, had no control over her eating and found it was too easy to eat convenient, fattening food which is tasty and hard to resist. She then found it hard to break her bad habits. Helen lost weight in a slimming club because the support from others in the same situation was more structured than the support she'd had at work. The slimming club empowered her to devise a strategy for overcoming her barriers to weight loss. She learned about healthy eating and how to manage her food cravings. She has conquered her weight and she is determined to maintain her weight by carefully controlling what she eats.

New way of thinking: Helen's vitamin D status went down when she started university. It would have dropped in the first term as autumn gave way to winter and to make matters worse as a student she spent a lot of time indoors studying. Away from home for the first time she stayed on campus, so there was relatively little walking to do outdoors between her halls and lecture theatres. And she spent a lot of the daytime in bed, recovering from her hectic nightlife. Added to that, her university in Manchester was further north than her home town of Plymouth, so she had moved to a region where ultraviolet-B levels were a little lower. After graduating, she worked in an office on an industrial estate, with no outside area or anywhere to walk to at lunchtime, so she got no sunlight during the working week.

The constant dieting meant although she always felt she had too much fat, in effect, her body thought otherwise. Her weight was constantly dropping below her set point and her body was always battling to regain it, while she was battling to lose it. During her pregnancy and after the birth, the demands on her vitamin D reserves were higher, so her calcidiol lowered even further, raising her set point higher.

She is now in a cold war with her body. She eats some fatty food and takes a multivitamin containing vitamin D, so her vitamin status is not as low as it was when she was trying different diets before. Her vitamin D status is more constant than when she was always changing her diet, but she is still below her set point and to remain at her present weight she will have to either continue to monitor her eating or she will have to improve her vitamin D status. Otherwise, she will regain the weight she has lost and possibly even more in the future.

Anna

Anna is a fitness instructor. She takes weight training and aerobics classes five times a week and does a lot of training in the gym herself. Her weight is 64 kg (10 stone or 140 pounds) and she would like to be 60 kg, (about 9.5 stone or 132 pounds) although she thinks her ideal weight is 55 kg (8 stone 9 lb or 121 pounds). She cannot lose weight, even though she eats what she thinks is a healthy diet (high carbohydrate, low fat, low calories). She is terribly frustrated as she thinks she is doing all the right things with regard to eating and exercise – she thinks she *deserves* to lose weight. As a fitness instructor, she wants to inspire and motivate her clients and believes she should set herself up as an example and she simply cannot understand where she is going wrong.

Old way of thinking: Although Anna does a lot of exercise, she must be eating more calories than she is using up. She probably eats more than she says, or perhaps more than she herself believes. She may be suffering from low self-esteem and is afraid of success. She should consider counselling to help examine her eating issues.

New way of thinking: Anna's set point is 64 kg or more and her body is working to maintain or raise her weight while she consciously tries to lower it. She thinks that by taking in less energy from food than she is using for exercise, her excess fat will be used as an energy source and will fall away. But, although it is true she is using more energy than she is taking in, her body is clinging on to the fat and her metabolism is adapting by becoming more efficient, so that she can use less energy to do the same amount of exercise. In addition, her body may be breaking down muscle to maintain the fat stores. While she thinks the fat is not needed, her body regards it as vital to survival.

Katie and Andy

Katie and Andy decided to lose weight together. They were both overweight when they met, and after nine years of marriage they had gained even more weight. They began to have health problems – Katie developed asthma and Andy had arthritis. When Andy started having chest pains, they decided to join a slimming club together. They started going for a walk together each day after work and after several months of losing weight, they took up cycling at weekends. A year later they are now keen on the outdoors and regularly go out for long cycle rides. They have both lost weight but are still dieting.

Old way of thinking: Katie and Andy fell into bad habits of eating and not doing exercise because they live in an obesogenic environment. They ate a lot of convenience food that was energy dense, they drove when they could have walked and took the lift when they could have used the stairs. By dieting, Katie and Andy took in fewer calories and by exercising, they used up more calories than they took in. Excess fat was broken down and used as energy to provide the difference. They were able to do this because they were motivated by health problems and supported by their love for each other. Anyone can do it if they really want to.

New way of thinking: Katie and Andy gained weight because their vitamin D status was low. Vitamin D deficiency also predisposed them to asthma, arthritis and heart disease. When they began their diet, they started walking outdoors every day, which increased their daily sunlight exposure. This raised their calcidiol levels, making it easier to lose weight and stick to the diet.

They still have to make an effort to eat less than they would like because their weight is still below their set point. Should they stop going outdoors they will find it very difficult to continue to control their eating, but if they continue with their outdoor activities they may find that their vitamin D status becomes high enough to maintain a normal weight with no effort at all.

Ryan

Ryan, a retail manager who enjoyed outdoor sport, had always been fit, healthy, active and slim. At the age of 30, he dislocated his kneecap and tore ligaments when playing football. His leg was in plaster for several weeks and he spent most of the spring and part of the summer off work, hobbling around in his flat. His weight went up from 70 kg (11 stone or 154 pounds) to 89 kg (14 stone or 196 pounds). He noticed that he was eating more but he didn't try to diet at all. He recovered from his injury well and went back to playing sport, but it took a year for his weight to go back down to its normal level.

Old way of thinking: Ryan gained weight because he was unable to do exercise, so he was using up fewer calories. He also ate more because he was at home feeling bored and eating gave him something to do. He lost weight once he went back to work, started doing exercise again and became too busy to eat so much.

New way of thinking: Ryan's vitamin D status was normally high enough for him to maintain a normal weight without any conscious effort at all. After the injury, he spent several weeks inside his flat, when he would normally be going to work and playing football, jogging and other sport. This meant the amount of everyday sunlight exposure that Ryan had experienced dropped quite dramatically and his vitamin D status fell. If he'd had a garden and had spent more time sitting outdoors, he may have increased his sunlight exposure and his weight may have remained stable, in spite of the period of doing no exercise. When Ryan went back to football he was still overweight, but the following year when he returned to his routine and his vitamin D status was restored, his set point went back to normal and he lost the excess weight, without any effort at all.

Vitamin D deficiency and health

This book has raised many questions about vitamin D and overweight. How much ultraviolet-B do we get, how much vitamin D do we need, how much should we take and for how long? These are all questions that need to be answered by future research studies and experience. Before we can decide on the best way to prevent and treat overweight, we need a better understanding of the vitamin D economy, both at a global level and a personal level. In the meantime, what is our current understanding, and how can we relate what we know to health and disease?

We can perhaps separate the consequences of vitamin D deficiency into two. The first is the fall in vitamin D that leads to cold adaptation. This is a normal physiological response and in cold conditions it helps us to survive. The problem for us is that we have adapted to the cold because of a fall in vitamin D, not because of a fall in temperature. Even when we live in a cold climate, we keep warm by controlling our microenvironment to create an artificial tropical climate, so we don't need the physiological changes.

When cold adaptation is mild it is of no consequence perhaps – we put on a little weight and we may increase our proportion of white muscle fibres and so on, and gradually we become overweight and less fit with age, but we remain healthy. But when cold adaptation is more severe, the changes themselves can become dangerous because we are not using up the additional energy reserves for shivering, nor are we facing the expected food shortage. We don't use up the stored fat and the extra glucose and we develop the diseases of diabetes and cardiovascular disease associated with overweight. We are adapting to the winter while living in a year-round summer and, just as a normal response by the immune system to an infection can make us very ill, the normal physiological response becomes more dangerous than the original threat.

The second consequence of vitamin D deficiency is that, having harnessed this product of photoreception for good use, we have become dependent upon it for our healthy physiological processes and, without it, we cannot maintain the normal functioning of our bodies, particularly when it comes to the development and renewal of tissues. When we are deficient in vitamin D we may end up with diseases because the tissues are not being properly renewed and because our immune system is not robust enough to fight off infections and other threats to our health. Vitamin D deficiency can therefore lead to disease because we lack the hormone calcitriol, whereas overweight results from low calcidiol.

When we think that overweight increases our risk of disease, it may be that it is vitamin D deficiency causing both overweight and disease independently. A disease (asthma, for example) may be more common in overweight people because they have vitamin D deficiency, but it may not be caused by overweight or even connected to overweight, other than the fact that both can result from vitamin D deficiency.

It also means we can suffer from vitamin D deficiency whether we are overweight or not. If you are not overweight because you control your weight by dieting or exercise and your body weight is below its set point, you may still be suffering from vitamin D deficiency.

Overweight can be good for health

It seems overweight can protect against the more severe effects of some diseases. In patients with chronic heart failure, those who are overweight or obese are less likely to die within a given period. In patients with chronic kidney disease undergoing haemodialysis, those who are overweight live longer than those whose weight is normal. This is called the obesity paradox since obesity, by medical definition, is unhealthy, yet, in some patients who are seriously ill, obesity can be an advantage. It is thought that extra reserves of energy help to protect the seriously ill from death, but it may also be that overweight patients have a better supply of vitamin D stored away than those who have less fat.

As we gain weight, we store vitamin D in our fat mass for later use – just as we store energy. Perhaps we are better at saving and rationing our vitamin D (and other nutrients) when we are preparing for food scarcity during the winter. Adaptation to the winter may include the instigation of rationing all resources throughout the body to cope better with the expected supply shortages. Therefore, adaptation to cold in response to lower vitamin D is healthier than not adapting to cold.

But it is not just in the seriously ill that being overweight is an advantage. People who are overweight tend to have higher bone mineral density and are less likely to suffer from osteoporosis and bone fractures. Adaptation to cold may involve more than just gaining weight and the metabolic syndrome. People who are overweight may be protected from bone disease because increasing bone mineral density is a natural part of the process of the body getting bigger – the heavier you are, the stronger your bones need to be so that they can continue support your weight. Alternatively, as part of the adaptation to save energy, perhaps the turnover of tissues is slowed down a little, including the constant removal and renewal of bone tissue, so that there is still enough to cope, whereas in osteoporosis, the bone turnover continues at a normal rate and, without the resources, the bones lose their density and strength. Those who do not gain weight in the face of a drop in vitamin D may not store vitamin D and can only use it as and when it is available. When there is none coming in, there are no stores to draw on in an emergency.

Weight loss and health

When you lose weight, you feel great partly because some of the vitamin D that you stored is released into your bloodstream. This may be why you feel better and it may also be why losing weight can help to lower blood pressure and reduce the effects of those other factors that make up the metabolic syndrome. The trouble is that unless the problem of vitamin D deficiency, which caused the overweight in the first place, is addressed, the benefits will be short-lived. This could be why, although weight loss can be beneficial in the short term, several studies have made the unexpected finding that weight loss is associated with excess mortality.

Losing weight can mean that you are healthier in the short term but not in the long term. Indeed, some studies suggest that weight loss is harmful and having a stable weight, even when overweight or obese, is healthier than losing weight. After bariatric surgery, the loss of fat can reverse or reduce the effects of the winter metabolism, so there are improvements in blood pressure and insulin resistance, for example, but vitamin D deficiency continues and bone loss is a long-term problem for people who have had bariatric surgery.

Overweight in population groups

Can vitamin D deficiency explain how overweight varies between different population groups? The overweight statistics are frequently divided into ethnic group, age group, gender, and socioeconomic status. There are differences between groups but they are often quite small and can detract from the fact that anyone of any gender, age or ethnicity, whether rich or poor, can be overweight. There is no population group that is unaffected by vitamin D deficiency or overweight. However, it is worth considering some of the differences and we will start with ethnicity.

Ethnicity

Numerous epidemiological studies have found differences between ethnic groups in the rate of overweight, or in the average body mass index. Some examples are given in the box below.

- *In Israel,* obesity is higher in the Arab population than the Jewish population.
- *In the USA,* the prevalence of overweight and obesity is lower among Asian Americans, (this includes people whose origins lie in the Far East, South-east Asia or the Indian subcontinent) and higher among non-Hispanic blacks, Native Americans and Pacific Islanders.
- *In New Zealand,* the highest rates of overweight are in Pacific Islanders, the lowest in Europeans, with Maoris in the middle.
- *In the UK,* black adults generally have a higher risk for obesity than whites and whites have a higher risk than Chinese.
- *In Australia,* Aboriginal and Torres Strait Islander people have almost double the rate of obesity of other Australians at the same locations.

It is interesting to note that the increase in overweight in the USA in the period 1988–2002 was the same in all groups. This confirms that the cause of the increase was the same across all groups, even though some were affected more severely than others to start with.

Is there any biological basis for the differences? In some cases, it is thought the measurement of overweight and the criteria for the metabolic syndrome vary with ethnicity. For example, Inuit and Far East Asians have relatively shorter legs than other populations and use of the standard body mass index cut-offs may overestimate the proportion of overweight in these populations. On the other hand, South Asians develop metabolic abnormalities at a lower body mass index than other groups, and it is thought that the body mass index cut-off should be lower in this group for this reason.

In many countries, ethnicity is associated with socioeconomic status; however, socioeconomic factors do not fully explain the differences. Furthermore, low social and economic status could be both a cause and a result of overweight. If you are overweight, particularly if you are severely overweight with health problems, you are more likely to have difficulties with education and pursuing a career. It is recognised that there is a complex interaction between genetic, cultural, social and economic factors, but can the differences be attributed simply to differences in vitamin D status?

Ethnic grouping is defined by self-description and there is no biochemical test than can determine which ethnic group you belong to. We might reasonably expect that there are genetic differences between ethnic groups. In fact, although it is possible to distinguish, for example, an East Asian group from an Oceanic group, it is a rough-and-ready sorting that may be useful on a worldwide basis, but when it comes to individuals or smaller groups, such as the British black people who are descended from the Caribbean region, ethnicity is probably less useful than distinguishing people by which football team they support. It remains possible that there are differences that have not yet been identified. Some groups may be more likely to have winter genes, for example, or differences in vitamin D metabolism. However, we can explain most of the differences by a combination of skin pigmentation and location.

Without doubt the ethnic groups with the highest rates of overweight are blacks living at middle latitudes, while blacks living in low latitudes have a much lower rate of overweight than average. This difference is not confined to overweight. Black African Americans have higher rates of high blood pressure than white Americans, but their blood pressure is also higher than black people who live in sub-Saharan Africa and the Caribbean. This suggests that our susceptibility to overweight and high blood pressure is more about where we live than being black.

Migration and vitamin D status

Many studies have found that the vitamin D status of immigrants is lower than indigenous populations. Why are black people living at middle latitudes more susceptible to vitamin D deficiency? Black skin has a greater concentration of melanin, which means black people need either a greater intensity of ultraviolet-B or a longer exposure than white people to make the same amount of vitamin D. In middle latitudes, as we go about our everyday business, those of us who are black might, as a population group, make less vitamin D than whites.

Skin pigmentation is not the only factor to affect the vitamin D status of different ethnic groups. Others include diet – for example, as a population group, black people drink less milk in adulthood than whites. In the USA milk is fortified with vitamin D but this attempt, for what it is worth, to improve the vitamin D status of the general population fails the section of the population who most need it.

Another important factor, particularly for women, is clothing. Clothing is an effective sunscreen – light coloured, loosely woven fabrics will allow some ultraviolet through, while tightly woven fabrics such as dark blue denim probably block all ultraviolet. Most Western-style clothing allows the head, hands, face and sometimes arms to be exposed to ultraviolet but Islamic-style clothing covers the head, sometimes the face, and the burqa covers the entire skin. This clothing style originated in low latitudes where the ultraviolet irradiance was intense and may not affect vitamin D production too much. However, at middle latitudes, and today even at low latitudes where ultraviolet intensity is perhaps lower than in the past, it may completely block all the available ultraviolet and prevent vitamin D production. In confirmation, several studies have found that veiled women tend to have lower calcidiol levels and higher weight than women who wear Western-style clothing.

The problem of getting enough vitamin D may be more severe for black people in general and this is clearly something that needs particular attention, but we should be wary of assuming that light-skinned people are not at risk of vitamin D deficiency. Indeed, white people might be more likely to protect their skin from sunlight than black people, so there is not always a simple divide.

Anyone, of any colour, of any ethnic group, who migrates to another country, will experience a difference in their ultraviolet environment that may affect their vitamin D status and consequently their health and body weight. It can even apply to anyone moving *within* a country, for example to higher latitude, lower altitude or more polluted area – even just down the hill to a town. In some cases migration can result in an improvement in vitamin D status, but the recent global trend has been for migrants to move from rural to urban, from lower to higher latitudes, and from higher to lower altitudes, since the trend is towards the urban–industrial towns and cities. The trend for all population groups, as we have seen, is towards a lower ultraviolet environment.

Wealth

There is a popular view that overweight is a problem of the poor and uneducated, but is it correct? Overweight is associated with wealth on a country-by-country basis. The epidemic of obesity started in wealthy countries, such as the USA and the UK, and we have seen that as a country becomes wealthier, overweight becomes more common, as with Brazil and China, for example. In low income countries the richest people tend to be the most likely to be overweight and as the country becomes wealthier, overweight rises faster among the poorest. In Africa for example, overweight is higher in the wealthiest but in recent years it has increased faster in the poor than in the wealthy. This reversal has been called the poverty-obesity paradox by Daniel Hruschka, an anthropologist at Arizona State University, because it contradicts the assumption that the wealthier become overweight because they have more food.

Within countries there can be differences in the prevalence of overweight between different regions. In Canada, for example, overweight is above average in the northern and Atlantic regions and below average in the southern and western regions. In Austria, there is a gradient of obesity running from east to west, with an obesity prevalence of 17 per cent in eastern Austria, falling to 12 per cent in western Austria. And in the USA, obesity ranges from less than 20 per cent in Colorado, Hawaii, Vermont and Connecticut to more than 30 per cent in Louisiana, Mississippi and West Virginia.

In addition to regional differences, clusters of high rates of obesity have been noted, called 'obesity hotspots'. For example, in the valleys in South Wales, Merthyr Tydfil, Torfaen, Blaenau Gwent and Caerphilly have 27 to 28 per cent obesity – above the average of 23 per cent for the whole of Wales.

In recent years there has been increasing recognition of a neighbourhood effect on overweight. A study of women in the USA, for example, by Supriya Krishnan and colleagues at Boston University, found that neighbourhood status had a greater effect than individual income or education on the incidence of overweight and type 2 diabetes.

In confirmation, Jens Ludwig and colleagues at the University of Chicago studied a 1990s social project called Moving to Opportunity in which families living in poor housing in five different states were offered help with housing costs so they could move to more costly housing if they wanted to. Ludwig found that ten years later the women of the families who had moved to a wealthier neighbourhood were less likely to have extreme obesity or to be at risk of diabetes than those who stayed in their poor neighbourhood. This finding suggests that you could prevent overweight by moving home.

When household wealth or individual wealth is studied in detail in relation to overweight, the results become confusing and contradictory. Many of these research studies have been done in the USA where it is difficult to disentangle the effects of economic status and ethnic minority status, although it appears that the ethnic disparities are not explained by socioeconomic factors (as discussed above) and, of course, severe overweight and poor health can make it difficult to get a good education and earn a high income. Over time, it has become clearer that it is the socioeconomic status of the *area* that is associated with overweight. It is national, regional and neighbourhood wealth, not personal or household wealth that is important when it comes to overweight.

We can make sense the disparities between countries, regions and neighbourhoods in terms of vitamin D. On a country-by-country basis, as economic activity in a country increases, urbanisation increases. Much of the population migrates from higher altitude and rural areas into low-altitude built environments with poorer housing and less outside space, swapping work on farms for indoor jobs. In addition, emissions from transport and industry increase the blocking of ultraviolet by the atmosphere.

Regional differences in overweight can be explained by many factors affecting ultraviolet availability, including the density of buildings, the local topography and the levels of atmospheric pollution blocking ultraviolet. Industrial areas most likely to have the highest level of ultraviolet blocking tend to be less attractive and therefore poor, although even the most attractive areas might suffer from low ultraviolet, if under flight routes, for example.

The effects of the local ultraviolet on your vitamin D status, and therefore your weight, will be greater if you live in the same place for all your life rather than if you move. Cities typically undergo a great deal of migration both in and out. To take London as an example, most people born in London do not stay there all their lives but move out at some point to the suburbs and beyond. On the other hand, most people who live in London at any one time were not born there and many were born in other countries. For this reason the effect of the local ultraviolet on the London population might not be apparent.

If you live in an area of low ultraviolet, its effects will be greatest if you live there all your life and spend a lot of time in the local area. If you are at home all day or work locally it will have a greater effect than if you commute to work in another area. Similarly if you spend a lot of time travelling, particularly abroad, you may escape the effects of your home ultraviolet levels.

Housing and working conditions tend to be characteristic of a neighbourhood and can affect the ability to make vitamin D. You can make vitamin D while you are sweeping your front step, mowing your lawn, cooking at the barbecue, or sitting on your balcony. You can make vitamin D while you are walking to the station, school or shops, or to get water, while cycling to work, or sitting or playing in the park. If you live in a home with no outdoor space you need to leave your residence before you can make vitamin D and you will make less vitamin D if you have no need to walk, or if for some reason you cannot walk easily and safely to and from local facilities.

In summary, we can explain the connection between the wealth of a country and overweight by ultraviolet blocking and we can explain the perceived connection between poor socioeconomic status by the geographical and industrial effects on regional and local ultraviolet. You are more likely to be overweight if you live in a poor area within a wealthy country because it is most likely to have a low ultraviolet intensity. It is ultraviolet poverty rather than economic poverty that is the problem when it comes to overweight. Inequalities in health have increased during the time that overweight has increased and it is possible that they can be attributed to lower ultraviolet.

Men, women and age

There are differences in the prevalence of overweight between men and women, or boys and girls, but they are small and inconsistent. In general, slightly more women than men are obese and slightly more men than women are overweight. There are greater differences between men and women in urban areas than in rural areas and the largest differences are found in the Middle East and North Africa. Some differences between men and women can be explained by pregnancy and childbirth, which can increase vitamin D deficiency. In many areas, women are more likely to work locally than men and therefore are affected more by the local ultraviolet levels. Men are more likely to work outdoors and women are more likely to diet. The disparities between men and women in the Middle East and North Africa could be explained by the differences in exposure to sunlight. Religious and cultural restrictions mean that some women in the Middle Eastern and North African countries spend less time outdoors than men and when they do go outdoors traditional clothing styles cover most or all of their skin.

Today, many young people are overweight, but almost everybody in my generation, born in the 1950s and 1960s, was slim throughout childhood and early adulthood, only becoming overweight in middle age. This can be explained at least partly by the fact that children get more sunlight exposure than adults. There is deep concern about the increase in the number of overweight children and yet the age group with the highest rates of overweight and obesity are currently in their middle ages – people in their forties, fifties and sixties – who were *not* overweight when they were children in the 1940s, 1950s and 1960s. For example, in the Health Survey for England 2007, obesity in boys and girls aged 2 to 15 years was around 15 per cent, but this was much lower than the highest prevalence of obesity of 30 per cent found in people aged between 45 and 74 years. Instead of asking what people are doing wrong to get fat, perhaps we should think about what children are doing *right* for most of them to maintain a normal weight. If we consider children at a typical primary school, they are sent out in the playground or field every day, except in extremely bad weather, for around half an hour twice a day. In addition, they tend to spend time outdoors in their leisure time, playing in the park, garden or street (though perhaps not so much these days). It has been estimated that we get most of our lifetime's exposure to sunlight in our first 18 years. As we get older, we tend to spend less and less time outdoors.

Weight gain with age is not inevitable

Many of us gain weight slowly as we get older and we think it is a normal part of ageing. Few people have the same slim physique at 50 years old as they had at 20 years old. In fact, those people who do not gain any weight in middle age are rare. We tend to accept that overweight comes with age, along with wrinkles and grey or balding hair. Is it possible that vitamin D deficiency is the common factor causing all these effects? If so, it is possible that weight gain with age is not normal, not inevitable and instead we should remain slim throughout our lifetime. We also accept ill health comes with old age and, as the population ages, it is inevitable that the diseases of old age, such as Alzheimer's disease and arthritis, will become more common. I wonder if, instead, with a healthy vitamin D status, it is possible we should remain slim and healthy throughout a long life until we die peacefully in our sleep.

Is vitamin D deficiency everywhere?

Michael Holick estimates that 50 per cent of the world's population is vitamin D deficient. In 2011, I watched a discussion about vitamin D in which a senior medical professional stated that the majority of North

Americans are not vitamin D deficient. He was bald and overweight and I thought he was probably vitamin D deficient. I must confess I look around me in the street and see vitamin D deficiency everywhere (at least I think so, but I must admit to being unusually preoccupied with the subject).

To find population groups who do not suffer from overweight we need to look away from modern, urban-industrial societies and look at history, or at those rare groups who still follow ancient ways of life, such as the hunter–gatherer tribes who spend most of their time outdoors wearing little or no clothing, or the smallholders in rural Africa or on mountain sides, such as found in the Talysh mountains in Azerbaijan. If we find people who get plenty of daily ultraviolet exposure and have consistently high levels of vitamin D, we will find people for whom weight is never a problem.

Vitamin D deficiency in other species

Overweight has been studied almost exclusively as a human problem and, even when it is noted that animals are overweight, the blame is placed on overfeeding by humans. But is it really just a human problem? Perhaps, a cow, standing in the field all day, and an alga, floating on the top of the ocean, can get all the ultraviolet-B they need even when there is not enough for us humans with our indoor habitats and clothing habits. But we need to consider whether other living things may also be suffering from low ultraviolet. Birds and bees, for example, have ultraviolet vision. If ultraviolet has lowered in recent years because of fossil fuel emissions, can they still find their way about so well? And, since vitamin D has not been studied in invertebrates how can we be sure they are not suffering from vitamin D deficiency?

The health and welfare of animals in captivity is a great concern. For example, a study by Ros Clubb of the RSPCA compared the life spans of 800 elephants in European zoos with wild elephants in Kenya's Ambesoli National Park and with tamed elephants in Myanmar's Myanma Timber Enterprise. The elephants born in zoos live for only about half as long as protected populations in other countries. The infant mortality rate of Asian elephants is twice that of Asian elephants in Burmese timber camps. The authors suggest stress and obesity as the most likely causes. I wonder if it is because the elephants in European zoos are living in a lower ultraviolet environment than their counterparts in Kenya and Burma.

Reports of species loss have been accelerating in recent years. In fact, the decline of species has been so great that some scientists, including Tony Barnosky and David Wake (who is also known as Commander Salamander), both of the University of California, Berkeley, suggest that we could be seeing the beginning of the sixth mass extinction event. There have been five mass extinctions – near the end of the Ordovician, Devonian, Permian, Triassic, and Cretaceous periods – when more than three quarters of species were lost.

It is amphibian species that appear to be suffering the greatest losses, which is curious because the amphibians survived the four previous mass extinctions (they did not appear until after the first mass extinction). Amphibian species have been declining since the 1980s. The Sierra Nevada Yellow-legged Frog is one of the best-studied examples. It has disappeared from more than 90 per cent of the area it previously inhabited, despite protection of its habitat, which is mostly in national parks and wilderness. Efforts to reintroduce it to these areas failed, resulting in hundreds of dead frogs.

Several causes for the decline in species are considered, including climate change, habitat destruction and infectious diseases. The decline in frogs is thought to be caused by an epidemic of a fungal disease called chytridiomycosis and more than a dozen factors may contribute to the decline in bee populations, but most scientists think it is linked to climate change. To my knowledge, although increased ultraviolet-B is one of the causes considered (even in the absence of evidence that ultraviolet *has* increased in the habitats), a *fall* in ultraviolet has never been considered as a potential cause of global biodiversity loss.

Overweight in other species

If animals are suffering from vitamin D deficiency, then they should also be suffering from overweight, if the winter response idea is correct. Overweight has been studied almost exclusively in humans, but there are numerous reports of overweight pets, mostly cats and dogs, but also horses. In addition a few studies have found that the body size of animals has increased in recent decades. An examination of museum specimens of otters in Norway and Sweden by Yoram Yom-Tov, of the Department of Zoology at Tel Aviv

University, revealed an increase in size in these animals in the last quarter of the twentieth century. And in the USA, Yan Klimentidis of the University of Alabama and a team of scientists looked at the weights of more than 20,000 animals in 24 populations that had been recorded for various scientific studies. The animals were of eight different species in different environments, including domestic dogs and cats, chimpanzees, macaques and other monkeys living in research centres, laboratory mice and rats, and feral rats captured in urban Baltimore. The body weight of all the species had increased in the 1980s and 1990s.

The End of the Great Epidemic of the Global Age

THE EPIDEMIC CAME TO an end once people realised that the 'obesity epidemic' and the 'vitamin D deficiency epidemic' were the same. They started to reverse the epidemic long before they successfully reduced the use of fossil fuels. People stopped worrying about their weight and started enjoying food again. They improved their vitamin D health by eating more fish, meat, eggs, milk and dairy food, taking vitamin D supplements and getting outdoors more often. The health services were able to do more to help people with vitamin D deficiency, rather than just trying and mostly failing to deal with the outward signs of it. Pharmaceutical companies developed drugs and skin creams to increase vitamin D levels that had a real and safe effect on weight. Slimming clubs and weight loss programmes of all kinds improved the health of their clients by incorporating vitamin D health into their services and eventually became vitamin D clubs. Policy-makers took action to increase vitamin D availability. They improved the food composition data; changed dietary advice, so that it was aimed at increasing rather than reducing nutrients; encouraged the provision of sunlight and outdoor spaces in housing and workplaces; reinstated school whole milk; and improved the monitoring of street-level ultraviolet. Farmers ensured that livestock were exposed to sunlight whenever possible and increased the vitamin D content of food. Lamps and sunbeds designed specifically for making vitamin D were made safe and accessible. Manufacturers of instrumentation produced a range of monitors for measuring ultraviolet. Supplement producers provided a wide variety of vitamin D supplements. It took time, but gradually people stopped gaining weight, started losing weight and the incidence of many diseases fell. No more children were diagnosed with type 2 diabetes. Overweight was eradicated and weight gain became a rare and easily treated condition.

Chapter 9

The Reversal Strategy

THE ORIGIN OF OVERWEIGHT lies in an ancient, primitive mechanism. One compound changes into another when a photon of sunlight with a wavelength in the ultraviolet-B part of the spectrum comes along. This change was used by some of the earliest life forms to detect sunlight and over millions of years of evolution it became a living barometer, letting the inside of the body know what the weather is like outside. By the time mammals had evolved, a fall in vitamin D had become a signal to adapt to the cold by getting fat and switching to a winter metabolism. Overweight, then, is an adaptation to the cold induced by the brain when it detects a fall in vitamin D.

Turning blind spots into sun spots

I should emphasise here again that this is all hypothetical, but for the rest of this chapter and the next I will assume it is true. Once we accept this idea as correct, it is natural to ask why, with all the thousands of studies of obesity, the obesity organisations and the obesity journals, it was not realised earlier. The simple answer is that vitamin D deficiency is multifactorial, which makes its observation complex, and obscures its connection to overweight. No amount of studying overweight and its associations would have pointed to vitamin D deficiency without concurrent work on vitamin D deficiency. It is not surprising that the connection between overweight and vitamin D deficiency was not obvious. We haven't known about the existence of ultraviolet for long and we are only just beginning to learn about vitamin D. Nevertheless, we should try to identify the blind spots that impeded our understanding of the cause of overweight and are exposed as discordance between the message in this book and prevailing messages about our environment and health. The first part of this chapter will review these blind spots and the last part will consider what we need to do to eradicate overweight in the future.

Vitamin D is not a bone vitamin

This book suggests that vitamin D deficiency causes overweight but, previously, you have been told vitamin D is a bone vitamin. There is no doubt that severe deficiency of vitamin D can result in bone disease, which can be reversed by raising vitamin D status. However, vitamin D is no more a bone vitamin than folate is a neural tube vitamin (lack of folate during pregnancy can cause neural tube defects in babies), or protein is a hair nutrient (lack of protein can result in loss of hair among other symptoms). Good bone health requires many nutrients and vitamin D is needed for aspects of health that are not related to bone. There is still much to learn about what vitamin D does, but we do know that calcitriol, the hormone derivative of vitamin D, has effects throughout the body.

It is salutary perhaps to read the following quotation about another vitamin – vitamin C (ascorbic acid) – by Albert Szent-Györgyi, the Hungarian-born biochemist who was awarded the Nobel Prize in 1937 for his discovery of vitamin C:

My own interest in ascorbic acid centered around its role in vegetable respiration and defense mechanisms. All the same, I always had the feeling that not enough use was made of it for supporting human health. The reasons were rather complex. The medical profession itself took a very narrow and very wrong view. Lack of ascorbic acid caused scurvy, so if there was no scurvy there was no lack of ascorbic acid. Nothing could be clearer than this. The only trouble was that scurvy is not a first symptom of a lack but a final collapse, a premortal syndrome, and there is a very wide gap between scurvy and full health.

Perhaps bone disease is the final collapse in vitamin D deficiency and there is a wide gap between bone disease and full health. We think of vitamin D as a bone vitamin because of history and the medical narrative linking vitamins with specific deficiency diseases, in this case, rickets. This view means that there have been almost no studies of vitamin D in invertebrates and it has been difficult for vitamin D researchers to convey the importance of vitamin D in preventing diseases not related to bone. Most importantly it has contributed to the failure to recognise the extent of vitamin D deficiency. The science tells us that vitamin D is more than a bone vitamin and that it is time to move on from this outdated concept.

Vitamin D deficiency is severe

This book suggests that we do not get enough vitamin D from sunlight and food. Previously you have been told you can get all the nutrients you need from a varied diet and there is no need to take vitamin supplements. You have been told you can get all the vitamin D you need by making it in sunlight as you go about your daily activities. You associate nutrient deficiencies with poverty and lack of education. You may have heard that some children have rickets because their parents did not let them play outside or made them wear ultraviolet-proof swimwear on the beach. But in my opinion, vitamin D deficiency is a result of being human, having an upright posture, wearing clothes, living in buildings and living outside the equatorial regions. Even further, I suggest that vitamin D deficiency is a problem for many – perhaps even all – living things. The mechanism of using ultraviolet photons to make vitamin D as a way of detecting sunlight probably evolved when our Sun was younger and ultraviolet was much stronger than it is today. Vitamin D deficiency, then, is a consequence of living on a planet that orbits a middle-aged star.

We need ultraviolet-B

This book suggests that we are increasingly deprived of ultraviolet-B. Previously, you have been told ultraviolet radiation is increasing because of the hole in the ozone layer and you are accustomed to being told to stay out of the sun because skin cancer levels are rising at an alarming rate. As far as public health authorities are concerned, ultraviolet radiation – especially ultraviolet-B – is a hazard, toxic, dangerous, and to be avoided. It is unusual to see the words 'ultraviolet radiation' without the word 'harmful' preceding them. Yet we don't say harmful sea, harmful air, or harmful mountains, although we can be harmed by all of those things. This use of the word harmful might often be intended to distinguish the harmful ultraviolet-C radiation from the helpful ultraviolet-B radiation, but the general impression given is that all ultraviolet is bad. The fact is that ultraviolet-B is potentially harmful and potentially beneficial, as are all things in nature.

Low ultraviolet is more dangerous than high ultraviolet

The depletion of the ozone layer brought the dangers of ultraviolet-B to our attention. People were right to fear the effect of ozone layer thinning. But they were unaware of the dangers of too *little* ultraviolet radiation. Ultimately we have greater defences against strong ultraviolet – clothing, buildings and sunscreen – than we have against weak ultraviolet.

In the future, if we are not vigilant in monitoring, we will be vulnerable to any increase in ultraviolet radiation, which might be caused by a change in the atmosphere or in solar activity. We must be aware of the effects on local ultraviolet from air traffic, fires and events such as earthquakes and volcanoes, as well as the effects on global ultraviolet from atmospheric changes and solar activity. The possible blocking of ultraviolet by fossil fuel emissions is one aspect of climate change that has been overlooked, but thanks to the thinning of the ozone layer, we now have the scientists with the expertise and instrumentation to be able to monitor it. We should be aware of the increase in ultraviolet that will occur when we are successful in our attempts to reduce emissions from industry and transport in the future. We also need to take ultraviolet into account when considering geoengineering projects to combat global warming.

We need to be aware of the danger that ultraviolet radiation could increase and cause harm, but the greater danger will always be when ultraviolet radiation decreases, because then we do not get enough vitamin D. It is vital that we are aware of the ultraviolet climatology and can adjust our exposure as necessary. It is also vital that we make good use of artificial ultraviolet sources when the ambient ultraviolet is weak. People working in sunlight-deprived conditions, such as in the Antarctic, or underground or in submarines, and those who are confined indoors by illness, need to compensate for the lack of ultraviolet. We should recognise ultraviolet as a basic environmental necessity.

We are adapting to the cold as the world gets warmer

This book suggests we are in the process of adapting to a cold climate. But how can this be, at a time when more of us have centrally-heated homes and there is an extensive discourse about global warming? How can we possibly be adapting to a cold climate when we are clearly not feeling colder? On the contrary we seem to be feeling hotter. We know all about global warming – there has been an increase in the temperature of the Earth and it is expected to rise further with devastating consequences. But is this increase in temperature – of 0.74°C over 100 years – sufficient to explain the massive rise in the number of air conditioners used? In 2003 a number of countries (UK, Canada, Denmark, Italy, Sweden and the USA) were hit by power cuts thought to be due to increased demand for power by air conditioning units. All were within a few weeks in August and September during a heat wave when several weather records were broken.

Is it really so much hotter? People suffer in the heat, but mainly in places like the USA and Europe, with mostly temperate climates. Perhaps the problem is that we are becoming physiologically adapted to the cold and this is making it harder to keep cool in hot summers. Extra fat along with the metabolic changes mean that it is easier to keep warm in the cold, but harder to lose heat in the warm. The reverse of this situation is that, should we manage to eradicate vitamin D deficiency and cure overweight, we will find it easier to keep cool in the summer but will suffer more from the cold of the winter. We may then experience an increase in excess winter deaths. The problem of dealing with seasons will always be with us. I cannot resist noting the irony if it turns out that our use of fossil fuels, to keep us warm in the winter and cool in the summer, is warming the Earth while causing us to adapt to the cold.

We need to eat fat

This book suggests cutting down on fat is not a good idea because it contains certain vitamins that are only found in fat. But previously you have been told fat is bad. The perception that fat is bad and a low fat diet is a healthy diet has widespread acceptance. If I were to suggest to an overweight friend that he or she should eat more fat, he or she would simply conclude I was mad. Low fat foods are so widespread that it can be difficult to find products containing normal proportions of fat. This is particularly true of dairy products. Semi-skimmed milk is now the standard milk offered in cafés, fast food outlets and canteens, for example. Flavoured milk drinks for children are made with skimmed and semi-skimmed milk, not whole milk, and most yoghurts are low fat. The supermarket shelves are dominated by low fat dairy products with the whole milk versions squeezed into a corner.

This situation has arisen because research into heart disease found an association between dietary fat and blood cholesterol levels, between blood cholesterol levels and atherosclerosis, and between atherosclerosis and heart disease. If we chop out the steps in the middle we get an association between dietary fat and heart disease. By the 1970s, dietary fat was the main target for the prevention of heart disease. As a result, average fat intake dropped from over 40 per cent of total calorie intake to 34 per cent in America. As expected, deaths from heart disease dropped and yet the incidence of heart disease did not fall, which suggests the drop in the number of deaths could have been due to improved treatment. Still, in the face of an epidemic of overweight, we might be forgiven for remaining anti-fat, since fat contains a high density of calories and too many calories, they say, make you fat.

One of the primary reasons why a reduction of fat is advocated is because it is seen as a no-risk option. With all of the population able to access more calories than they need, it surely cannot do anyone any harm to cut down the amount of fat they consume. In America, obesity was fairly constant from the early 1960s to 1980. With the subsequent fall in fat intake, you would expect a fall in obesity but in fact it increased (from 14 per cent to over 22 per cent). In the case of heart disease, the hypothesis has been adjusted. It is now not total dietary fat that is harmful, but the *type* of fat, so we now have *good fats* and *bad fats*.

Advice on dieting was dominated by cutting down on fat in the 1980s and 1990s until people realised that it was not only unhealthy but almost impossible to eat a very low fat diet. Now the advice is to eat some fat, but not too much. Still, I have not seen any advice to replace the vitamins lost when switching from whole milk to low fat milks, even for 2-year-old children. Nutritional advice seems to ignore the fact that micronutrients (vitamins) and essential fatty acids are reduced along with the targeted macronutrient (fat) and it ignores the fact that if we cut down on one thing we might compensate by eating more of another. The obsession with reducing macronutrients may have resulted in deficiencies of micronutrients. Nutritional advice seems to have lost its way – surely it should be all about making sure we get the nutrients we need.

Body weight is self-regulated

Previously you have been encouraged to control (or maintain) your weight by various means, but this book has shown that body weight is controlled physiologically and the mechanisms controlling weight are powerful. Of the many papers I have read for this book, one of my favourites was the edited transcription of a discussion at the weekly Grand Rounds in the Department of Medicine, University of Washington School of Medicine. In this discussion, David Weigle (now Professor of Medicine having specialised in treating overweight patients as well as doing research into obesity) pointed out that health care for the obese was hampered by four commonly held beliefs that he regarded as myths. These beliefs are:

- 1. Body weight is set by acquired food habits and desires.
- 2. Body weight can be controlled by choosing the right diet.
- 3. Dieting is to be encouraged.
- 4. Body shape is not significant.

He described the evidence for the set point of body weight (much of which has been discussed in this book) and that weight loss by dieting is doomed to failure. He pointed out that the failure of dieting is further evidence for the existence of a set point and he said the health hazards of being moderately overweight are overstated.

This paper is called *Human Obesity – Exploding the Myths* and it was published as long ago as 1990. Since then, myths 3 and 4 have received some attention. Rather than dieting, "healthy eating" is encouraged, and it is now recognised that waist size is an important predictor of health, following the realisation that overweight is more than just an excess of fat. But clearly this paper did not explode the myth about what controls body weight, a myth that continues to prevail more than 20 years after the paper was published.

The set point theory is not fully accepted and, where it is acknowledged, it is thought of as being skewed to protect against starvation but not against overfeeding, i.e. the body weight set point is a *minimum* body weight and the regulatory mechanisms only kick in when the body weight drops below the set point and not when body weight goes above it. Perhaps this is understandable when we look at the distribution of body weight in the population – the range is huge and is skewed to overweight. It is also understandable when we consider our personal experience that weight gain is easy but weight loss is difficult. But these observations are phenomenological and they are concerned only with humans.

The existence of a body weight set point explains why dieting doesn't work in the long term and why none of the drugs developed so far has proved to be effective for the long term and without serious side effects. Much of the research into overweight becomes nonsense if you accept there is a body weight set point. Research into the putative contributors to the rise in overweight – fast food, convenience food, lack of physical education in schools, walking to school, watching TV – is driven by lay opinion rather than science. Studies examining these factors only make sense if they completely ignore the scientific evidence for the body weight set point. I wonder how much difference it would have made if David Weigle's presentation had been successful in exploding the first two myths in 1990 and if research for the following 20 years had been aimed at finding the cause of the elevation of the set point.

Overweight is not personal

You have been told that overweight is caused by making the wrong choices, but in my book, overweight is not personal. Instead, I have suggested that the risk of vitamin D deficiency is a particular problem for humans, that it must have affected some of our ancestors, and that it affects millions of us around the world today. Even further, I suggest it is a global problem affecting many living things today and has done so in the past.

Overweight occurs when caloric wealth is combined with vitamin D poverty. It is a consequence of the environment we happen to be in. We have no awareness of the vitamin D availability of our environment and therefore cannot possibly make any choices about it, so how can we be to blame? Overweight is a result of the circumstances we find ourselves in. It is a matter of luck. Lucky you, if you were born of vitamin D-rich parents, live in an area of high ultraviolet intensity and grew up with a vitamin D-rich diet. Unlucky you, if you were born vitamin D-poor, live in an area that is polluted, at high latitude and low altitude. You wouldn't be so overweight if you were born at a different time, or lived in a different place, or had a different job.

The explanation of the origin of overweight in my book is very different to the messages that tell us overweight is a consequence of personal factors, over which each of us has the finest control. If you are overweight it is not because you have *unresolved negative emotions* (more likely you are just not happy about being overweight), nor is it because you are *in a comfort zone* (more likely you are struggling to get comfortable), nor is it because you are *in denial* (instead, others are in denial about the obvious fact that you wouldn't be overweight if you had any choice). You don't eat because you *experience sadness as an emotional emptiness that you try to fill with food* (you eat because you are hungry). It is not because you *live near a fast food restaurant* (maybe you do but so do thin people). It is not because you have *bad habits*, *self-esteem issues* or *suffer from misfortune* (perhaps you do but they have nothing to do with your weight). It is not because you are *addicted to food* (perhaps you are but that's because you really will die without it). It is not because you need to be *educated about healthy choices* (if you are, it might make you even more overweight). Overweight is not a punishment for doing a bad thing or being a bad person. It is time to see overweight as just another condition that might afflict anyone, like asthma, indigestion, or baldness. It is not a matter of choice and should not form the basis for prejudicial assumptions about an individual's state of health or personal characteristics.

The hegemony of lifestyle choices

Allow me to pontificate. People *don't want* to be overweight, they *don't choose* to be overweight and if dieting and exercise worked there wouldn't be millions of overweight people. It makes biological sense that there is a set point for body weight, otherwise we would see an enormous amount of variation in body weights in other animals as well as ourselves, for all of the time, everywhere, throughout history. Overweight *cannot* be caused by excess food supply, otherwise overweight would have been much higher in the developed world than it was before the 1970s. Overweight affects *all* countries, *all* sections of society and *all* population groups. It *cannot* be attributed to genes or education. People aren't overweight because they haven't been taught about healthy eating.

I once read a commentary about cancer in a newspaper in which the writer said disease is caused not by the environment but by lifestyle, but biologically, there is no distinction between lifestyle and environment. What the writer meant, of course, was that disease is not caused by anything in the environment over which the individual has no control, but by those things in the environment – lifestyle – which the individual *can* control. The hegemony of individual lifestyle choices as the cause of ill health and overweight has serious consequences and can explain why overweight continues to spread, why the suffering goes on year after year and why nobody knows what to do about it.

People talk about lifestyle choices as though they are as easy as choosing between a red and a green jumper, as if anyone would choose to be overweight or to be ill. I may be able to choose whether to eat chicken or beef at the supermarket but I have no control over how that meat was produced, I don't know which farm the meat came from, I don't know how old it is, and it may not even be the meat I think it is. The concept of choice over lifestyle is overestimated as, in practice, the individual choices that each of us can make in everyday life are limited. Furthermore, the promotion of choice as a cause of ill health has the effect of limiting choice, because the importance of making the right choices becomes dictatorial. Health advice is interpreted as commandments, which must be followed and those who do not follow it are treated as sinners who will pay a mortal penalty later in life.

Not that there hasn't been some excellent scientific research into overweight. A good example is the work of the Earlybird Diabetes Study, which aimed to study a cohort of children to find out more about the determinants of obesity and diabetes. One of its key findings is that children do not become overweight because they are driven to school and not given enough exercise – instead it found the amount of exercise a child does is controlled from within and that overweight precedes a fall in activity. Unfortunately, research such as this is not taken on board because it contradicts firmly held beliefs, which are based upon lay opinion. While writing this book I have repeatedly been astonished to see evidence regarding dieting, healthy eating and activity that contradicts the public messages ignored or misreported in favour of the lay explanations.

The attribution of overweight to lifestyle choices leads inexorably to the victim-blaming model. This leads to the assumption that anyone who is overweight *must* have eaten too much and not done enough exercise. In other words, illness and overweight result from being bad, while leanness and good health result from being good. The attribution of the determinants of ill health to the choices of the suffering individuals is nothing new. During the plagues of the fourteenth century, Flagellants were people who flogged themselves in the belief that their self-imposed suffering would move the Lord to be compassionate and spare them from the plague. More recently, tuberculosis was said to be caused by dissolute and immoral living, before the discovery of the tuberculosis bacterium. We may like to think that we are moving away from superstitious medicine to scientific medicine, but it is clear that we still have a long way to go.

It is not only cruel and unjust to blame the overweight for their predicament, it also prevents proper investigation of the true determinants of overweight. The most important and dangerous consequence of the hegemony of lifestyle choices as causes of disease is that it results in a pointillist kind of epidemiology, in which the focus on individuals prevents us from standing back and seeing the big picture. When thousands or millions of people are afflicted by the same condition, it doesn't make sense to blame individual sufferers.

The Great Depression of the 1930s was a worldwide economic downturn triggered by a stock market crash in the USA, which affected just about every country in the world, with unemployment one of the devastating effects. In 1933 in the UK, unemployment was 2.5 million, which was 25 per cent of the workforce, but in some towns unemployment was as high as 70 per cent. The cause of the depression is debatable, but it is clear in retrospect that soaring unemployment was a global effect of the worldwide economic conditions – the shrink in the money supply, a sharp decline in international trade and a fall in production as demand decreased. But *at the time* the worldwide view was not so easy to see and many people blamed unemployed individuals for getting themselves into the situation because they didn't want to work, while the unemployed often blamed themselves for their predicament.

Today we have the advantage of being able to take a worldwide view quite easily. We know that overweight is not just a problem in one individual, in one community, one region or one country. We can see it affects millions of people around the world and people of all ages, ethnicity, socioeconomic status – no section of society appears to be immune to overweight. We can see, also, how individuals *and* populations make the transition from normal weight to overweight. A report produced in 2007 by the UK's Foresight Programme took a strategic review of obesity and acknowledged that the individual approach was doomed to failure. The report noted strong parallels between climate change and obesity in that, to effectively tackle both these problems, the involvement of scientists, government, businesses and civil society are needed to improve the environment. The report therefore recommended a common approach to both obesity and climate change, although there was no suggestion as to a link between their causes. In spite of its visionary scope, the report was, as usual, firmly based on the assumption that obesity is caused by an imbalance of calories consumed and calories expended.

Overweight in context

We need to consider the context of overweight. At various points in this book I have mentioned the possible health consequences of vitamin D deficiency beyond overweight. It is often said that we are better fed, healthier and living longer than ever before. But is it true? Our traditional measures of health are life expectancy and infant mortality. But although infant mortality is relatively low, the rate of births by *Caesarean* section is high. And although life expectancy is higher than it has ever been, are we really healthier?

Take a moment to imagine what would happen if we suddenly had no access to medicine of any kind – no hospitals, pharmacies, ambulances, no surgery, drugs, no physicians, nurses, midwives, pharmacists, dentists. How many babies and mothers would die at birth? If there were no *Caesarean* deliveries, how high would infant mortality be? How many people would die of diseases such as asthma, diabetes and epilepsy who at present are dependent on drugs to control their conditions? We recognise the importance of healthcare and spend tens of billions of pounds every year on it, but it may have given us a false impression of our ability to survive. Medicine is keeping us alive; it is not making us healthy.

It is often said that because the population is living longer there are greater demands on the health services. This would make sense if the increase in life expectancy was due largely to a reduction in deaths by accidents or murders. But if we are living longer because we are in better health, then surely we should be healthier and *less* likely to become ill with old age. If we live longer because we are healthier, our demands on the health services should go down, or at least remain the same. But while a proportion of people live long and healthy lives, some live for a long time with illnesses, sometimes for many decades. The greatest inequalities in health can be found among the elderly. Take a group of 80-year-olds and you will find a vast range of health states – from being fit and well enough to work with many active years to come, to being severely disabled and dependent on others. We accept this as normal, but perhaps it isn't inevitable.

The truth is that illness and disability is widespread – not just among the elderly – and perhaps we have not taken on board just how extensive ill health is today. In the UK, the USA and other countries, the number of people claiming long-term benefits due to sickness has increased in recent years, particularly in the 1990s (when overweight also increased). For example, in the UK the number of people claiming Invalidity Benefit then Incapacity Benefit was fewer than 1 million in 1971, but had risen to 2.5 million in 2006. This increase is usually attributed to a decline in the labour market and that the benefits system encourages people to avoid work and to become dependent on benefits. The consensus is that there was no reason for any increase in disability or illness in the population. In 1994, John Major, the Prime Minister at the time, summed up the thoughts of many people when he said:

Frankly, it beggars belief that so many people have suddenly become invalids, especially at a time when the health of the population has improved.

But has the health of the population really improved? It doesn't appear so when we look at some other measures of health:

- According to the General Household Survey in the UK, the prevalence of longstanding illness in adults and children went up from 21 per cent in 1972 to 35 per cent in 2002.

- Total expenditure on health in European countries rose from 4–8 per cent of GDP in 1970 to 8–12 per cent in 2006, and in the USA it went up even more from around 7 per cent to around 16 per cent of GDP.

- The number of prescriptions has increased – for example the average number of prescriptions dispensed in the UK almost doubled from 6.6 per person in 1980 to 11.6 per person in 2000, and trebled to 18.3 in 2010.

- There are reports that specific diseases are increasing in prevalence, for example, allergies, asthma, autism, diabetes, coeliac disease, gout, some cancers and depression, to name just a few at random.

The rise in chronic illness has occurred at the same time as the rise in overweight, so overweight needs to be considered in the context of the increase in ill health generally, rather than assuming one causes the other. It has to be considered whether vitamin D deficiency, and perhaps other nutritional deficiencies, underlies much of the ill health we suffer today. Vitamin D deficiency may not directly cause cancer, for example, but it is conceivable that vitamin D deficiency increases the risk of cancer by impairing defensive mechanisms. During the time that overweight has increased, the disparities in overweight have got wider and the inequalities in health have also increased, in spite of efforts to bridge the gap. When a resource is plentiful, almost everyone can get enough to meet their needs, but as a resource becomes more and more depleted, the inequalities get sharper with fewer people getting all they need, more people getting less than ideal, and a greater number suffering severe deprivation. Vitamin D poverty has the potential to explain the recent increase in chronic ill health and its regional distribution, as well as the persistence of the inequalities in health and deprivation, particularly racial and regional disparities.

How to eradicate overweight

When a disease is prevalent in a population, there is always a simple relationship between the cause and the disease, and when the cause is eradicated, the disease will mostly disappear. The many different influences on vitamin D status – pollution, latitude, diet, clothing, skin pigmentation, occupation and others (you can find a list in question 2 of Chapter 10 Crisps) – make the cause of overweight appear to be complex and confusing, but the cause can be put simply as vitamin D deficiency. Tackling overweight can become simple once you understand its biological origin. We don't need to deal with overweight – instead we need to deal with vitamin D deficiency. I think we can be optimistic that once we have dealt with vitamin D deficiency, overweight will no longer be an epidemic. It will become a rare condition, and mostly acute rather than chronic, to be found in a few people unfortunate enough to have a genetic susceptibility, or a predisposing illness, or who are on medication on which weight gain is unavoidable. When it does occur, it will be easily treated before it gets too severe.

The trouble is that tackling vitamin D deficiency will not be so simple and may take some considerable time – perhaps as long as a generation. I have shown in this book how and why I think vitamin D deficiency causes overweight, but to tackle overweight it would help if we can understand the cause of vitamin D deficiency which has resulted in the dramatic rise in overweight in recent years and in this respect, this book offers questions rather than answers.

The cause of the vitamin D famine

It is evident that we make less vitamin D than in the past because changes in our daily lives have reduced our casual exposure to sunlight, we have increased the use of protection from sunlight to avoid skin cancer, and there has been an increase in pollutants in the atmosphere that absorb ultraviolet. At the same time, changes in our diet have reduced our vitamin D intake, including the decline in whole milk consumption and fat consumption, and changes in food production methods have reduced the amount of vitamin D in our food. In addition, there has been an increase in medication that can potentially lower vitamin D status. It seems that all these things combined have caused a rise in vitamin D deficiency in the period in which overweight has increased, but no doubt some contributed more than others.

It is reasonable to consider whether the dramatic increase in overweight resulted from a dramatic fall in vitamin D – the onset of a vitamin D famine. Is there a single major contributing factor among the list of many factors causing vitamin D deficiency? In this regard, I think it is important to stay on the fence until we have more information. We clearly need more research and there is a danger of jumping to premature conclusions, turning our attention to one putative cause and ignoring all the others. I think it is important to address all the different things that affect our vitamin D status. Our response to health problems has a tendency to be simplistic – the surgical extirpation of anything associated with disease is carried out with the assumption that its removal can have no harmful consequences. A more thoughtful, multifaceted approach, using slow thinking rather than fast thinking, would be safer and more effective.

In the meantime here is a summary of my thoughts at the time of writing. I think the massive rise in the prevalence of overweight, wherever it occurs, can be attributed to increases in fossil fuel emissions – mainly aircraft emissions but also from power generation, road transport, shipping and industry. The regional variations (at a given time) can be attributed to both emissions and geographical differences such as latitude, altitude, topography, building cover and weather. Individual variations (within the same region) can be attributed to time spent outdoors, diet, occupation, clothing types and skin pigmentation.

Perhaps we shouldn't get too carried away with vitamin D – I have no doubt there are other nutrient deficiencies and many other causes of ill health – but when we put together the problems of overweight, increasing ill health, the biodiversity crisis, the rise in unusual weather and global warming we should consider if they can all potentially be traced to fossil fuel emissions.

The proof of the pudding is in the eating and in this case, the proof of the hypothesis is in reversing vitamin D deficiency. If we can eradicate vitamin D deficiency worldwide, we should see a dramatic fall in overweight in the population. As individuals, we can all do something to increase our vitamin D levels, but the trouble is, as I know from my own experience, getting more vitamin D is not easy (if it was we would not have such a problem with overweight, of course). There is little vitamin D in food, we don't know how much we can safely take in supplement form and getting more sunlight is easier said than done. To deal with overweight on a population basis, we need to change our vitamin D environment to make it more abundant. We need to end the vitamin D famine.

A vitamin D rich environment

As individuals we can all do more to raise our vitamin D status by getting more exposure to sunlight, eating foods such as fish that contain vitamin D and taking a vitamin D supplement. If you are a public health or medical professional and are reluctant to raise recommended intakes of vitamin D and reverse the sunlight protection advice, you can at least ensure that the current recommendations are implemented. This means encouraging people to take the small amounts of 5, 10, or 15 micrograms per day of vitamin D, which will do no harm except to the most sensitive people.

We can immediately pay more attention to groups who are at most risk of vitamin D deficiency, such as black people, the elderly and veiled people living at middle and high latitudes. But we should note these are 'greater risk' rather than 'at risk' groups – we need to get away from the idea that vitamin D deficiency only affects a minority of the population. (And perhaps we should be asking why the problem of vitamin D deficiency in greater-risk groups was not already being addressed.) We can provide vitamin D supplements for pregnant women, nursing mothers and babies. We can consider whether patients with broken bones should have either a vitamin D test and/or supplementation and consider whether generalised aches and pains in adults and growing pains in children could be caused by vitamin D deficiency. We could stop recommending reduced fat milk and dairy products until there is evidence that they are more beneficial than whole milk and reconsider the provision of school milk.

Challenges for the longer term

It is fine for me and others to say that we need to get outdoors more, but it is not easy. First there is the weather. Is there any point in going outside when it is raining or very cloudy, and even if there is, who wants to go out in the rain? While writing this book I have tried to eat my lunch outdoors every day but many days it is too cold, too windy or too wet and some days it is too hot. Even on a fine day you have to contend with insects biting your skin and landing on your food or drink, the noise of traffic, aircraft, electric garden tools, barking dogs and chirping birds. Even the most comfortable chair is not as comfy as the sofa and if you use an upholstered chair you have the bother of having to put it away and take it out each day, whereas the sofa is just there indoors waiting for you to sink into it whenever possible. If you use a laptop or mobile screen, you can't see the screen properly because of the sunshine. If you use paper for writing or reading it gets blown about in the breeze. Unless you have a secluded garden you are visible to the neighbours and perhaps passers-by. If you have hay fever, you expose yourself to pollen; if you are on a busy road you expose yourself to pollution. If you have no garden or balcony you must walk to a place to sit. If you have no place to sit nearby you will have to drive. If you work indoors and cannot open a window or have no facilities to have your lunch outdoors – or are too busy to stop work to have lunch – you are confined indoors when the sun is out.

Some of these problems can be overcome by improving our outdoor places and ensuring that workplaces have outdoor lunch areas, that canteens and cafes have outdoor seating. We can also allow more sunlight into indoor facilities. Sunlight normally enters a building only through windows on the side, not from above. Artificial light is designed to enable us to see and for this it needs to replicate visible light, not ultraviolet radiation. The spectrum of artificial light is very different to the spectrum of the Sun. Richard Hobday, in his book *The Light Revolution*, points out that buildings throughout history have been designed to maximise sunlight, but in the middle to late twentieth century the importance of sunlight was forgotten. As artificial lighting and heating have improved, buildings have become bigger and many rooms inside a large building have no sunlight at all, including rooms in which people work all day long and hospitals where the sick go to get better. Building design can be improved to maximise the sunlight penetration into the interior, by the use of windows, skylights and sun-tubes. Window glass manufactured to allow transmittance of ultraviolet-B would have to be used. Conservatories can be built in workplaces to provide a comfortable, sheltered area with maximum sunlight.

Sunbeds and sunlamps

Sunbed usage is often compared to smoking as a source of harm that can cause cancer and induce a dangerous addiction in some of our youngsters. Some cancer experts aim to have sunbeds banned altogether. But with regard to getting more vitamin D, sunbeds could be of enormous benefit as they can overcome many of the difficulties in getting sunlight described above.

They can be used in winter, when there is little or no ultraviolet-B and when it is too cold to expose your skin to sunlight. Furthermore, they can be used to expose the whole naked body in private, with no fear of embarrassment or offence. Instead of comparing their usage to smoking, we should perhaps compare them to swimming pools, which can be dangerous if used unsupervised and particularly if used by children without adult supervision. But used safely, with proper regulation, monitoring and supervision, they can bring benefits to health.

At present sunbeds are designed to produce a tan but what we need instead are sunbeds that are designed to produce vitamin D. These may need to have a lower output and a narrower spectrum so that they emit more ultraviolet-B and less ultraviolet-A than at present. It might be ideal if they were to mimic the summer spectrum and irradiance of local ultraviolet-B. We need the manufacture of good quality sunbeds and sunlamps designed specifically to make vitamin D, regulation to ensure they are safe, and improved access, with sunbeds available in every high street, shopping centre, workplace and hospital. Only a short exposure time would be needed – perhaps five minutes or less – so you could pop in to use the sunbed in your lunch hour.

At the moment the people who need to use sunbeds the most – black and elderly people – are the people who are least likely to use them. If sunbeds were designed to make vitamin D, perhaps we could have them designed specifically for different skin types. Perhaps a high-tech sunbed would be able to measure skin type, work out how much time needed to make a given amount of vitamin D, and automatically set its timers so it is not left up to the individual to try to guess how long he or she needs to be on it. We are accustomed to using artificial (non-solar) sources of lighting and heating, so why not artificial sources of ultraviolet?

Food

The concentration of vitamin D in food is very low when compared to other nutrients. One possible reason is that animals exposed to sunlight all day have a daily supply of vitamin D and have no need to store it, but it is also possible that our livestock are suffering from vitamin D deficiency for mostly the same reasons as humans. These low concentrations mean it is difficult for us to get much vitamin D from our diet. In addition, we do not have much information about how much vitamin D is contained in different foods, how it changes according to the way the food is produced, and how much it has changed over time.

For example, I choose eggs laid by free-range hens because I expect them to have more vitamin D than eggs laid by indoor hens, but what do I know about how much vitamin D the eggs contain? I am not aware of any studies comparing vitamin D levels in eggs from housed and free-range hens. In any case, it will depend on how much time the free-range hen actually spent outdoors, how much ground-level ultraviolet-B was available and perhaps how old the hen was at the time the egg was laid.

How can we get more vitamin D in food? The most obvious way is to add it to the food – called fortification. Some foods are already fortified with vitamin D but there is potential to increase the amounts added and to extend fortification to other foods. There are several objections to fortification: it is not reliable; it increases intake throughout the population without targeting those who need it, which is potentially harmful; it takes away choice; and it isn't natural.

When foods that should have been fortified have been randomly analysed for the actual amount of vitamin D, they have not always had the correct amounts. In one case, when the amount of vitamin D in fortified milk was measured, over half the milk had not been fortified at all and only 5 per cent had the correct amount of vitamin D. Most studies found that fortified foods have less than the stated amount of vitamin D, but there is a greater danger from errors which result in high amounts added. The only known cases of vitamin D toxicity caused by eating food occurred when the food was accidentally fortified with excessive amounts of vitamin D.

Perhaps the greatest argument against fortification is that it hasn't worked. Fortification has been used for years in many countries, all of which suffer from severe deficiency in vitamin D. In the USA, for example, milk has been routinely fortified with ergocalciferol since the 1930s, but this did not prevent widespread vitamin D deficiency and overweight. One explanation is that the level of fortification is not sufficient – the guideline amount is 100 IU per 8 ounces, which is roughly 10 micrograms per litre. Another is that ergocalciferol is used for fortification rather than cholecalciferol. Ergocalciferol is less effective than cholecalciferol in raising serum calcidiol. In addition, to my knowledge the possibility that it competes with cholecalciferol and calcidiol in milk has not been investigated. If it does, it is possible that fortification of milk with ergocalciferol may actually reduce the amount of vitamin D you get from milk, in a manner similar to the reduction in cholesterol by plant sterols (which lower the amount of cholesterol reaching the bloodstream by competing for absorption in the intestine).

Perhaps more importantly, the consumption of milk, fortified or not, has gone down dramatically in the period in which overweight has increased. The consumption of these fortified drinks and food vary enormously between individuals. The food or drink may not be eaten or drunk in sufficient amounts, or by the people who need it the most. Fortification of foods such as milk, margarine and cereals do nothing to target those who are in the greatest need. On the other hand, some people might be sensitive.

Fortification is not sufficient, in any case, to correct deficiencies, even where it increases calcidiol levels. In order to correct deficiencies it would probably be necessary to fortify to very high levels, which would put non-deficient individuals, particularly children, at risk of overdose. Overall, fortification may be too little, too indiscriminate and too risky. Certainly, we need to be aware that fortification is not the simple solution it may appear to be.

An alternative to fortification is to improve the vitamin D status of the livestock from which our food is produced. This might be a safer way of increasing the amount of vitamin D in food, since the health of the livestock would be a way of monitoring the safety of the food. The vitamin D status of livestock could be improved by either supplementing feed with vitamin D or by ensuring exposure to ultraviolet, whether from sunlight or sunlamps (preferably sunlight) and monitored by taking regular measurements of circulating calcidiol.

It is known that both layer hens and broiler chickens have benefited from fish oil in the feed or exposure to ultraviolet. This has been done mainly due to animal welfare concerns but of course a healthy animal makes healthy food. Pirjo Mattila and colleagues at the Agricultural Research Centre of Finland have shown that feeding hens with additional vitamin D increases the amount of cholecalciferol and calcidiol in egg yolks. They found that cholecalciferol in the feed was more effective at raising the vitamin D content of the yolk than ergocalciferol and that feeding higher amounts of vitamin D increased the bone strength in the layer hens. Ensuring livestock have a healthy vitamin D status improves their health and well-being and increases our vitamin D status. I wonder if many of the food scares we have had in recent decades could have been avoided if the livestock had a healthy vitamin D status.

The vitamin D content can also be increased in other foods. Sundar Koyyalamudi and colleagues at the University of Western Sydney, Australia showed that the concentration of vitamin D in button mushrooms could be increased considerably by exposing the mushrooms to ultraviolet radiation for an hour just before harvesting. Mushrooms could be a potentially rich source of vitamin D, particularly for vegetarians and vegans, if this practice became widespread. Algae may also be a good source of vitamin D. Increasing food diversity may also help – for example, in the UK fish is usually eaten only once a week and only 16 types of fish are eaten on average compared to 33 in France.

In summary, we need better food composition data, more information about how diet affects vitamin D status, and we need to consider how we can get more vitamin D into food, to benefit the livestock *and* the consumer.

Can we get enough vitamin D from sunlight?

There is no doubt that sunlight has both risks and benefits, and as people have become more aware of the problem of vitamin D deficiency attention has been given to finding the best way to get vitamin D while minimising the risks. Scientists like Alfio Parisi and David Turnbull, at the Centre for Rural and Remote Area Health, University of Southern Queensland, Australia, are investigating many different aspects of sunlight exposure. Their research will help us to make more vitamin D in sunlight with greater safety in future. But a critical question that needs to be addressed is whether it really is possible to make all the vitamin D we need by simply trying to get outdoors more.

Earlier I mentioned the difficulties in getting outdoors, but even if we could get out a great deal more than we do, would it be enough? Research done by Ann Webb and Ola Engelson indicated that it is possible if you have skin type 2 (fair skin), but it would be very difficult for black or Asian people to get enough vitamin D from sunlight alone, and in practice it is probably impossible for any skin type to get enough exposure at middle and high latitudes in cold weather when only the face and hands can be exposed. We need to consider whether the amount of ultraviolet reaching the Earth's surface is strong enough for us to make enough vitamin D to be healthy and, if not, would we be able to take enough vitamin D in the form of supplements to compensate? Can our bodies cope with metabolising the amount we need?

We don't know whether ground-level ultraviolet has fallen in recent decades and, if so, by how much. If it has fallen by a huge amount, say, it is possible that an intake of vitamin D that would have been toxic for most people 50 years ago is today a minimum requirement. Should this be the case, we may need to accept that at least some of us will depend upon sunbeds, supplements and pharmaceuticals to keep our vitamin D levels at a healthy status. We might be dependent upon artificial sources of ultraviolet-B in the future, not only for humans, but also for our pets, animals in captivity, livestock, wild birds, animals and plankton.

A vitamin D wish list

Many of the questions posed in this book can only be answered by future research. In the meantime, there are many opportunities for creative minds in this area and I would be interested to hear any suggestions you have. Here is my own vitamin D wish list:

More vitamin D in food

As discussed above, we can raise the amounts of vitamin D in our food by giving cholecalciferol supplements to livestock that provide our meat, eggs, and milk and expose mushrooms to ultraviolet radiation one hour before harvesting.

Better supplements

A wide range of vitamin D supplements in many different doses, in flavoured chews or syrups as well as capsules, vitamin D dropper bottles that measure a precise amount with each drop and are suitable for babies, and 'vitamin D butter' – butter with high amounts of added vitamin D, so you can just spread it on your toast.

DIY calcidiol tests

Home testing kits that measure calcidiol instantly. You take a pinprick of blood and drop it onto a piece of blotting paper, insert it into a machine and it reads your calcidiol level.

Personal ultraviolet-B dose monitors

I would like to be able to calculate how much vitamin D I am making in any sunbathing session. To do this I would need an instrument that can measure my minimal erythemal dose (MED), perhaps with an electronic skin scanner, so I can work out how much vitamin D I can make, given a particular dose of ultraviolet-B. If it could measure personal MED it would be more accurate than the skin typing used at present. Ideally, this would be combined with a personal ultraviolet-B monitor displaying the ultraviolet-B irradiance in millijoules per square centimetre. Then it should be possible to calculate how much ultraviolet-B we are getting in the sunlight, or how much is given out by a lamp. With both these instruments it should be possible to calculate how much vitamin D is made with each MED and to calculate how much exposure time we need to get a given dose of vitamin D. We would also be able to see how our MED goes up as our vitamin D status increases. It would be ideal if all this could be done by one instrument that can be worn around the neck or on the wrist, or as an app for a mobile phone.

Ultraviolet-B monitors everywhere

Personal ultraviolet-B monitors that measure ultraviolet-B in millijoules per centimetre and can be worn all day, household ultraviolet-B monitors, ground-level ultraviolet-B monitors in the street, in the park and other outdoor locations, with displays so we can all see how much ultraviolet-B is in the area and a worldwide network of ground-level ultraviolet-B monitors so that trends in regional and global ultraviolet-B can be monitored.

Better sunbeds

Sunbeds that are designed to emit ultraviolet radiation mimicking the local intensity and local spectrum and designed for making vitamin D, rather than for tanning. Sunlamps that can be easily fitted indoors, perhaps over the bed.

Outdoor facilities

Workplaces with outdoor facilities or sunlit conservatories so that workers have access to sunlight even when they have to work indoors, and all homes to have a garden, yard, balcony or conservatory so that everyone has access to sunlight at home.

Indoor sunlight

Buildings with lighting designed to emit ultraviolet-B when needed, window blinds that allow ultraviolet radiation to be controlled and architecture that maximises sunlight entry into buildings. Windows made of glass designed to maximise transmittance of ultraviolet-B.

Pharmaceutical solutions

There is enormous potential to develop pharmaceuticals to increase vitamin D in different ways. At the moment, pharmaceutical preparations of vitamin D are used for the treatment of the skin condition psoriasis. These contain a drug that is similar to calcitriol and is available on prescription, but are relatively new and untested for simply raising calcidiol levels. Further research is needed to work out the best way to raise calcidiol – we know that cholecalciferol is slightly more effective than ergocalciferol but we don't yet know how safe and effective calcidiol might be. Other ideas for increasing vitamin D are:

- Creams and sprays that can be applied to the skin that either contain cholecalciferol and/or 7-dehydrocholesterol to increase the amount of vitamin D made when exposed to ultraviolet-B.

- Drugs that block the breakdown of vitamin D, or increase the rate of conversion from precalciferol to cholecalciferol and from cholecalciferol to calcidiol.

- Drugs that lower the conversion of precalciferol to lumisterol and tachysterol so that we can make vitamin D for longer (although we don't yet know if these versions of vitamin D are functional).

Investigating the effects of existing drugs on vitamin D metabolism may produce fruitful results with regard to dealing with overweight. For example, a few studies have found that statins can increase calcidiol. These reports need to be confirmed and the mechanisms are not understood, but they suggest the possibility that statins can be used to raise vitamin D.

Weight loss in the future

When it comes to losing weight, the facilities that are already in existence can adapt their approach to incorporate vitamin D status. Instead of trying to control our eating we will be trying to raise and keep up our vitamin D levels. Perhaps we will join a club that aims to help and support us while we increase our vitamin D. We will attend weekly sessions with others and have our calcidiol measured as well as our weight. There we might get advice on how to get outdoor exercise, or just get outdoors, to increase our exposure to sunlight safely and improve our vitamin D intake through diet and supplements. Or we might read a magazine – perhaps called *The Sunlight Monitor* – that has regular features telling us about the ultraviolet-B intensity at places to go on holiday, advice on getting sunlight safely, recipes that include foods containing vitamin D, home-improvement projects which can increase the amount of sunlight coming into our homes, ideas for things to do outdoors, places to visit and pubs and restaurants where we can eat outdoors, and the best supplements to take. We might go to a sunbed facility where the lamps are designed for making vitamin D with little risk of sunburn or skin cancer. We might buy a cream or spray to put on our skin that increases the amount of vitamin D we make when exposed to ultraviolet-B. If we are severely overweight we might need to attend a vitamin D clinic where our calcidiol will be monitored and a medical professional will prescribe appropriate medication that will help to improve our vitamin D status. If we are rich, we might go to a high-altitude clinic in a beautiful setting to kick-start our weight loss.

Once we understand what we need to do to raise our vitamin D status and keep it high, the fat will just fall off by itself and stay away – *for good.* There is every reason to be optimistic that overweight can be eradicated in the future and that, if you are overweight, no matter how severely, or for how long, you can look forward to a splendid future in which you will be able to lose weight and maintain a normal weight for the rest of your life without having to restrict your diet.

Suntithenai

At this time, the beginning of the twenty-first century, we have been reminded how vulnerable we are to the forces of nature: that climate changes, and that we can take nothing for granted if we wish to survive. It is no coincidence that the title of this book echoes the title of Darwin's work *The Origin of Species*. To understand ourselves, and our problems, we need to look beyond our everyday human experience, to learn from our beginnings as humans, and the beginning of life millions of years ago. The origin of overweight is not a matter of just food, or of energy equations, it is a matter of understanding the nature of us, and all living things, and where we are in the universe. Darwin showed us that we are not so different from animals, that we are indeed animals and part of 'one grand natural system'. One hundred and fifty years later our understanding of evolution is still in its early stages but it is clear that the 'grand natural system' is probably far grander than Darwin ever envisaged. In recent years James Lovelock showed us that we can understand the Earth as a living system, and the study of physics and astronomy has shown us that even the universe seems to be evolving.

We may seemingly separate ourselves from the vagaries of nature and our environment when we protect ourselves from the climate and industrialise our food production, which we needed to do to survive, especially in cold climates. But every so often we need to remind ourselves that we are part of nature, interdependent living systems within living systems, not just dependent on nature and not just responsible for nature, but constituents of it. We are moving away from the thinking of the past – that we are special and the world is there to be used and conquered for our benefit – but we have a long way to go before we 'get' that we are no more or less important, and no more or less vulnerable than other living things, and that we still have much to learn about our fundamental physiological relationship with our environment. We have an instinct that the weather, the climate, and the well–being of the Earth are connected to our human health, but we depend on science to reveal the mechanisms.

The narrow focus on energy balance has resulted in a desperate grasping of one solution after another (by individuals, by health researchers and by public authorities), doomed to fail because they are simply different versions of the same thing, based upon the same old thinking. It is incontestable that we need scientific research in different disciplines that seem, on the face of it, entirely unconnected. This book exemplifies everything I love about science. When you hear about the research that scientists do – whether it is a study of the muscle fibres used in shivering, or where in the body a hormone receptor can be found, or a study of the life cycle of stars, or an analysis of the DNA in an ancient skeleton – you might wonder what the point is, when it seems to be of no interest to anyone in the world except for a few scientists. Yet who would imagine that all these things would be of significance in a book about overweight? No amount of research into overweight, even if it had been more scientific and rigorous, would have found the link with vitamin D deficiency, if vitamin D deficiency and many other seemingly unconnected fields were not being studied at the same time.

On 22 February, I also encountered rays alongside violet in the colour spectrum of colours – outside it – by means of horn silver. They reduced even more strongly than violet light itself and the field of these rays is very wide. More to come soon.

Johann Wilhelm Ritter in 1801

It has been difficult though not impossible to conceive how two such apparently different agencies, light and vitamin, should have the same effect.

Harry Steenbock and Archie Black in 1924

Ultraviolet radiation was discovered at the beginning of the nineteenth century by the German physicist Johann Wilhelm Ritter, who, inspired by the discovery of infrared by William Herschel, set out to look for radiation beyond the violet of the visible spectrum. He was looking for something that could not be seen, could not be felt (unlike infrared, which was discovered by its heat) and might not even exist. He found it by its ability to blacken silver chloride and he called it 'oxidising rays' to distinguish it from Herschel's 'calorific rays'. Little was made of his discovery at the time, as his contemporaries did not quite know what to make of it.

Around a hundred years later, in the early twentieth century, vitamin D was discovered by the concerted efforts of a number of nutritional scientists, who were looking for a factor that prevented the disease rickets. They established that this unknown factor was a constituent of food that also, inexplicably, seemed to be present in sunlight. It was Harry Steenbock and Archie Black who discovered that the factor could be produced in food by irradiation with ultraviolet. Perhaps in the early twenty-first century we will discover just how important both ultraviolet radiation and vitamin D are for our health and for the rest of the living world.

Chapter 10

Crisps

Short answers to 100 questions about overweight

Vitamin D

1. What is the cause of overweight?
Vitamin D deficiency.

2. If it's that simple, why didn't anyone realise earlier?
The trouble is, the amount of vitamin D we get is affected by many different things so no one is going to find the link between vitamin D and body weight just by looking at weight or just by looking at vitamin D. It is only after you have made the link that it becomes obvious. The amount of vitamin D we make can be affected by many things, as shown in the following list:

Altitude
Buildings
Climate
Clothing
Digestive health
Genotype
Ground cover (e.g. snow, grass, or concrete)
Housing
Latitude
Leisure activities (affects time spent outdoors)
Medication
Nutrition (intake of vitamin D-containing foods – eggs, fats, fish, meat, milk and dairy products)
Occupation (affects time spent outdoors)
The ozone layer
Particulates in the atmosphere (e.g. sand, smoke or dust)
Pollution from air traffic, ground traffic and industry
Season
Skin properties (e.g. skin thickness and colour)
Smoking
Solar output
Sunbathing
Sunscreen
Supplement intake.
Terrain (e.g. hillsides, valleys, basins)

3. Why are healthy levels of vitamin D underestimated?
The amount of vitamin D we need to be healthy was originally based on whether you have rickets or not, but we now know that vitamin D does more than just keep bones healthy – it is required for all-round good health. We didn't have the technology to measure vitamin D in people until a few years ago and it appears that the first estimate of healthy levels was too low. In addition, it was thought we can make all the vitamin D we need by getting a little bit of exposure to sunlight as we go about our daily business –

a view that doesn't take into account that we spend less time outdoors than in the past. Furthermore, we may not be able to make as much vitamin D today because ultraviolet-B is blocked by fossil fuel emissions.

4. Why do people who are overweight tend to have low vitamin D levels?
Overweight is *caused* by low vitamin D. To make matters worse, as the body gets bigger it needs more vitamin D to keep overall levels up and it tends to store more.

5. Why do some people who are overweight have normal vitamin D levels?
Vitamin D status is assessed by measuring the concentration of calcidiol in the blood. This reflects recent input, so it is still possible to have higher vitamin D for a short term but without it having any effect on weight (if you have been getting some sunlight recently, for example) particularly if you have been overweight for a long time. We don't yet know how low your vitamin D level has to be, or for how long, before you gain weight, or how high it has to be before you can lose weight.

6. How can losing weight result in higher vitamin D levels?
Vitamin D is stored in fat, so when you lose weight you may be releasing some of your stored vitamin D from the fat into the bloodstream. It means that if you have your calcidiol measured when you have just lost some weight, it may be higher than normal. This raised calcidiol might make you feel better and help you to keep losing weight, but it is temporary.

7. Why haven't vitamin D supplements caused weight loss in trials?
At the time of writing very few trials have been done to test whether increasing vitamin D helps with weight loss. Some trials have found small reductions in body fat and other health benefits but none has shown the dramatic effects on weight loss that you can get by dieting. (Similar trials of vitamin D for other health conditions such as cancer and cardiovascular disease have also had limited effect.) The trouble is that the trials were short and didn't actually treat the vitamin D deficiency. It might be that we just don't yet know the best way to treat vitamin D deficiency, and losing weight by taking vitamin D might take longer than using traditional methods, or it might be that removing the cause is not the cure, just as giving up smoking can help prevent lung disease but cannot cure it once the disease has set in. We need to have a better understanding of how much vitamin D we need

and the best way to treat vitamin D deficiency. In the meantime, there is no doubt that most of us, whether overweight or not, will benefit from increasing our vitamin D levels.

Cold adaptation

8. What is the point of overweight?
Overweight is a way of getting bigger so you can survive in a cold climate. The extra fat helps to keep your core body temperature from falling, even in extremely low temperatures. It also provides a store of energy to help you to survive the inevitable food shortages. The point of overweight is to protect you from cold and hunger.

9. Why would we be adapting to the cold when it's not getting colder?
We (and other living things) detect cold by an ancient, outdated method – we measure the amount of sunlight by making vitamin D. When there is not much sunlight, vitamin D falls and our bodies prepare for surviving the cold.

10. If we need to adapt to the cold, why don't we grow fur like other animals do?
It seems we lost most of our hair at some point in our evolution. It may have been to allow more sunlight to get to our skin for making vitamin D or to allow us to lose heat by sweating when temperatures are high.

11. Why is overweight associated with the metabolic syndrome?
Gaining weight is just one way of protecting our core temperature. Others include changes in the circulation and changes in energy metabolism. The metabolic syndrome is our winter metabolism. Both overweight and the metabolic syndrome together are a way of surviving extreme cold.

12. Why are the muscles of overweight people different from people of normal weight?
Some studies have revealed that overweight people tend to have more of the white fibres and fewer of the red fibres in their muscles than lean people, and that the more fat they have, the fewer the red fibres. The composition of the muscles can change and white fibres are responsible for high intensity shivering. It is theoretically possible that the fibre type changes when we become overweight so that muscle is better suited to shivering, rather than exercise. When people who are overweight go on a diet, or have bariatric surgery, those with the highest proportion of red fibres in their muscles lose

the most weight. This is one possible explanation as to why some people find it easier to lose weight than others. If you have fewer red fibres, you may be more cold-adapted than other people. If so, it will make it harder for you to lose weight, but the only way to tell is to have a muscle biopsy analysed in a laboratory.

13. Why is overweight associated with changes in fats and glucose and with insulin resistance?

Overweight is associated with high levels of glucose and fats circulating in the blood and higher amounts of fat in the muscle. Fats and glucose can be used as fuels in the muscle for exercise or shivering. When we become adapted to the cold, the muscles need an extra supply of fuels and may also need a different set of fuels for shivering than for exercise. People who are overweight and insulin resistant, or have type 2 diabetes, have higher than normal amounts of triglyceride in their muscles. Similarly, higher amounts of triglyceride are also found in the muscle of endurance-trained athletes. In athletes, the extra triglyceride is there to meet the demand for long-term exercise, but in people who are overweight it is there to meet the demand for long-term shivering. Insulin resistance refers to higher levels of glucose in the blood, which are normally lowered by insulin. This may occur because the muscle fibre type has changed and the muscles are no longer taking up glucose at the normal rate. The higher glucose level in the blood may also be necessary to provide an extra reserve of fuel.

14. Why is overweight associated with high blood pressure?

One of the ways we keep warm in the cold is by altering the constriction and dilation of the blood vessels, to prevent heat being lost from the blood to the outside air. It is possible that increased constriction is the cause of higher blood pressure in people who are overweight. This can also explain why blood pressure measurements tend to be higher in the cold.

15. Why is exercise beneficial for the metabolic syndrome?

Exercise, particularly endurance exercise, can increase the proportion (or capacity) of red fibres. Furthermore, exercise will help to use up the extra fuels that have been made available for shivering. Exercise may therefore act as a substitute for shivering.

16. Why is exercise sometimes difficult for overweight people?
When you are overweight and cold-adapted, your muscles and metabolism are more suited to shivering than to exercise. This can make exercise much harder than normal. If your muscle, for example, is composed of fewer red fibres and more white fibres you will find exercise more difficult. Endurance and power exercise such as running or weight training will be particularly hard.

17. What links hypertension, insulin resistance, dyslipidaemia and all the different alterations in metabolism found in association with overweight?
All the changes can be understood as part of our winter metabolism. Our 'normal' metabolism is suited to a warm environment, while our winter metabolism is suited to a cold one. It only appears to be abnormal and to cause problems because we are not living in the cold. Even when we live in cold climates, we create an artificial tropical climate with heating so we do not need these physiological adaptations.

18. How does the metabolic syndrome lead to diabetes and cardiovascular disease?
The winter metabolism changes the pattern of energy storage so that we have more glucose and lipids in our blood, but when we are not exposed to the cold they are not used up. So the higher glucose leads to more insulin produced until eventually the pancreas cannot produce enough insulin to keep the glucose concentration down and diabetes develops. Cardiovascular disease can result from the extra lipids in the blood forming plaques and eventually blocking blood vessels causing heart disease or stroke.

19. Why do Inuit have lower blood pressure and lipid levels in relation to body mass index or waist circumference than Canadian populations?
This could be because they are exposed to colder temperatures. The winter metabolism becomes a medical problem when we are not exposed to the cold temperatures for which our physiology has become prepared.

20. Why has the demand for air conditioning increased?
As we become adapted to the cold, we find it harder to cope with hot weather. Overweight reduces our surface area in relation to our body mass, which means we have less skin in contact with the air and lower heat loss in relation to the amount of heat we produce. Furthermore, our winter metabolism can make it harder to lose heat. All this means we are

uncomfortable at warm temperatures and need to use artificial means to keep cool.

21. Why are we getting taller as well as fatter?
There has been an increase in height as well as weight in the population. Children who are overweight tend to grow faster and end up as taller adults than their normal-weight counterparts. Once we reach adulthood, we cannot gain height, so the only way to increase our size is by getting fat, but children can get bigger by growing taller as well as fatter. Being taller means we have a lower surface area in relation to our size and more capacity to store fat and then we have a better chance of surviving in a cold environment.

22. Why do overweight children enter puberty earlier?
It has been noted that children are reaching puberty at younger ages than in the past and that overweight children tend to start puberty earlier than normal weight children. One possible explanation is that vitamin D deficiency causes the onset of earlier puberty because it maximises the chance of producing children in a cold environment in which life expectancy is low. Vitamin D deficiency could explain why earlier puberty is more common in the overweight but also affects normal weight children.

The rise in overweight

23. Why has overweight increased in the past 40 years?
Overweight has increased because vitamin D deficiency has increased in this time, but then we must ask: why has vitamin D deficiency increased? There are several reasons. In contrast to the period between the 1930s and 1960s when sunlight and vitamin D were valued, for the rest of the twentieth century their benefits were forgotten. We have been getting less sunlight and less vitamin D from our food during the period in which overweight increased. Every way in which we get vitamin D has been affected. We stopped putting babies outdoors, we stopped walking to the shops, we stopped working outdoors, we stopped sunbathing, we stopped school milk, and we ate fewer eggs and less fish. By the turn of the century there was no concern about the amount of vitamin D in the diet, while sunlight was regarded as a harmful carcinogen to be avoided at all costs. Our view of sunlight had swung from healing to hazardous and the voices of vitamin D

experts imploring that something must be done about vitamin D deficiency were falling on deaf ears.

24. But the rise in overweight has been dramatic, so is there one main cause of vitamin D deficiency?
Pollution from burning fossil fuels may have blocked the ultraviolet-B from getting to the ground and reaching our skin, which we need to make vitamin D. Emissions from transport, particularly aviation, have risen dramatically and could potentially explain the rise in overweight and its geographical distribution.

How location affects weight

25. Why is overweight more common in some countries than others?
Some countries are more vitamin D-deprived than others. Several things about the location of a country affect the amount of ultraviolet-B its inhabitants can get. The intensity of ultraviolet-B at the ground level is affected by global location (latitude), the local geography (altitude, valleys, basins, mountains) and the composition of the atmosphere (weather, pollution). These factors will also affect the amount of vitamin D in the food produced in the country. The amount of sunlight exposure people get depends upon the location, society and customs (weather, the built environment, clothing styles, employment). The amount of vitamin D in the diet will depend on the food production methods and the different foods in the local diet. In addition, the skin pigmentation of population groups differs from one country to another.

In summary, we would expect overweight to be more prevalent in urban areas, in polluted areas, at low altitudes, in valleys, in people living in tenements and tower-block housing, in people who work indoors, in people who wear extensive clothing, in people with darker skin, and in people who eat a low fat diet. Because there are so many different factors affecting vitamin D status, there is not a simple relationship between any one of the factors and overweight. To illustrate the complexity of the geographical distribution of obesity, the next questions are about a few specific examples.

26. Why are you more likely to be overweight if you live in the UK than in France?

The observation that the French have low rates of cardiovascular disease and obesity in comparison to other countries, in spite of having what is regarded as an unhealthy lifestyle – smoking, drinking a lot of wine and a diet that is rich in butter, cream, cheese, paté and pastries – has been called the French paradox. It has spawned a couple of best-selling books and led to detailed analysis of the way that French people eat and the benefits of drinking wine. But is it all about vitamin D?

Without having any data to compare vitamin D levels between the people living in the UK and France, we can infer that people living in the UK are more likely to be vitamin D deficient than people living in France. At a position between latitudes 41° N and 51° N, France lies midway between the equator and the North Pole, whereas the UK lies further north, between latitudes 49° N and 61° N. Compared to UK, France is a more rural country and may have less pollution (it is the smallest emitter of carbon dioxide of the G7 countries). The French diet is lower in carbohydrates and richer in saturated fat than the British diet, with more dairy products, particularly butter and cheese and more fish (which contain vitamin D). In France, for instance, 33 types of fish are eaten, compared to only 16 in the UK. All these factors could result in higher vitamin D levels in people living in France than those in the UK.

27. Why are you are more likely to be overweight if you live in Mississippi than in Colorado?

In 2008 the adult obesity rate in Mississippi was 32 per cent compared to only 19 per cent in Colorado. Why is there such a big difference between these two states of the same country? Latitude certainly doesn't explain it. Colorado lies between latitudes 37° N to 41° N (roughly the same latitude as Athens and Madrid). But Mississippi is further south with latitudes 30° N to 35° N (similar to Cairo 30° N and Tel Aviv 32° N). So, on the basis of latitude alone, you would expect to find more overweight among people living in Colorado than Mississippi. How about altitude? Colorado is in the Rocky Mountain region and is well known for its scenery – mountains, lakes and plains and rivers, its abundant sunshine and clear nights – whereas Mississippi is known for its humidity. The mean elevation of Colorado is

2,073 metres (6,800 ft) with the highest point Mount Elbert at 4401 metres (14,438 ft), and the lowest the Arikaree River at 1,010 metres (3,315 ft). But Mississippi is at lower altitude with a mean elevation of 91 metres (300 ft) – the highest point being Woodall Mountain at 246 metres (806 ft) and the lowest the Gulf of Mexico at 0 metres.

This difference in altitude could affect ultraviolet irradiance at ground level. It has been estimated that ultraviolet irradiance increases by 10 per cent with every kilometre, so people living in Colorado could be getting around 20 per cent more ultraviolet-B as they go about their daily business than people living in Mississippi. In addition, more than 90 per cent of the Colorado population is white, compared to 62 per cent of the Mississippi population. We can therefore immediately see two reasons – altitude and proportion of white population – why we would expect people living in Colorado to have better vitamin D status, and therefore more likely to be overweight, than people living in Mississippi.

28. Why are you more likely to be overweight if you live in Mexico City than in Paris?

A friend went on a sightseeing holiday to Paris and lost 2 kg (5 pounds) in weight. A similar holiday in Mexico City left her 3 kg (6 pounds) heavier. She was puzzled by this as she was convinced that there was no great difference in her calorie intake or output between the two holidays – she ate as well in Paris as she did in Mexico City and did as much walking in Paris as in Mexico City. At latitude 19° N, Mexico City is closer to the equator than Paris at 48° N, so the difference in latitude does not explain it. Mexico City is at 2240 metres above sea level, while Paris is at 35 metres (115 ft) to 130 metres (427 ft), so altitude does not explain it. Mexico City lies in a high altitude basin – in fact it is in the crater of an extinct volcano – and has lower atmospheric oxygen levels and stronger sunlight than lower altitudes. These geographical features contribute to a high pollution level, so high that Mexico City is one of the world's most polluted cities. The biggest contributors to pollution are sulphur dioxide and ozone, both of which absorb ultraviolet-B. Differences in the amount of blocking of ultraviolet by pollution could mean that while my friend was walking about the tourist sites, she got more ultraviolet and therefore made more vitamin D in Paris than she did in Mexico City.

29. Why are you less likely to be overweight if you live in Japan?
The low rate of overweight in Japan, combined with the longest life expectancy in the world (and lower rate of age-related diseases) has led to a comparison of Japanese diets with others and the books *Japanese Women Don't Get Old or Fat* and *The Japan Diet* by Naomi Moriyama. In Japan the typical diet is low in meat and dairy products but high in fish and shellfish. Fish, mostly fatty fish, is a major part of the diet in Japan and contributes to their higher vitamin D intake than other countries. Whale meat, seaweed and mushrooms are also eaten, all of which may be good sources of vitamin D. Japan's life expectancy is highest in Okinawa, its poorest prefecture, which contradicts the view that affluence lengthens life and the Okinawa Diet is promoted for weight loss and long life. But could it be because at latitude 26° N, Okinawa lies 1,000 kilometres south of Tokyo on the Japanese mainland and has a subtropical climate? Typical calcidiol levels are around 60 compared to 40 in the UK and the extremely low levels seen in Europe and North America in winter are rare in Okinawa.

30. Why are people who live in sunny places overweight?
Ultraviolet-B is the only component of sunlight that can produce vitamin D. It is fairly weak and is easily blocked by gases and particles in the atmosphere. Dust, sand, smoke, emissions from industry and transport, volcanic emissions and anything that changes the composition of the atmosphere can block ultraviolet without blocking the rest of sunlight. This means that even if you live in a sunny place with low ground-level pollution, it is still possible to be ultraviolet-deprived and suffer from vitamin D deficiency and you can be overweight even if you get lots of sunlight. *Sunlight does not equal ultraviolet.*

Inequalities in overweight

31. Why are some people more overweight than others?
Even at the same location, with the same diet and lifestyle, some people are more overweight than others. The main reason is that some people are more vitamin D-deficient than others. In addition to all the environmental factors affecting vitamin D (see question 2) your vitamin D status is probably affected by genetics. And even when two people have the same vitamin D

status throughout life, their weight may be different because of their dieting history.

32. Why are you more likely to be overweight if you are black than if you are white?
The darker your skin, the more of the black melanin it contains and the more ultraviolet-B is absorbed or scattered in your skin before it gets to make vitamin D. If you are black you might need to spend much longer in the sunlight to make the same amount of vitamin D than you would if you were white. You probably make less vitamin D as you go about your daily business and may have had lower vitamin D levels throughout life. If you are black and live in a middle or high latitude place like Canada or northern Europe, you might not be able to get enough sunlight to make all the vitamin D you need. You may need to take a vitamin D supplement or use a sunbed to keep your vitamin D at a healthy level.

33. Why are you more likely to be overweight if you eat processed foods than a traditional diet?
Traditional diets often contain fish, meat and dairy products containing vitamin D whereas the modern diet contains more processed foods such as biscuits and breakfast cereals, sugar and carbonated drinks, which contain little or no vitamin D. For example, when populations such as Inuit or the Pacific Islanders change from their traditional diet to a western diet, they eat less fresh fish and other seafood (the best food sources of vitamin D) and they become overweight. However, other factors, such as the blocking of ultraviolet by transport emissions may be more important.

34. Why are you more likely to be overweight if you are a king or a queen?
Kings and queens may be expected to spend much time indoors. This does not apply to members of the reigning British Royal Family who are well known for their love of the outdoors. But previous kings and queens were overweight, for example, William the Conqueror, King John, Henry VIII, Queen Anne, George IV and Queen Victoria. Suzannah Lipscomb, a research curator at Hampton Court Palace and Oxford scholar, said that the year 1536 transformed Henry VIII. In January that year, Henry fell from his horse in a jousting accident that knocked him unconscious and opened an

old leg wound. We could speculate that his injury caused a dramatic fall in vitamin D status simply because he stopped going outdoors.

35. Why are women sometimes more overweight than men?

There are no consistent differences in overweight between men and women, particularly in Europe and the USA, but statistics show quite big differences between men and women in urban areas of Middle Eastern countries. One reason women might be overweight more often than men is that their vitamin D status falls when they have a baby, and another is that men are more likely to work outdoors. The greater difference in Middle Eastern countries could be caused by differences in clothing, where veiling is common among women. The more skin covered by clothing, the less vitamin D you can make when outdoors, and extensive covering by clothing, including veiling, can leave little exposed skin in which to make vitamin D as you go about your daily business. If you wear such clothing, particularly in middle and high latitude countries, you may need to take a vitamin D supplement or use a sunbed to compensate.

36. Why are you more likely to be overweight if your friends and family are overweight?

You are likely to have similar vitamin D levels to your friends and family because they live in the same area as you and share the same activities, so are exposed to similar levels of ultraviolet-B.

37. Why are you more likely to be overweight if you are an adult than if you are a child?

There is great concern among health professionals that childhood obesity is increasing. And yet in every country, overweight is always more common in adults than in children. Overweight is increasing faster among adults than it is among children in all countries studied with the exception of Australia. Children probably have higher vitamin D levels than adults because in primary school they usually spend around half an hour in the morning and half an hour at lunchtime outdoors (except in the most extreme weather) and are more likely to spend free time outdoors playing in the garden or park. They also drink more milk than adults. As they grow up they spend less time outdoors, drink less milk, and it becomes more difficult to maintain vitamin D status.

The socioeconomic environment

38. Why does economic development increase overweight?
On a worldwide basis, there is a link between overweight and economic development. This can be seen clearly in countries where overweight becomes more common as the country experiences economic growth. In these countries, overweight has been traditionally associated with wealth but, as the economy grows, becomes more common in the poor. In general, vitamin D availability is high in ancient societies, is high among the poorer sectors in agricultural societies and is low among all sectors in industrial societies. Vitamin D deficiency spreads with economic development.

39. Why don't people who follow ancient ways of life suffer from overweight and the metabolic syndrome?
Many of the remaining hunter–gatherer groups, such as the San people of Botswana, live in tropical regions and wear little or no clothing so their exposure to ultraviolet-B is high. Those who live in the higher latitudes, for example, the Darhad, compensate for their low ultraviolet environment by having more milk, fish or meat in their diet.

40. Why is overweight more common among the wealthy in agricultural societies?
In societies based on traditional agriculture, most people work outdoors and get plenty of vitamin D. The wealthier sections of society do not need to work outdoors, so they make less vitamin D. The combination of low vitamin D and high calories means they are more likely to become overweight than the poorer sections of society.

41. Why is overweight sometimes more common in the poor in urban–industrial societies?
Within countries, there is not a strong correlation between socioeconomic status and vitamin D status, so there is not a strong association with overweight. But in general, poorer people are more likely to live in built-up environments, near industrial areas, near airports and motorways and in tenements or tower block housing lacking outdoor space.

42. Why are you more likely to be overweight if you live in an urban area than a rural one?
Urban areas have more building cover (which shades the sunlight), more concrete (which absorbs ultraviolet-B), more pollution from transport and industry (which blocks ultraviolet-B), and you are less likely, perhaps, to spend your leisure time outdoors. You may spend some time underground, in basement floors and underground railways and subways (where ultraviolet-B doesn't reach). In addition, urban areas tend to be in low-altitude valleys and basins where the ultraviolet irradiance is lower than on plateaux and hillsides.

43. Why can't various socioeconomic factors be clearly linked with overweight?
There is a popular view that people who are disadvantaged are more likely to be overweight. However, although some studies find links between overweight and social and economic factors within countries, such as divorce, living alone, poor education and unemployment, the association is often weak and other studies fail to confirm the link. Although people who live in urban-industrial areas may be at an ultraviolet-disadvantage, and some of the links with poor socioeconomic status can be explained by the higher proportion of black people in this sector, particularly in the USA, these effects are masked by the many different things influencing vitamin D status. On an individual basis, there is no direct connection between vitamin D status and economic wealth, education, employment status or family circumstances. No section of society in an urban-industrial environment is immune to vitamin D deficiency and therefore, no section of society is immune to overweight.

Food

44. How have changes in food consumption lowered vitamin D?
Over the period in which overweight has increased, we have been eating less of all the foods containing vitamin D – fish, eggs, meat and animal fat, and milk and dairy products, such as cream and butter. This is partly because food processing has moved from the home to the marketplace (so we eat less fresh food) and partly because of the drive to lower fat intake. The diet regarded as healthy today is low in vitamin D.

45. How does food processing contribute to overweight?

Food technology has resulted in the replacement of foods that contain vitamin D with foods that do not. Manufactured juice drinks have replaced milk as the standard children's drink, and butter and lard have been replaced with vegetable oils for spreading and cooking. These processed foods contain less vitamin D.

46. How do modern farming practices contribute to overweight?

The twentieth century saw a trend towards keeping livestock indoors, particularly chickens and pigs and, more recently, cows. Livestock kept indoors will have less exposure to sunlight and therefore lower vitamin D levels than those kept outdoors. The meat, milk and eggs they produce will then have less vitamin D. Farmed salmon have less vitamin D than wild salmon, possibly because the feed contains less vitamin D.

47. Do trans fats cause overweight?

The process of turning oil into fat by hydrogenation results in the production of *trans* fats, which are normally found only in small amounts in unprocessed food. Hydrogenated vegetable oils are used in many processed foods, including chocolates, biscuits, desserts, stocks and soups, as well as margarine. There is some evidence that *trans* fats in these foods can cause greater weight gain than polyunsaturated fats, even though they make up only about 7 per cent of the total fat intake in the USA. One possible explanation is that hydrogenated oils lower vitamin D intake by replacing animal fats in the diet (which contain vitamin D) with vegetable oil (which probably does not). It is also possible that vitamin D absorption or metabolism is affected by different fatty acids.

48. Do soft drinks containing high-fructose corn syrup cause overweight?

In the USA, the increase in overweight has occurred at the same time as an increase in the consumption of drinks containing high-fructose corn syrup and there is a view that these drinks may be the single cause of the increase in overweight. Much research has been conducted into this possible cause but the evidence is inconclusive. In 2007, an expert panel decided that high-fructose corn syrup has no greater effect on weight than other sources of energy. In Australia, the consumption of all forms of sugar fell during the period in which overweight increased and diabetes tripled. This has been called the Australian paradox. If there is an association, it may be because sweetened fruit-based drinks have largely replaced milk as a popular drink, particularly as the standard drink for children. Milk contains vitamin D, whereas fruit-based drinks do not.

Milk

49. How is the decline in dairy consumption related to overweight?
Over the past 30 to 40 years, we have been drinking less milk in total and switching from whole (full fat) milk and dairy products to reduced fat versions, at the same time as overweight has increased. Milk was provided in schools between the 1920s and the 1970s. Anyone born after 1980 did not receive free school milk and since then, fruit-based drinks have replaced milk as the standard children's drink. Today, children as young as two years old are given semi-skimmed milk in place of whole milk.

50. Why is full fat dairy better than reduced fat versions?
The fat of milk contains fat-soluble vitamins (as well as essential fatty acids) including vitamin D. When the fat is removed, these nutrients are also removed. Low fat dairy means low vitamin dairy.

51. What effect does milk and dairy fat have on weight and the metabolic syndrome?
Many studies done around the world have demonstrated that, in general, the more milk and dairy foods in the diet, the less likely people are to be overweight or to have the metabolic syndrome. In weight loss trials, people who were told to have more dairy lost more weight than other participants. It has also been found even though increasing dairy increases total calorie intake, it does not increase weight because it raises the metabolic rate.

52. Why do some studies show the opposite, viz. the more milk and dairy in the diet, the higher the weight?
Some studies have found that the more milk and dairy in the diet, the more weight is gained. And sometimes in the same study, it has been found that some people weigh less when they have more milk and dairy foods, while for others it is the opposite. Why these contradictory results? One possible reason is that the studies do not distinguish between low fat milk and full fat milk and dairy foods. This is because most studies assume that calcium is the

critical component, but milk contains many different nutrients, including vitamin D. Even if calcium is the critical component, vitamin D increases the absorption of calcium, so may still be important. If vitamin D is the critical component, then the effect of milk and dairy will depend on whether it is fortified with vitamin D and whether it is full fat or not. In fact, some studies in which the amount of dairy fat has been measured have found that the more dairy fat in the diet, the lower the weight of individuals.

53. Why are milk and dairy foods a better source of vitamin D than most people think?

The vitamin D content of milk appears to be very low. However, it depends on the vitamin D status of the animal at the time it was milked and may be higher in summer, for example, than in winter, but food composition tables do not take season into account. The vitamin D in milk is (like the other nutrients in milk) bioavailable – which means we are more likely to absorb it from milk than from some other foods. As well as cholecalciferol, milk also contains vitamin D in the form of calcidiol, which is a more potent form of vitamin D than cholecalciferol (and is not included in the food composition tables). Most people have milk and dairy foods on a daily basis, so even if the amount of vitamin D you get from these foods *is* small, at least you are getting some every day.

54. Why might cutting down on dairy fat make us gain weight?

When we want to lose weight, many of us cut down on dairy fat by switching from whole milk to skimmed, semi-skimmed or 1 per cent milk, and by choosing low fat versions of dairy products such as yoghurts, cream and butter. We think that by cutting down on fat and calories we will lose weight or at least not gain any more. But when we cut down on dairy fat we also cut down on fat-soluble nutrients including essential fatty acids, vitamin A, vitamin E and vitamin D. Even for children, advice to cut down on dairy fat is never accompanied by advice to replace the lost nutrients. A lower fat diet is therefore a lower nutrient diet. Furthermore, vitamin D is absorbed more easily by the digestive system when it is accompanied by fat in the diet, so even if you add vitamin D to low fat milk, it may not be absorbed so well as from whole milk. There is, in fact, no evidence that cutting down on dairy fat can prevent overweight or help us to lose weight and some evidence that it does the opposite.

The theories

55. Why doesn't the thrifty genotype hypothesis explain overweight?
The thrifty genotype hypothesis is based on the idea that we have inherited a tendency to gain weight when food is available, because weight gain enabled our ancestors to survive famines. The main weakness of this idea is that it doesn't explain why people put on weight when they do. The winter response hypothesis can explain all the things that the thrifty genotype cannot. Theoretically, surviving the cold must have been a selective pressure for some of our ancestors, in addition to famines. No thrifty genes have been discovered because genes are less important than environment as the cause of widespread overweight. Almost all of the differences between individuals can be explained by differences in vitamin D status, which is mostly affected by environment. Nevertheless, genes do have a small effect – some genes are known to make a difference to weight in rare cases and there may be others as yet unidentified that affect the way vitamin D is metabolised.

56. How does vitamin D deficiency and overweight fit in with Barker's foetal origins hypothesis?
David Barker, Professor of Clinical Epidemiology at the University of Southampton, proposed that undernutrition in the womb could cause changes that lead to coronary heart disease later in life. His hypothesis is now widely accepted and has been extended to include obesity and the metabolic syndrome. The amount of vitamin D available in the womb during foetal development will affect development. There are critical windows of development and the stage at which the foetus is exposed to the lowest and highest level of vitamin D may affect development in different ways. It is possible that low vitamin D at one or more stages will, by epigenetic modifications, predispose the baby to weight gain and metabolic changes that prepare the baby for survival in a cold climate.

57. What can vitamin D deficiency and overweight tell us about Bergmann's rule?
Bergmann's rule is that animals living in cold environments are bigger than their counterparts living in warmer places. The evidence for Bergmann's rule

has so far been conflicting and confusing. It has been assumed that the stimulus for an increase in body size in response to the cold is cold itself. It is possible that some of the contradictory observations can be explained by differences in ultraviolet radiation or vitamin D rather than temperature.

Why obesity research produces confusing results

58. Why is evidence for the obesogenic environment unclear?

The obesogenic environment is assumed to be one in which there is a plentiful food supply and low demand for exercise. But it is both low vitamin D and high calories combined that result in overweight. Without taking into to account the vitamin D availability, the research that has been done so far has been missing the primary cause of overweight.

59. Why don't obesity maps show any obvious correlation with any one factor?

The multitude of factors affecting vitamin D deficiency mean there is no simple relationship between just one of those factors (latitude, for example) and overweight. Once you start looking at all the factors, you can start to see a correlation. Any study looking at the relationship between overweight and environment would have to consider all the things listed in the answer to question 2 to observe a direct link between vitamin D deficiency and overweight.

60. Why has overweight increased even though our calorie intake and fat intake have not?

National food surveys reveal that the average calorie intake has reduced in the UK since the 1970s and, in the USA, although calorie intake has increased, the average weight gained is less than would have been predicted based on the calorie intake. It appears we can get fatter on fewer calories. The simple answer to this conundrum is that the equation *calories in minus calories out equals calories stored* cannot be applied in a strict sense to the human body. Population studies show a gradual increase in overweight, suggesting that everybody has been getting slowly fatter. That view can be misleading. In truth, in any given period, some people have gained weight fast, others slowly, some lose weight and some (most) people maintain a stable weight. There is no doubt that you need an increase in calories to gain weight initially and without an adequate supply of food a population will not be able to gain weight no matter how widespread or severe vitamin D deficiency is. But while some people are increasing their calorie intake and gaining weight, others are remaining overweight while keeping their calorie intake at a steady level, or even reducing their calorie intake. And because the body adapts to store energy and restrict energy expenditure, you can remain overweight on fewer calories than you ate when you were slim.

61. Why are people gaining weight, even though the proportion of fat in the diet has gone down?
This has been called the American paradox, although the paradox is not confined to America. There is not a direct relationship between intake of fat and weight. Vitamin D is a fat-soluble compound, so lowering fat will lower vitamin D, which will result in an increase in weight.

62. Why have studies failed to demonstrate a direct relationship between the prevalence of overweight and modern eating habits, such as the increased consumption of fast food?
The amount of food you eat is driven by your physiology and not the number or type of food outlets available where you live. Once your fatstat has risen and you need to gain weight you may be more likely to take advantage of the convenience of a fast food restaurant nearby, but you will gain weight (unless you diet) no matter how far you live from a fast food restaurant. On the other hand, if your fatstat is stable, you won't eat more just because there is a fast food restaurant in your neighbourhood. Some of the evidence can be explained by reverse causality – as we need more food to gain weight, the demand for fast food restaurants might increase, but they do not cause overweight.

63. Why have the studies failed to demonstrate a direct relationship between overweight and activity?
Nobody becomes overweight *because* they watch TV, are driven to school, or don't do enough PE. If there is a relationship it is the other way around – overweight causes energy conservation and makes exercise difficult. Inactivity does not cause overweight. Overweight causes inactivity. It has been proposed, by Terence Wilkin of the Peninsula Medical School, that we have an activitystat (just like our fatstat). Like eating, how much exercise you do is determined by your physiology, rather than your opportunities. The results of studies into the relationship between exercise and the built environment

are conflicting and confusing. If the studies were to distinguish between indoor and outdoor exercise, they might see a correlation. Walking (or any activity) outdoors usually involves exposure to sunlight and will increase your vitamin D status, so a built environment that encourages walking may result in better health and less overweight in the local population. The built environment that encourages walking is a vitamin D-friendly environment.

64. Why do some overweight people find exercise difficult?
Once you have become cold-adapted, you will be less inclined to exercise because your body is trying to conserve its energy. In addition, your muscles may become adapted to shivering and are less suited to exercise. Furthermore, prolonged vitamin D deficiency may cause muscle and bone weakness making exercise very difficult.

65. Why are efforts to improve health and weight control not working?
They do not address the real cause of overweight, which is vitamin D deficiency. Current initiatives involve encouraging exercise and healthy eating. Exercise will be beneficial if it is done outdoors. Even indoor exercise can help by using the muscles that have been prepared for shivering, but although it may stave off the metabolic syndrome and its consequences, it may not make any difference to weight, especially in the long term. In any case, many people who are overweight cannot tolerate much exercise. Healthy eating always includes lowering the amount of fat in the diet, which lowers vitamin D, so efforts to improve the diet may actually make the problem worse.

Weight gain

66. Why is weight normally stable in most people?
Normally, an increase in the amount of fatty tissue in the body would cause a switch between the activation of the energy accrual and energy dissipation circuits in your brain, so that you stop storing fat by becoming less hungry and using up energy until your body weight reaches its set point. This switching probably occurs all the time to ensure your weight remains stable even though you might eat different amounts and do different amounts of exercise from day to day. There is no need to consciously control your weight – your physiology does it for you.

67. Why is energy homeostasis normal in people who are overweight?
When overweight was less common, researchers assumed that people became overweight because of a fault in the normal mechanisms controlling body weight, but many years of research has found such problems are rare. In most people overweight occurs because the set point has been raised, but there is no fault with the system. Appetite and energy expenditure are controlled just as well when you are overweight as when you are slim.

68. Why do overweight people have high levels of leptin?
Leptin is released by the fat cells and the more fatty tissue you have, the more leptin you produce, so it is not surprising that people who are overweight have high levels of leptin. High levels of leptin are expected to lower appetite so that you go back to a normal weight, but this doesn't happen in overweight people. The reason is that the body weight set point has been raised and leptin will remain high until the set point is attained.

When leptin is given to overweight people, it does not seem to have any effect and this has led to the idea that there is leptin resistance, i.e. something has gone wrong with energy homeostasis, or (the more popular idea) that falling leptin after starving ensures weight is gained but there is no opposite effect. What actually happens in overweight is that the set point has been raised to a higher point so the level of leptin at which you switch from energy accumulation to energy dissipation is higher. Overweight people have higher levels of leptin even when their body weight is stable. Giving overweight people injections of leptin will only result in weight loss if the amount of leptin is high enough to fool the brain into thinking the body weight is higher than the set point and, of course, the levels need to be kept high by repeated injections. Furthermore, leptin is not the only signal involved and may eventually be overcome by other signals.

69. Why does post-starvation obesity occur?
While you think your fat is an extra source of energy your body doesn't need, your body regards it as essential. When you lose weight below your set point, your body will go into starvation mode *whether you are overweight or not* at the time. It adjusts the way it uses energy so that in future it will use less energy to do the same activity and when you regain weight it will be in the form of fat, even if you lost some as muscle.

70. How can you be more overweight than someone else, even though you eat less?
There is no doubt that you need to eat to gain weight and, in general, people who are overweight tend to eat more than their lean counterparts and eat more energy-dense foods. However, some overweight people claim to eat little and/or to eat a healthy diet but they are never believed. Instead, they are accused of lying and eating in secret. No doubt some do so, and it is a sign of the social stigma of overweight that eating – a perfectly natural thing that all living things need to do – has become something to be ashamed of. But it is also possible that they are telling the truth because they can maintain a high body weight on little food. After weight loss, energy expenditure is reduced and energy is more likely to be stored as fat. This means that you can remain overweight even though you eat less than you did when you were thin. It also means that to lose weight, you may need to eat much less than you did when you were a normal weight.

71. Why might we prefer to eat a chocolate bar to an apple?
When we are in a phase of energy accrual, we need to gain weight and might prefer foods with a lot of calories, like chocolate, so that we can gain the weight quicker. If we eat more energy-dense food it is not just because it is available and heavily marketed, but because we *need* it.

72. Why do we put on weight at certain times?
We put on weight when our vitamin D level drops. We don't know whether it needs to drop below a certain level (and this may differ from one person to another), whether it needs to drop for a certain time, or whether it simply needs to drop. This is something we cannot understand until further research is done. In the meantime, we can see that anything causing a drop in vitamin D will, sooner or later, cause overweight. The following questions are about some specific examples.

73. Why do we gain weight after illness or injury?
After illness, or injury, we often spend more time indoors and our vitamin D level will fall. If you stop going out every day to work or school, or if you cannot get out due to illness or disability, you will get less exposure to ultraviolet-B and your vitamin D level will fall without you being aware of it. If you spend time in hospital, your vitamin D level is certain to fall as no

efforts are made to compensate for the lack of sunlight exposure. In addition, some medication can lower vitamin D levels.

74. Why do university students sometimes gain weight?
Weight gain in the first year at university is very common. So common, in fact that in the USA it is known as Fat Fresher Syndrome, or Freshers 15 because the average student gains 15 pounds (around 7 kg). In recognition of the problem, university refectories have made more effort to provide salads rather than the traditional pie and chips. Some have gone further and introduced fitness clubs and healthy living courses and cookery classes. It is thought to occur because many students are away from home for the first time, do not know how to cook, or have the facilities to do much cooking, are inclined to drink alcohol more and eat more energy-dense convenient food away from the supervision of their parents than they do at home (paradoxically, since parents are generally blamed for their children's overweight). An alternative explanation is that intense studying involves being indoors – attending lectures and seminars, library work, reading and writing – and, particularly when students start college in the autumn term, studying might cause vitamin D levels to fall even further that they would normally at that time of year. Furthermore, freshers often live on campus and have only a short distance to travel between their residence and places of study so are not exposed to much sunlight while travelling.

75. Why do people who work in the Antarctic sometimes gain weight?
In the Antarctic, the ozone layer is thin and the snow and ice reflects ultraviolet, but because of the low angle of the Sun, the need for confinement and to wear extensive thick clothing, to protect against the cold, people who work there tend to experience a drop in their vitamin D levels. Not surprisingly, weight gain has been reported in people who work in the Antarctic as well as in expeditioners.

76. Why do people who work on submarines sometimes gain weight?
Personnel working on submarines experience a complete lack of sunlight for the period of submersion and do not normally compensate with alternative sources of vitamin D. Several studies have shown that calcidiol falls in personnel when deployed on submarines for several weeks or more. In a 1995 study, for example, 20 sailors experienced an average drop in their

calcidiol levels from 78 to 48 after 2 months and, in a 2005 study, 51 sailors experienced a drop from 65 to 50 after 49 days. Not surprisingly, it has also been reported that submariners gain weight during submersion.

77. Why do some people gain weight when they give up smoking?
Many people gain weight when they give up smoking and people who have given up smoking are more likely to be overweight than both people who have never smoked and people who continue to smoke. It is generally believed that smoking is an appetite suppressant. There has been no research on the effect of smoking on vitamin D, but it is known that smoking activates the liver enzymes that are responsible for detoxification and it is theoretically possible that smoking increases the conversion of cholecalciferol to calcidiol by stimulating the liver enzymes. If so, we would expect smokers to have a faster turnover of vitamin D, with higher calcidiol levels but lower stored cholecalciferol. This could mean that smokers become depleted of vitamin D earlier in life than non-smokers and may be another reason why smoking is bad for our health. It is possible that when you give up smoking and stop producing the higher levels of liver enzymes, your calcidiol will fall abruptly, the body weight set point will rise and you will gain weight.

Eating and weight loss

78. Why can some people eat what they like without ever gaining weight?
Some people seem to be able to eat as much as they like, never do exercise and never gain weight. These people may simply have had plenty of vitamin D throughout their lives, so their body weight set point has never changed. Another possibility is that they are unable to gain weight, in spite of vitamin D deficiency. It is at least theoretically possible, for example, that they produce more leptin than normal. If so, they have the problem that they have less capacity for storing vitamin D. Others may keep their weight down by exercise. It is important that if you are thin, you do not assume you must be getting plenty of vitamin D. Since you have less fat, your stores of cholecalciferol may be lower and it might be more important for you to maintain a regular intake of vitamin D.

79. Why do some overweight people feel addicted to food?
When the set point is higher than the body weight, you are in a state of energy accrual. You have a bigger appetite so that you will eat more and

increase your weight. Until the set point is reached you will be more hungry than usual. The more you try to restrict what you eat, the harder your body will work to make you gain weight.

80. Why is it so hard to lose weight?
Your body tries to maintain your weight to a set point or fatstat. When you try to lose weight you are trying to get your weight below the set point. At the same time, your body is trying to keep it at the set point. So if, for example, your set point is 70 kg and you want to be 60 kg, you must overcome your body's powerful homeostatic systems that are trying to keep it at 70 kg. It can be done, but it needs a project management plan, plus an enormous amount of determination, motivation and willpower and it feels like a battle because you are fighting your powerful physiology, not just your habits.

81. Why do some people seem to find it easy to lose weight?
Some people find it easier to lose weight than others because of differences in vitamin D status and dieting history. If your vitamin D level is raised, your set point will go down. If it goes down from 70 kg to 60 kg, for example, you will find it easy to lose the 10 kg. You will find that you don't want to eat so much, or you may find that you lose weight without changing what you eat or exercise. The weight will fall off (and walk out of the cat-flap) without any effort. You might be pleased with yourself that you have achieved what others cannot, without realising that it was easier for you.

For the same reason it can be easier for one person to lose weight sometimes than at other times. Firstly, your vitamin D status may be different at different times, so, for example, you might find it easier to lose weight in the summer than in the winter. Secondly, you may find it harder with each successive attempt to lose weight because each time you lose weight your body goes into a starvation mode and makes adjustments to conserve energy in future.

82. Why hasn't anyone invented a pill for losing weight that works well?
None of the weight loss drugs raise vitamin D status, so they do not treat the cause of overweight. Drugs that reduce fat absorption don't work very well because lowering appetite or reducing fat absorption has the same effect as dieting – they make the body work even harder to reach the body weight set

point. And they will also reduce the absorption of vitamin D. If you take a vitamin D supplement to counteract the absorption problem, you may find that the pills help – but it will be the vitamin D supplements, not the diet pills. Appetite suppressants usually work on the brain to make us less hungry. If you eat less because your appetite is lower, your body will find other ways of conserving energy. Appetite suppressants work in the short term but are less effective once these other mechanisms kick in.

83. Why don't low fat diets work very well?
Vitamin D is a fat-soluble vitamin, so it is found only in fat or oil (in the fat of whole milk, butter, cheese, cream, yoghurt, eggs, meat, lard and fish). When you cut down on fat intake, you also cut down on vitamin D intake. This will lower your set point even further and make losing weight even harder. Low carbohydrate diets such as the Atkins diet have been relatively successful, possibly because increasing fat helps to raise the vitamin D levels and in turn lower the set point. Furthermore, with the Atkins diet there was no overall restriction on calories, so there was no need for the body to go into starvation mode.

84. Why does sustained weight control require sustained effort?
After you have lost weight, your body is still trying to gain weight to reach the set point so you need to fight against all the powerful physiological mechanisms trying to increase your weight. The battle will go on for the rest of your life unless you can lower your set point by raising your vitamin D status.

85. Why is yo-yo dieting bad for your health?
Each time you diet, your body goes into starvation mode, doing everything it can to conserve energy, diverting resources away from non-essential to preserve the essential. It may even break down muscle in order to preserve fat and when you gain weight the regain in weight will be mainly in the form of fat rather than muscle. If you have been on diet after diet, as many overweight people have, you will gain weight much quicker and on less food than someone who has never dieted.

86. Why do people lose weight at high altitudes?
It is known that spending time at high altitudes results in weight loss. At higher altitudes the intensity of ultraviolet-B is usually greater so you can

make more vitamin D in any given time of exposure to sunlight. With a rise in vitamin D, the set point lowers and it is easier to lose weight.

Mothers and babies

87. Why do some women gain weight after childbirth?
Vitamin D is required by the growing foetus, which obtains its vitamin D as calcidiol from the mother's circulation. The amount of vitamin D-binding protein increases during pregnancy so there is more carrying capacity to cope with the amount needed for both mother and baby. During the pregnancy, the mother's vitamin D status gradually falls. By the time the baby is born, the mother's reserves can be exhausted, leaving her severely deficient for months after the birth. This could lead to excess weight gain during the pregnancy and after the birth (and perhaps to other postnatal problems). If she goes on to have more children, she will experience repeated falls in vitamin D with each birth and this can explain why mothers tend to be more overweight the more children they have.

88. Why do mothers with sons gain more weight than mothers with daughters?
I have noticed that, generally speaking, mothers with sons tend to gain more weight after childbirth than mothers with daughters. This is a personal observation and I know of no evidence for it, but if it is true, it could be because boys use more of the mother's vitamin D than girls, since it is known that there are differences between boys and girls in growth in the womb.

89. Why are you more likely to be overweight if you were born in the winter?
In the nine months you spent in your mother's womb, the amount of vitamin D available would have changed with the seasons. If you were conceived in the winter, spent your second trimester in the spring and were born in the summer, your mother's vitamin D status would have improved throughout your time in her womb. On the other hand, if you were conceived in the summer and born in the winter, vitamin D would have fallen in your second trimester and possibly deficient in the third trimester. We don't know what the requirements for vitamin D are in the womb at different times of development, so we don't know how vitamin D deficiency might affect development at different stages. Is it possible that vitamin D deficiency in the third trimester causes winter adaptation at birth? A couple of studies have shown a greater likelihood of being overweight if you were

born in the winter. However, the effect is only slight, suggesting vitamin D status throughout life is more important.

90. Why is there no clear evidence regarding the effects of breastfeeding on overweight?
Numerous studies have examined whether babies fed on formula milk are more likely to be overweight than breastfed babies, but the results are conflicting and many do not find any differences. The vitamin D status of the breastfed baby depends on the vitamin D status of the mother, the season of birth, and whether the baby has vitamin D supplements or not. It is likely that babies given formula milk or breastfed and given vitamin D drops will have higher vitamin D levels than breastfed babies who are not given vitamins. On the other hand, if the mother has a very good vitamin D status, then breastfeeding might be better. It is also possible that vitamin D status affects the ability to breastfeed. The conflicting evidence may become clear once vitamin D status of the mother and vitamin D intake of the baby are taken into account.

91. Why are babies who gain weight rapidly in the first week of life more likely to become overweight adults?
If vitamin D deficiency at birth predisposes weight gain, there is no reason why it shouldn't begin immediately after birth. It is not surprising, then, that the greater the vitamin D deficiency, the longer and heavier the baby tends to be at birth.

92. Why are you are more likely to be overweight if you have overweight parents?
The main reason is that you share your environment with your parents, so your vitamin D status will be similar in most cases. You live in the same place, you eat the same food and you may do similar activities. For example, if your parents live in a sunny area and spend much time outdoors, you will probably do the same. If your parents live in a highly polluted area, stay indoors a lot and don't eat fish or eggs, or drink milk, you will probably do the same. Your vitamin D status is therefore likely to be similar to your parents, particularly when young. Shared genetics may play a role, but the vitamin D environment is more important.

93. Why are you more likely to be overweight if your mother was older when you were born?
The increase in overweight has coincided with a rise in the average age of the first-time mother, and there is some evidence that you are more likely to be overweight if your mother was older at the time of your birth. As vitamin D tends to become depleted with age, an older mother is more likely to have become deficient in vitamin D than a younger mother. The child of an older mother is more likely to be vitamin D deficient in the womb and more likely to become cold-adapted, which could mean he or she will gain weight quicker or at higher levels of vitamin D.

Health and disease

94. Why is overweight associated with health problems?
Vitamin D deficiency can cause both overweight and disease.

95. Why is the link between overweight and some diseases stronger than others?
There are theoretically two ways in which vitamin D deficiency can be bad for your health. One is related to the winter response and is a *vitamin* deficiency and the other is due to a deficiency of the *hormone* calcitriol, which is a derivative of vitamin D. It may be possible to suffer from calcitriol deficiency without becoming overweight and to be overweight without suffering from calcitriol deficiency

- *Deficiency of the vitamin* – When vitamin D is low, we become adapted to the cold. We gain weight and our metabolism is switched to its winter setting. When we are not exposed to extreme cold, this winter metabolism becomes harmful and can lead to cardiovascular disease, diabetes and stroke. The association between overweight and these diseases is strong because they result from the consequences of being adapted to a cold climate. Other conditions such as early puberty may also result from the winter response.

- *Deficiency of the hormone* – Calcitriol is the hormone made from vitamin D. Calcitriol deficiency can result in poor health, just as any hormone deficiency can cause ill health, because there is not enough to enable normal functioning. The diseases that result are less strongly associated with overweight because they may actually be caused by other factors, but having low calcitriol leaves us more susceptible. For example, a disease may be caused by an infection (e.g. tuberculosis) that can be fought off by our immune system, but if we have calcitriol deficiency our immune system is less able to fight off the infection. An autoimmune disease (e.g. multiple sclerosis) may also be more likely when calcitriol is deficient.

96. How can overweight be good for your health?

Sometimes people who are overweight live longer than thin people – for example heart surgery patients, people with heart failure, and dialysis patients. In the elderly, overweight (though not obesity) is better for health than normal weight. Low body weight is a risk factor for osteoporosis. Overweight may help protect you from vitamin D deficiency diseases because vitamin D is stored in fat and if you are thin you have less storage capacity for vitamin D. This means that when crisis comes, the thin person may simply run out of vitamin D, particularly when elderly, while an overweight person still has some in reserve. If so, this is one good reason for staying overweight. If you are thin, it might be more important for you to ensure that you have a regular intake of vitamin D as you may have low reserves.

97. How can losing weight be bad for your health?

Losing weight can be beneficial in the short term because some of the effects of the winter metabolism may be caused directly by the presence of extra fat. Take away the fat and you take away these effects. In addition, fat is the storage depot for cholecalciferol, so when you lose fat, these stores of vitamin D are released into the blood and it is possible that they are converted to calcidiol. So as far as your brain is concerned, you have been out in the sunshine lately, your body weight set point drops a little and you feel great because you have more vitamin D available. But in the long term, your stores of vitamin D have gone down, so there is less available in an emergency. Perhaps by the time you are older, you run out of vitamin D sooner that you otherwise would have done. When you have a medical problem – an infection, say – your body cannot recover so well. This could be why people who have lost weight show an improvement in certain health measurements in the short term – their blood pressure goes down, for example – but this doesn't translate into better health and longer life in the long term.

98. Why is there a loose connection between overweight, ageing, smoking and many diseases?

It is theoretically possible that vitamin D underlies many of these observations, although it cannot be the sole cause. Vitamin D deficiency increases with age. Smoking may increase vitamin D deficiency in the long term. Signs of ageing, such as grey hair, wrinkles and baldness, could be consequences of vitamin D deficiency. So as we get older and our vitamin D drops, we show the signs of ageing and become more susceptible to illness. Smoking might hasten the process by increasing the turnover of vitamin D and lowering reserves. It doesn't mean that there aren't other causes of disease – for example, infections, exposure to toxic chemicals and so on – but perhaps with vitamin D deficiency we are less able to deal with these challenges when they come along. What for one person (with plenty of vitamin D) might be dealt with without producing any symptoms, in another person (with moderate vitamin D deficiency) could cause a short illness, and in another (with severe vitamin D deficiency) might result in a disabling or terminal disease.

99. Why do some types of medication cause weight gain?

Certain types of medication are known to cause weight gain as a side effect, particularly antipsychotics, antiepileptics, some antidepressants, insulin and other drugs that control glucose. Researchers have found that antiepileptic drugs increase the breakdown of vitamin D by activating a detoxification protein called the pregnane X receptor, which in turn increases the amount of a liver enzyme that breaks down vitamin D. Other drugs known to activate the pregnane X receptor include taxol, rifampicin and HIV-protease inhibitors such as ritonavir and saquinavir, and also the herbal medicine St. John's Wort. All these drugs may lower vitamin D when taken in the long term. It is possible that increasing vitamin D intake could overcome this side effect.

100. Why does psychiatric treatment often result in overweight?
Vitamin D deficiency is common in psychiatric patients. Admission as an inpatient in hospital, whether psychiatric or not, usually involves spending much time indoors, so we would expect vitamin D to fall soon after admission. The added problem for psychiatric patients is that many of the antipsychotic medications, such as those used to treat schizophrenia, depression and bipolar disorder, cause weight gain – as much as 27 kg (60 pounds) in some cases – which could be due to their effect on the metabolism of vitamin D. (See the notes for a list of psychotropic drugs that cause weight gain.)

Thank you for reading

APPENDIX

A summary of research findings into overweight and vitamin D

Overweight and vitamin D deficiency have things in common

Vitamin D deficiency and overweight are found in the same places and in the same people. Both are pandemic – they affect millions of people around the world. Both affect all population groups – men and women, boys and girls, rich and poor, black and white, young and old. In some populations, there is a higher prevalence in black people rather than white people, and in women rather than men for both vitamin D deficiency and overweight.

Both are risk factors for a range of diverse diseases and medical conditions including those that are very common, such as diabetes mellitus, heart disease and high blood pressure. On the other hand, the risk factors for both vitamin D deficiency and overweight are similar – living in urbanised, industrial societies. In contrast, living in rural areas, at high altitude, or in traditional hunter–gatherer or pastoral societies seems to protect from both vitamin D deficiency and overweight.

People who are overweight have low levels of vitamin D

In the 1970s, John Haddad at the Washington University Medical School developed a method for measuring vitamin D that involved measuring calcidiol, which is a form of vitamin D that circulates in the blood and is the best measure of vitamin D status. One of the first groups of people he measured with his newly developed assay was a group of patients who had undergone surgery for obesity. He found their vitamin D levels were low and it was assumed to be a result of the surgery. This made sense as bone disease was common in patients after bypass surgery and thought to be because the surgery made it more difficult to absorb fat-soluble vitamins like vitamin D.

To test this assumption, in the 1980s, Juliet Compston at Cambridge University decided to look at patients *before* they had surgery and she found their vitamin D levels were extremely low. Over the next few years, several researchers confirmed that patients who had been treated for obesity with surgery were at risk of vitamin D deficiency and other studies revealed, like Compston's, that vitamin D deficiency was common in patients with obesity even before surgery. Since then, a multitude of studies have found that people who are overweight tend to have lower levels of vitamin D and are more likely to be vitamin D deficient than people of normal weight. This is true of men, women, boys and girls. Vitamin D is also lower in people who have the metabolic syndrome – high cholesterol, high blood pressure and other abnormalities often associated with overweight.

The amount of fatty tissue is related to the amount of vitamin D

Vitamin D levels are correlated with the amount of fat in the body. There are many ways of measuring overweight – body mass index, waist circumference, waist to hip ratio, weight, total body fat, and percentage body fat. An increase in body mass index, for example, could be caused by an increase in muscle, and it is possible to have a high level of fat around the organs (visceral fat) without being defined as overweight using the body mass index. But many studies have found that vitamin D levels are inversely related to fat mass. In other words, the lower the level of vitamin D, the higher the amount of fat there is in the body. In fact, people with higher amounts of fat are three times more likely to be vitamin D deficient – even those who are not overweight. It should be pointed out that this is a general observation found when looking at a group of people. Some overweight people have high vitamin D and some thin people have low vitamin D, but when you look at a population of people – and this has been done for very large groups of thousands of people – there is a general trend between lower vitamin D and greater amount of fatty tissue in the body.

Vitamin D genes influence weight

Many gene variants have been found to affect weight and a handful of studies show that some of the gene variants known to affect vitamin D might also affect weight. But we still know very little about how genes influence vitamin D and weight.

Vitamin D is active in fat cells

Laboratory studies have shown that vitamin D is active in fat cells and can actually prevent them from developing into mature cells. We also know that the hormone calcitriol derived from vitamin D is a controller of cell development and both fat cells and bone cells originate from the same stem cells. This is a fascinating scientific area but at the moment it is not clear what role calcitriol has in the normal processes of fat cells.

Explanations

There is now no doubt that there is a link between overweight and vitamin D deficiency and researchers have hypothesised that vitamin D may play a role in obesity, but no conclusions can be made about the link. The connection could just be coincidence, both happening at the same time by chance, although this seems very unlikely since the studies find a significant correlation between them.

If there is a connection between the two, there are several possible explanations. One possibility is that vitamin D deficiency is one of the physiological and metabolic abnormalities caused by overweight. Another early idea was that people who are overweight become vitamin D deficient because they are less inclined to expose their skin to sunlight or to sunbathe. The most popular idea at the moment is that overweight leads to vitamin D deficiency – or at least it appears to – because vitamin D is measured in the blood and stored in the fat. The more fat a body has, the more storage space there is for keeping vitamin D tucked away. So people who are overweight are not really vitamin D deficient but just appear to be, because there is less circulating in their blood.

The evidence for this view comes from four observations. Firstly, a study including a large number of gene variants in thousands of people in Europe found that although body mass index genes could affect vitamin D, the variants in vitamin D genes did not affect body mass index. Secondly, vitamin D levels are related to the amount of fatty tissue more strongly than other measures of overweight such as weight, body mass index or waist circumference and this relationship is found in people of all weights, not just people who are overweight. Thirdly, when people are given vitamin D supplements the level of vitamin D in the blood rises, but the more fatty tissue they have, the less it rises. Fourthly, weight loss whether by surgery, dieting or exercise, causes an increase in vitamin D in the blood.

All this suggests that when vitamin D enters the body, it goes into fat rather than the blood. Then, when you go on a diet or weight loss programme and lose fat, the vitamin D is released into the blood. However, there is some evidence against this idea. People who have less vitamin D in their diet are more likely to be overweight and, although vitamin D in the blood rises after weight loss, it appears to be temporary and it goes back down, even when weight loss continues. The rise in vitamin D in the blood after supplementation is not related to fat in all studies. As for the genetic studies, this book shows how our environment is more important when it comes to our vitamin D status and genes can only play a small role, except in rare cases. An alternative explanation is that the larger amount of tissue means more vitamin D is required to maintain the same concentration – in other words, people who are overweight need more vitamin D and it is harder for them to get enough to avoid vitamin D deficiency.

Vitamin D deficiency predicts overweight

There is some persuasive epidemiologic evidence that vitamin D deficiency causes overweight rather than the other way around because it can predict overweight. In other words, vitamin D deficiency comes first, and then overweight follows some years later. For example, in a 2006 study of a group of children in Bogota, the children with low vitamin D had a larger amount of fat 2 years 6 months later than those with higher vitamin D. And, in 1996, in a study of 2,500 adults in Norway, those with low vitamin D were more likely to become overweight or obese over the next 11 years than those with high vitamin D. One study in Spain, by Inmaculada González-Molero, found that people were more likely to develop diabetes over the next 6 to 8 years if they had low vitamin D – in fact, not one of the people in the study whose calcidiol level was above 75 nmol/l developed diabetes. In a study starting in 2002, she also found that people with vitamin D deficiency were more likely to become obese over the next three to five years, whereas obesity did not predict vitamin D deficiency. Another interesting study found that low levels of calcidiol in mothers during pregnancy predicted higher fat mass in their children at age 4 and 6 years old.

Trials

If vitamin D deficiency causes overweight, then it should be possible to prevent overweight, and perhaps lose weight, by increasing vitamin D intake. No trials have yet been done to assess the prevention of overweight using vitamin D and, so far, only a few short-term trials of vitamin D supplementation to treat overweight have been done, with limited results. There certainly have been no reports of any dramatic weight loss by taking vitamin D and we cannot expect to take vitamin D and lose weight with the same short-term results as dieting. Vitamin D deficiency has been linked to many diseases and health conditions, but, so far, trials of supplementation have not demonstrated the results policy-makers would like to see. Policy-makers like to see solid evidence from large randomised controlled clinical trials, but controlled trials are not appropriate in this instance, since, ethically, there cannot be a control group in whom the deficiency is not corrected. Perhaps for this reason, trials of vitamin D in overweight have not aimed to correct deficiency but instead have used vitamin D supplements as if they were a drug rather than a vitamin. This is understandable when we are accustomed to seeing fast, dramatic results in the treatment of overweight and when we regard nutrient deficiencies as mild and easily reversed in a few weeks. But vitamins are not drugs and clinical trials of vitamins, while they might provide useful data, will never be able to replicate the long-term, well-nourished state. A meta–analysis of studies looking at vitamin D supplementation and premature death, found that only when vitamin D supplements were taken for three years or longer, was there any effect on mortality. It is possible that it will take three years or more of supplementation before any effect is seen on weight, but none of the trials to treat overweight have lasted that long – most are for six months or less. In this book, I argue that we are currently suffering from a profound and severe vitamin D deficiency that will require a change in the global environment. To deal with the obesity epidemic, we need long-term solutions.

Hypotheses

I hope that the hypothesis presented in this book makes sense to the people suffering from overweight in the real world. The real test of it will be in the experiences of individuals and populations in future years. Nevertheless, it is a scientific hypothesis that is testable by various methods used in mainstream science. The hypothesis is that overweight is an adaptation to the cold that is induced by the brain when it detects a fall in vitamin D. This can be split into two main hypotheses, each of which could be found to be correct independently of the other. These are:

1. That overweight is an adaptation to the cold.

2. That overweight is caused by vitamin D deficiency.

For the main hypothesis to be correct, a third hypothesis linking the two hypotheses above is required:

3. That a fall in vitamin D induces a winter response.

The first hypothesis predicts:

4. That overweight confers an advantage in the cold.

5. That losing weight lowers protection against cold.

The second hypothesis predicts:

6. That the maintenance of vitamin D sufficiency will prevent overweight (in individuals of normal weight) or result in weight loss (in overweight individuals).

7. That a fall in vitamin D status will cause overweight (in individuals of normal weight) or result in weight gain (in overweight individuals).

These hypotheses can be refined and broken down to yield many testable research questions. Testing prediction 6 will be a challenge because the definition of vitamin D sufficiency and the treatment of vitamin D deficiency are debatable, as outlined in Chapter 2 Vitamin D Poverty.

NOTES, REFERENCES AND FURTHER READING

Introduction

My article in Medical Hypotheses

Foss YJ. Vitamin D deficiency is the cause of common obesity. Med Hypotheses. 2009 Mar;72(3):314–21.

The most cited and downloaded articles in the journal

The most cited articles published in *Medical Hypotheses* since 2008, extracted from Scopus can be found on the website for Elsevier: www.elsevier.com and the most downloaded on the website of Science Direct: www.sciencedirect.com

Overweight

I use the term 'overweight' to refer to all categories of overweight and obesity, however defined. The definition of obesity varies but for adults it is usually BMI of 30 or higher, or waist measurement of more than 94 cm for men and 80 cm for women. For children you need to refer to a chart.

BMI = body mass index, which can be calculated by dividing your weight in kilograms by the square of your height in metres.

Body weights are given in kilograms. For anecdotes, body weights are also converted to their approximate equivalent in stones and pounds.

Chapter 1 Helpful Radiation

Ultraviolet

For the sake of readability, I frequently use the terms 'ultraviolet' and 'ultraviolet-B' as a shorthand for 'the ultraviolet', 'ultraviolet radiation', 'ultraviolet irradiance', 'ultraviolet light' or similar.

The measurement of ultraviolet radiation

Most people use the unit mJ/cm^2 (millijoule per square centimetre) or J/m^2 (joule per square metre).

$1\ mJ/cm^2 = 10\ J/m^2$.

Some people use the unit mW^{-s}/cm^2 (milliwatt-second per square centimetre), which is equivalent to mJ/cm^2 (a watt-second is the same as a joule).

Dose is the amount absorbed. Dose is usually measured in MED (minimal erythemal dose) which is the amount that turns a white skin perceptibly pink. This varies depending on skin type and exposure but a standard value of 250 J/m^2 is used for the UV index.

Irradiance is higher than dose as not all of it is absorbed.

The UV index is a calculated value on a linear scale from 1 to 15. One unit on the scale is the equivalent of 0.42 MED per hour.

In practice, ultraviolet irradiance at any one time and place is highly variable. In addition, the response of exposed skin is also highly variable, making predictions using these calculations very difficult.

Forms of vitamin D

There are two forms of the vitamin available:

1. Ergocalciferol, also called vitamin D_2
2. Cholecalciferol, also called vitamin D_3.

Both of these forms might be referred to as calciferol. There is just a small chemical difference between the structure of ergocalciferol and cholecalciferol but as a nutrient, cholecalciferol appears to be a little more effective than ergocalciferol.

Calcidiol and calcitriol

Inside the body calciferol may be stored or it may be converted to calcidiol. Calcidiol is the form of vitamin D that travels around in your bloodstream. How is your vitamin D status? To find out you need to have some blood taken and the concentration of vitamin D is measured. It is the concentration of calcidiol in the blood that is used to assess your vitamin D status. When we talk about vitamin D deficiency, we usually mean that the calcidiol concentration in the blood is low.

For the sake of readability, I frequently use the term 'calcidiol' or 'calcidiol level' to refer to 'serum calcidiol concentration' (often called 'serum 25-Hydroxyvitamin D concentration' or '25-OHD').

Calcidiol can in turn be converted to a hormone called calcitriol. This is the derivative of vitamin D that is involved in the development of cells, in helping us to absorb calcium and in the immune system. Calcitriol is regarded as the active form of vitamin D.

Sometimes there is confusion about whether or not vitamin D is a hormone. The simple answer is that calciferol (whether ergocalciferol/vitamin D_2 or cholecalciferol/vitamin D_3) is the vitamin and calcitriol is the hormone.

Sunlight and vitamin D

Norman AW. The history of the discovery of vitamin D and its daughter steroid hormone. Ann Nutr Metab. 2012;61(3):199-206.

Deluca HF. History of the discovery of vitamin D and its active metabolites. Bonekey Rep. 2014 Jan 8;3:479.

Holick MF, Jenkins M. The UV Advantage. 2003 ibooks.

Hobday R. The Healing Sun. 1999 Findhorn Press.

Holick MF. The Vitamin D Solution: A 3-Step Strategy to Cure Our Most Common Health Problems. 2011 Plume Books.

The website of the National Earth Science Teachers Association (NESTA) provides a good introduction to solar radiation, electromagnetic radiation and the atmosphere. The address of the home page is www.windows2universe.org and for information about ultraviolet radiation select Sun, Radiation, Electromagnetic Radiation, Ultraviolet.

UV can be used to kill bacteria in wounds

Thai TP, Keast DH, Campbell KE, Woodbury MG, Houghton PE. Effect of ultraviolet light C on bacterial colonization in chronic wounds. Ostomy Wound Manage. 2005 Oct;51(10):32–45.

UV vision in birds

Bennett ATD, Cuthill IC. Ultraviolet vision in birds: What is its function? Vision Res. 1994 Jun;34(11):147–8.

Intensity of UV required to make vitamin D

Webb AR, Kline L, Holick MF. Influence of season and latitude on the cutaneous synthesis of vitamin D_3: exposure to winter sunlight in Boston and Edmonton will not promote vitamin D_3 synthesis in human skin. J Clin Endocrinol Metab. 1988 Aug;67(2):373–8.

Matsuoka LY, Wortsman J, Haddad JG, Hollis BW. In vivo threshold for cutaneous synthesis of vitamin D_3. J Lab Clin Med. 1989 Sep;114(3):301–5.

Emissions from industry and transport block ultraviolet-B

Agarwal KS, Mughal MZ, Upadhyay P, Berry JL, Mawer EB, Pullyei JM. The impact of atmospheric pollution on vitamin D status of infants and toddlers in Delhi, India. Arch Dis Child. 2002 Aug;87(2):111–3.

Barnard WF, Saxena VK, Wenny BN, DeLuisi JJ. Daily surface UV exposure and its relationship to surface pollutant measurements. J Air Waste Manage Assoc. 2003 Feb;53(2):237–45.

Elminir HK. Sensitivity of ultraviolet solar radiation to anthropogenic air pollutants and weather conditions. Atmos Res. 2007 May;84(3):250–64.

Climate in the UK
Hulme M, Barrow E. Eds. Climate of the British Isles: Present, Past and Future. 1997 Routledge.

UV and vitamin D in urban canyons
McKinley A, Janda M, Auster J, Kimlin M. In vitro model of vitamin D synthesis by UV radiation in an Australian urban environment. Photochem Photobiol. 2011 Mar–Apr;87(2):447–51.

Glass and UV radiation
Parker JM. Professor of Glass Science and Engineering, University of Sheffield. 2011 (personal communication).

Sunscreen
Matsuoka LY, Ide L, Wortsman J, MacLaughlin JA, Holick MF. Sunscreens suppress cutaneous vitamin D_3 synthesis. J Clin Endocrinol Metab. 1987 Jun;64(6):1165–8.

Clothing
Matsuoka LY, Wortsman J, Dannenberg MJ, Hollis BW, Lu Z, Holick MF. Clothing prevents ultraviolet-B radiation-dependent photosynthesis of vitamin D_3. J Clin Endocrinol Metab. 1992 Oct;75(4):1099–103.

Effect of sunlight on skin
Rees JL. The genetics of sun sensitivity in humans. Am J Hum Genet. 2004 Nov;75(5):739–51.

Pigmentation
Slominski A, Tobin DJ, Shibarhara S, Wortsman J. Melanin pigmentation in mammalian skin and its hormonal regulation. Physiol Rev. 2004 Oct;84(4):1155–228.

Rees JL. The genetics of sun sensitivity in humans. Am. J. Hum Genet. 2004 Nov;75(5):739–51.

Matsuoka LY, Wortsman J, Haddad JG, Kolm P, Hollis BW. Racial pigmentation and the cutaneous synthesis of vitamin D. Arch Dermatol. 1991 Apr;127(4):536–8.

Tadokoro T, et al. Mechanisms of skin tanning in different racial/ethnic groups in response to ultraviolet radiation. J Invest Dermatol. 2005 Jun;124(6):1326–32.

Official vitamin D content of foods
Department of Health Manual of Nutrition (Twelfth Edition) 2012 The Stationery Office.

1978 paper states that milk contains 0.5 micrograms of vitamin D
Moore JH. Cows' milk fat and human nutrition. Proc Nutr Soc. 1978 Dec;37(3):231–40.

A study in Italy of vitamin D in cows' milk
Bulgari O, Caroli AM, Chessa S, Rizzi R, Gigliotti C. Variation of vitamin D in cow's milk and interaction with ß-lactoglobulin. Molecules. 2013 Aug 22;18(9):10122–31.

Calcidiol content of foods
Uusitalo U, Kronberg-Kippila C, Aronsson CA, Schakel S, Schoen S, Mattisson I, Reinivuo H, Silvis K, Sichert-Hellert W, Stevens M, Norris JM, Virtanen SM; The TEDDY Study Group. J Food Compost Anal. 2011 Jun;24(4–5):494–505.

Calcidiol more potent than cholecalciferol
Ovesen L, Brot C, Jakobsen J. Food contents and biological activity of 25-hydroxyvitamin D: a vitamin D metabolite to be reckoned with? Ann Nutr Metab. 2003;47(3–4):107–13.

Re-analysis of vitamin D content in foods
Hill TR, O'Brien MM, Cashman KD, Flynn A, Kiely M. Vitamin D intakes in 18–64-y-old Irish adults. Eur J Clin Nutr. 2004 Nov;58(11):1509–17.

Children's diets
Prynne CJ, Paul AA, Price GM, Day KC, Hilder WS, Wadsworth ME. Food and nutrient intake of a national sample of 4-year-old children in 1950: comparison with the 1990s. Public Health Nutr. 1999 Dec;2(4):537–47.

The Family Food Survey
Department for Environment, Food and Rural Affairs. Family Food: A report on the 2003–4 Expenditure and Food Survey. 2005 The Stationery Office.

Vitamin D in food
Fox BA, Cameron AG. Food science, nutrition and health (Sixth Edition). 1995 Edward Arnold.

Fat
Dixon LB, Ernst ND. Choose a diet that is low in saturated fat and cholesterol and moderate in total fat: subtle changes to a familiar message. J Nutr. 2001 Feb;131(2S–1):510S–526S.

The composition of foods
Foster R, Lunn J. 40th Anniversary Briefing Paper: Food availability and our changing diet. Br Nutr Found Nutr Bull. 2007 Aug;32(3):187–249.

Figure 17 shows a fall in the consumption of whole milk and rise in reduced fat milks.

Figure 20 shows falls in the consumption of butter, margarine and cooking fat.

Table 15 shows changes in the fat content of meat.

Switching from whole milk to skimmed or semi-skimmed milk
Jenkins TC, McGuire MA. Major advances in nutrition: impact on milk composition. J Dairy Sci. 2006 Apr;89(4):1302–10.

Fats required for the development of the brain and nervous system
Van de Weyer C. Changing diets, changing minds: how food affects mental wellbeing and behaviour. 2006 Sustain.

This report is available from the website of the food campaign group Sustain: www.sustainweb.org

Bourre JM. Effects of nutrients (in food) on the structure and function of the nervous system: update on dietary requirements for brain. Part 2: macronutrients. J Nutr Health Aging. 2006 Sep-Oct;10(5):386-99.

A 'healthy' diet lowers calcium and vitamin D
Merrill RM, Aldana SG. Consequences of a plant-based diet with low dairy consumption on intake of bone-relevant nutrients. J Womens Health. 2009 May;18(5):691–8.

The composition of foods changes over time
Thomas D. The mineral depletion of foods available to us as a nation (1940–2002) – a review of the Sixth Edition of McCance and Widdowson. Nutr Health. 2007;19(1–2):21–55.

Poultry
Fleming RH. Nutritional factors affecting poultry bone health. Proc Nutr Soc. 2008 May;67(2):177–83.

Fish cannot make vitamin D even when exposed to sunlight
Takeuchi A, Okano T, Sayamoto M, Sawamura S, Kobayashi T, Motosugi M, Yamakawa T. Tissue distribution of 7-dehydrocholesterol, vitamin D_3 and 25-hydroxyvitamin D_3 in several species of fishes. J Nutr Sci Vitaminol (Tokyo). 1986 Feb;32(1):13–22.

Vitamin D content of fish
Chen TC, et al. Factors that influence the cutaneous synthesis and dietary sources of vitamin D. Arch Biochem Biophys. 2007 Apr 15;460(2):213–7.

Chapter 2 Vitamin D Poverty

Circulating calcidiol is the best marker of vitamin D status
Schmidt-Gayk H, Bouillon R, Roth HJ. Measurement of vitamin D and its metabolites (calcidiol and calcitriol) and their clinical significance. Scand J Clin Lab Invest Suppl. 1997;227:35–45.

Determination of normal range for vitamin D
Haddad JG, Chyu KJ. Competitive protein-binding radioassay for 25-hydroxycholecalciferol. J Clin Endocrinol Metab. 1971 Dec;33(6):992–5.

Zittermann A. Vitamin D in preventive medicine: are we ignoring the evidence? Br J Nutr. 2003 May;89(5):552–72.

Haddock L, Corcino J, Vazquez MD. 25(OH)D serum levels in the normal Puerto Rican population and in subjects with tropical sprue and parathyroid disease. P R Health Sci J. 1982;1:85–91.

Vieth R. Critique of the considerations for establishing the tolerable upper intake level for vitamin D: critical need for revision upwards. J Nutr. 2006 Apr;136(4):1117–22.

Experts believe the 'normal' values are actually deficient
Hollis BW. Circulating 25-hydroxyvitamin D levels indicative of vitamin D sufficiency: implications for establishing a new effective dietary intake recommendation for vitamin D. J Nutr. 2005 Feb;135(2):317–22.

Vieth R. What is the optimal vitamin D status for health? Prog Biophys Mol Biol. 2006 Sep;92(1):26–32.

Dawson-Hughes B, Heaney RP, Holick MF, Lips P, Meunier PJ, Vieth R. Estimates of optimal vitamin D status. Osteoporos Int. 2005 Jul;16(7):713–6.

Vitamin D levels in Hawaiians
Binkley N, et al. Low vitamin D status despite abundant sun exposure. J Clin Endocrinol Metab. 2007 Jun;92(6):2130–5

Vitamin D levels in Maasai and Hadza
Luxwolda MF, Kuipers RS, Kema IP, Dijck-Brouwer DA, Muskiet FA. Traditionally living populations in East Africa have a mean serum 25-hydroxyvitamin D concentration of 115 nmol/l. Br J Nutr. 2012 Nov 14;108(9):1557–61.

Vitamin D supplements and bone health markers
Hollis BW. Circulating 25-hydroxyvitamin D levels indicative of vitamin D sufficiency: implications for establishing a new effective dietary intake recommendation for vitamin D. J Nutr. 2005 Feb;135(2):317–22.

Vieth R, Ladak Y, Walfish PG. Age-related changes in the 25-hydroxyvitamin D versus parathyroid hormone relationship suggest a different reason why older adults require more vitamin D. J Clin Endocrinol Metab. 2003 Jan;88(1):185–91.

Lips P. Vitamin D physiology. Prog Biophys Mol Biol. 2006 Sep;92(1):4–8.

Heaney RP, Dowell MS, Hale CA, Bendich A. Calcium absorption varies within the reference range for serum-25-hydroxyvitamin D. J Am Coll Nutr. 2003 Apr;22(2):142–6.

Bischoff-Ferrari HA, Dietrich T, Orav EJ, Dawson-Hughes B. Positive association between 25-hydroxy vitamin D levels and bone mineral density: a population-based study of younger and older adults. Am J Med. 2004 May 1:116(9):634–9.

Recommended dietary allowances
Dietary Reference Values for Food Energy and Nutrients for the UK, Department of Health 1991: Report of the Panel on DRVs of the Committee on the Medical Aspects of Food Policy (COMA). 1991 Stationery Office Books.

Fox BA, Cameron AG. Food Science, Nutrition and Health (Sixth Edition). 1995 Edward Arnold.

Vieth R. Vitamin D supplementation, 25-hydroxyvitamin D concentrations, and safety. Am J Clin Nutr. 1999 May;69(5):842–56.

Vieth R, Fraser D. Vitamin D insufficiency: no recommended dietary allowance exists for this nutrient. CMAJ. 2002 Jun 11;166(12):1541–2.

Recommended intakes
Commonwealth of Australia National Health and Medical Research Council. Nutrient reference values for Australia and New Zealand including recommended dietary intakes. 2006; 127–38.

Health Council of the Netherlands. Evaluation of the dietary reference values for vitamin D. The Hague: Health Council of the Netherlands 2012; publication no. 2012/15E.

National Research Council. Dietary reference intakes for calcium and vitamin D. 2011 The National Academies Press.

Department of Health Manual of Nutrition (Twelfth Edition). 2012 The Stationery Office.

Upper levels in Europe

European Food Safety Authority Panel on Dietetic Products, Nutrition and Allergies. Scientific opinion on the tolerable upper intake level of vitamin D. EFSA Journal 2012;10(7):2813.

Michael Holick, believes that many patients with osteomalacia are diagnosed with fibromyalgia

Holick MF. Optimal vitamin D status for the prevention and treatment of osteoporosis. Drugs Aging. 2007;24(12):1017–29.

Vitamin D is needed for much more than preventing bone disease

Holick MF, Chen TC. Vitamin D deficiency: a worldwide problem with health consequences. Am J Clin Nutr. 2008 Apr;87(4):1080S–6S.

Human milk

Dawodu A, Tsang RC. Maternal vitamin D status: Effect on milk vitamin D content and vitamin D status of breastfeeding infants. Adv Nutr. 2012 May 1;3(3):353–61.

Vitamin D in pregnancy and lactation

Hyppönen E, Boucher BJ. Avoidance of vitamin D deficiency in pregnancy in the United Kingdom: the case for a unified approach in national policy. Br J Nutr. 2010 Aug;104(3):309–14.

Wagner CL, et al. Circulating 25-hydroxyvitamin D levels in fully breastfed infants on oral vitamin D supplementation. Int J Endocrinol. 2010(2010) Article ID:235035, 5 pages.

Hollis BW, Johnson D, Hulsey TC, Ebeling M, Wagner CL. Vitamin D supplementation during pregnancy: double-blind, randomized clinical trial of safety and effectiveness. J Bone Miner Res. 2011 Oct;26(10):2341–57.

Vitamin D toxicity

Jones G. Pharmacokinetics of vitamin D toxicity. Am J Clin Nutr. 2008 Aug;88(2):582S–6S.

Soon after vitamin D was discovered, experiments showed how high doses of vitamin D resulted in excessive levels of calcium. In the earliest experiments, large doses of cod-liver oil were given to rats, and it is not possible to be sure whether the ill effects were due to vitamin D, vitamin A or some other constituent of the oil. Vitamin D_2 (ergocalciferol) was used later both for fortifying food and for treating patients. We cannot be certain that the problem is vitamin D itself. At the same time, there were reports of large doses causing no harmful effects, so the situation was somewhat confused.

Between the 1930s and 1950s there were reports of overdoses resulting from incorrect amounts of vitamin D being added to fortified foods. After the Second World War, milk in the UK was fortified with 25 micrograms per quart (just under a litre). In addition, bread, flour and cereals were fortified with vitamin D and it has been estimated that babies at the time had between 50 and 75 micrograms per day. This was blamed for an increase in a type of hypercalcaemia in babies in the 1950s. This hypercalcaemia affects babies and children from a few months to a few years old, and can result in problems with growth and development. It was noted to be higher in the UK than in Canada and the USA and this difference was thought to be because of differences in the vitamin D content of milk. However, this condition was later characterised by John C.P. Williams, a registrar at Greenlane Hospital in Auckland, and is now called Williams syndrome or Williams–Beuren syndrome. It is caused by a chromosome deletion which results in the loss of genes.

It was thought that Williams syndrome caused abnormal vitamin D metabolism, and that this was the cause of the hypercalcaemia. In other words, it was thought people with Williams syndrome are particularly sensitive to vitamin D toxicity. But since then, although abnormal vitamin D metabolism has been found in some children with Williams syndrome, others have hypercalcaemia with normal vitamin D levels and many are quite normal for both vitamin D and calcium. Furthermore, the deleted genes have all been identified and none is involved in vitamin D or calcium metabolism. Overall it is estimated that hypercalcaemia occurs in about 15 per cent of children with Williams syndrome. It is still not understood whether the rise in vitamin D intake had anything to do with hypercalcaemia in babies.

Hollis BW, Wagner CL. Assessment of dietary vitamin D requirements during pregnancy and lactation. Am J Clin Nutr. 2004 May;79(5):717–26.

Cagle AP, Waguespack SG, Buckingham BA, Shankar RR, Dimeglio LA. Severe infantile hypercalcaemia associated with Williams syndrome successfully treated with intravenously administered pamidronate. Pediatrics. 2004 Oct;114(4):1091–5.

Cuthbertson WF. Vitamin D activity of plasma in idiopathic hypercalcaemia Proc Nutr Soc. 1963;22:146–53.

Martin ND, Snodgrass GJ, Cohen RD, Porteous CE, Coldwell RD, Trafford DJ, Makin HL. Vitamin D metabolites in idiopathic infantile hypercalcaemia. Arch Dis Child. 1985 Dec;60(12):1140–3.

Medical Research Council Conference on Hypercalcaemia held in 1957
Aetiology of idiopathic hypercalcaemia. Br Med J. 1960 January 30;1(5169):335–6.

In Finland, the recommended intake of vitamin D for infants was lowered
Hollis BW, Wagner CL. Assessment of dietary vitamin D requirements during pregnancy and lactation. Am J Clin Nutr. 2004 May;79(5):717–26.

Recent studies have cast doubt upon the earlier studies that formed the basis of decisions about the recommended intakes
Heaney RP, Davies KM, Chen TC, Holick MF, Barger-Lux MJ. Human serum 25-hydroxycholecalciferol response to extended oral dosing with cholecalciferol. Am J Clin Nutr. 2003 Jan;77(1):204–10.

Bischoff-Ferrari HA, Giovannucci E, Willett WC, Dietrich T, Dawson-Hughes B. Estimation of optimal serum concentrations of 25-hydroxyvitamin D for multiple health outcomes. Am J Clin Nutr. 2006 Jul;84(1):18–28.

Enteque seco
Boland RL. *Solanum malacoxylon*: a toxic plant which affects animal calcium metabolism. Biomed Environ Sci 1988 Dec;1(4):414–23.

Braun U, Diener M, Camenzind D, Thoma R, Flückiger M. Enzootic calcinosis in goats caused by golden oat grass (*Trisetum flavescens*). Vet Rec. 2000 Feb 146;6:161–2.

Napoli JL, Reeve LE, Eisman JA, Schnoes HK, DeLuca HF. *Solanum glaucophyllum* as source of 1,25-Dihydroxyvitamin D_3. J Biol Chem. 1977 Apr 25;252(8):2580–3.

Vitamin D transportation
Haddad JG, Matsuoka LY, Hollis BW, Hu YZ, Wortsman J. Human plasma transport of vitamin D after its endogenous synthesis. J Clin Invest. 1993 Jun;91(6):2552–5.

This study compared ergocalciferol (vitamin D_2) supplements to ultraviolet exposure. It is possible that cholecalciferol (vitamin D_3) supplements would not be transported in chylomicrons; however this has not been confirmed.

Heaney RP, Horst RL, Cullen DM, Armas LA. Vitamin D_3 distribution and status in the body. J Am Coll Nutr. 2009 Jun;28(3):252–6.

Michael Holick advises that people with obesity need more vitamin D
Holick MF. MrOs is D-ficient. J Clin Endocrinol Metab. 2009 Apr;94(4):1092–3.

Robert Heaney argues low vitamin D in obesity is a matter of dilution
Drincic AT, Armas LA, Van Diest EE, Heaney RP. Volumetric dilution, rather than sequestration best explains the low vitamin D status of obesity. Obesity (Silver Spring). 2012 Jul;20(7):1444–8.

Calcidiol has to be in excess of 375 to cause hypercalcaemia
Vieth R. The mechanisms of vitamin D toxicity. Bone Miner. 1990 Dec;11(3):267–72.

Accidental overdoses of vitamin D and the role of liver enzymes
Jones G. Pharmacokinetics of vitamin D toxicity. Am J Clin Nutr. 2008 Aug;88(2):582S–6S.

Paracelsus
Deichmann WB, Henschler D, Holmsted B, Keil G. What is there that is not poison? A study of the Third Defense by Paracelsus. Arch Toxicol. 1986 Apr;58(4):207–13.

Vitamin D in pregnancy
Wagner CL, Taylor SN, Dawodu A, Johnson DD, Hollis BW. Vitamin D and its role during pregnancy in attaining optimal health of mother and fetus. Nutrients. 2012 Mar;4(3):208–30.

Calcidiol response to supplementation
Heaney RP, Armas LA, Shary JR, Bell NH, Binkley N, Hollis BW. 25-Hydroxylation of vitamin D_3: relation to circulating vitamin D_3 under various input conditions. Am J Clin Nutr. 2008 Jun;87(6):1738–42.

Vieth R, Chan PC, MacFarlane GD. Efficacy and safety of vitamin D_3 intake exceeding the lowest observed adverse effect level. Am J Clin Nutr. 2001 Feb;73(2):288–94.

Wortsman J, Matsuoka LY, Chen TC, Lu Z, Holick MF. Decreased bioavailability of vitamin D in obesity. Am J Clin Nutr. 2000 Sep;72(3):690–3. Erratum in: Am J Clin Nutr. 2003 May;77(5):1342.

Supplementation of 125 and 250 micrograms per day found safe
Heaney RP, Davies KM, Chen TC, Holick MF, Barger-Lux MJ. Human serum 25-hydroxycholecalciferol response to extended oral dosing with cholecalciferol.

Women who were breastfeeding took 160 micrograms per day with no ill effects
Wagner CL, Hulsey TC, Fanning D, Ebeling M, Hollis BW. High-dose vitamin D_3 supplementation in a cohort of breastfeeding mothers and their infants: a 6 month follow-up pilot study. Breastfeed Med. 2006 Summer;1(2):59–70.

Large single doses
Leventis P, Kiely PD. The tolerability and biochemical effects of high-dose bolus vitamin D_2 and D_3 supplementation in patients with vitamin D insufficiency. Scand J Rheumatol. 2009 Mar-Apr;38(2):149–53.

von Restorff C, Bischoff-Ferrari HA, Theiler R. High-dose oral vitamin D_3 supplementation in rheumatology patients with severe vitamin D_3 deficiency. Bone. 2009 Oct;45(4):747–9.

Diamond TH, Ho KW, Rohl PG, Meerkin M. Annual intramuscular injection of a megadose of cholecalciferol for treatment of vitamin D deficiency: efficacy and safety data. Med J Aust. 2005 Jul 4;183(1):10–12.

Participants received a single dose of 100,000 IU (2,500 micrograms) cholecalciferol
Ilahi M, Armas LA, Heaney RP. Pharmacokinetics of a single, large dose of cholecalciferol. Am J Clin Nutr. 2008 Mar;87(3):688–91.

One microgram of cholecalciferol raises calcidiol by less than 1 nmol/l
Heaney RP, Davies KM, Chen TC, Holick MF, Barger-Lux MJ. Human serum 25-hydroxycholecalciferol response to extended oral dosing with cholecalciferol. Am J Clin Nutr. 2003 Jan 77(1):204-10

This was confirmed by other studies
Binkley N, Gemar D, Engelke J, Gangnon R, Ramamurthy R, Krueger D, Drezner MK. Evaluation of ergocalciferol or cholecalciferol dosing, 1,600 IU daily or 50,000 IU monthly in older adults. J Clin Endocrinol Metab. 2011 Apr;96(4):981–8.

Aloia JF, Patel M, Dimaano R, Li-Ng M, Talwar SA, Mikhail M, Pollack S, Yeh JK. Vitamin D intake to attain a desired serum 25-hydroxyvitamin D concentration. Am J Clin Nutr. 2008 Jun;87(6):1952–8.

Although 10 micrograms makes little difference in adults, it does have a significant effect in babies
Wagner CL, et al. Circulating 25-hydroxyvitamin D levels in fully breastfed infants on oral vitamin D supplementation. Int J Endocrinol. 2010(2010) Article ID:235035, 5 pages.

The average calcidiol level is around 50 nmol/l in UK
The National Diet and Nutrition Survey: adults aged 19 to 64 years. 2004 The Stationery Office (Section 4 Blood Analytes).

Vitamin D scientists argued for higher recommended intakes
Vieth R, et al. The urgent need to recommend an intake of vitamin D that is effective. Am J Clin Nutr. 2007 Mar;85(3):649–50.

The Institute of Medicine increased Dietary Reference Intakes for vitamin D
National Research Council. Dietary Reference Intakes for calcium and vitamin D. 2011 The National Academies Press.

Fierce criticism of the IOM report
Heaney RP, Holick MF. Why the IOM recommendations for vitamin D are deficient. J Bone Miner Res. 2011 Mar;26(3):455–7.

A review of supplementation studies
Heaney RP, Armas LA, Shary JR, Bell NH, Binkley N, Hollis BW. 25-Hydroxylation of vitamin D_3: relation to circulating vitamin D_3 under various input conditions. Am J Clin Nutr. 2008 Jun;87(6):1738–42.

In this paper, Robert Heaney, Bruce Hollis and colleagues studied the metabolism of vitamin D in participants who took different amounts of vitamin D supplements or had exposure to ultraviolet-B. They assembled data from six different studies:

1. Unpublished. Eleven participants received 4,000 IU of cholecalciferol in an unpublished study by N. Bell of the University of South Carolina.

2. Wagner CL, Hulsey TC, Fanning D, Ebeling M, Hollis BW. High-dose vitamin D_3 supplementation in a cohort of breastfeeding mothers and their infants: a 6-month follow-up study. Breastfeed Med. 2006 Summer;1(2):59–70.

In this study, 19 women who were breastfeeding received either 160 micrograms per day or 10 micrograms per day. This study showed that it is safe to give 160 micrograms per day to lactating mothers. It increased the amount of vitamin D in the milk.

3. Heaney RP, Davies KM, Chen TC, Holick MF, Barger-Lux MJ. Human serum 25-hydroxycholecalciferol response to extended oral dosing with cholecalciferol. Am J Clin Nutr. 2003 Jan;77(1):204–10.

In this study, 67 healthy men living in Omaha were given different amounts cholecalciferol for approximately 20 weeks in the winter. They were split into four groups taking 0, 25, 125 or 250 micrograms per day. Their calcidiol average was 70 nmol/l at the start. It was calculated from the change in their calcidiol levels that each microgram of vitamin D raised calcidiol by 0.70 nmol/l and that they used a total of 96 micrograms of vitamin D per day. About 80 micrograms of this was obtained from the body's stores and the rest was needed in supplements to maintain their calcidiol levels. Without taking in at least 12.5 micrograms per day, their calcidiol concentration fell during the winter. Heaney concluded that healthy men seem to use 75 to 125 micrograms per day and 80 per cent of their need is obtained from stored cholecalciferol.

4. Binkley N, et al. Low vitamin D status despite abundant sun exposure. J Clin Endocrinol Metab. 2007 Jun;92(6):2130–5

Twenty participants received sunlight exposure in Hawaii.

5. Armas LA, et al. Ultraviolet-B radiation increases serum 25-hydroxyvitamin D levels: the effect of UVB dose and skin color. J Am Acad Dermatol. 2007 Oct;57(4):588–93.

Sixty-nine participants received UV (three sessions per week of UV from a light box for 4 weeks.

6. Ilahi M, Armas LAG, Heaney RP. Pharmacokinetics of a single, large dose of vitamin D_3. Am J Clin Nutr. 2008;87:688–91.

30 participants received a single dose of 100,000 IU cholecalciferol.

Notes on these dose–response studies reviewed by Heaney:

One dose of 100,000 IU (2,500 micrograms): cholecalciferol rose immediately on day 1 but calcidiol rose more slowly over the next 7 days. Calcidiol rose by 34 nmol/l. Cholecalciferol then fell rapidly back to normal over the next 7 days, but calcidiol fell slowly, going back to normal by 112 days (16 weeks, i.e. 3–4 months). This suggests cholecalciferol was converted to calcidiol at a rate of 25 micrograms per day.

4,000 IU per day (100 micrograms per day), 5,500 (137.5 micrograms) and 11,000 (275 micrograms) per day: Cholecalciferol rose over 3 weeks then plateaued. Cholecalciferol average was what you would get from 40 micrograms per day.

Calcidiol rises rapidly at first but once it gets to 80 to 100 nmol/l, it rises more slowly, suggesting that all the enzymes are sitting around waiting for more cholecalciferol to come in but once it gets to about 80 to 100 nmol/l the enzymes are busy and more has to be made to meet the demand. Overall the results suggest that all the daily input is converted at first, but after about 80 nmol/l about 40 per cent of the daily input is converted to calcidiol and the remainder is being stored.

Heaney makes three conclusions:

Firstly, at typical inputs of cholecalciferol it is all quickly converted to calcidiol.

Secondly, conversion of cholecalciferol is limited by the availability of the enzyme and when input is above about 50 micrograms per day the unconverted cholecalciferol is stored.

Thirdly, the production of calcidiol must be in excess of consumption of calcidiol.

Between 80 and 100 nmol, the calcidiol rise slows down and becomes steady, which suggests that this is the start of normal status. This is close to the 80 to 100 nmol/l at which calcium and parathyroid hormone levels become normal, so this is further evidence that calcidiol should be above 80 nmol/l.

Vitamin D intakes to maintain calcidiol
Cashman KD, et al. Estimation of the dietary requirement for vitamin D in healthy adults. Am J Clin Nutr. 2008 Dec;88(6):1535–42.

In this study 245 healthy adults in Ireland and Northern Ireland received 0, 5, 10 or 15 micrograms of vitamin D for 22 weeks between October and April 2006. Average calcidiol was around 70 nmol/l. Cashman et al. calculated that around 40 micrograms per day is required to prevent calcidiol from falling below 80 nmol in the winter. This extrapolation has been criticised by Vieth in: Vieth R. Experimentally observed vitamin D requirements are higher than extrapolated ones. Am J Clin Nutr. 2009 Oct;90(4):1114–5.

Vieth R, Chan PC, MacFarlane GD. Efficacy and safety of vitamin D_3 intake exceeding the lowest observed adverse effect level. Am J Clin Nutr. 2001 Feb;73(2):288–94.

In this study 61 healthy volunteers in Toronto had either 25 micrograms or 100 micrograms per day for 5 months starting in January. Average calcidiol at the start was 40 nmol/l. At 3 months, the peak was 69 in the 25-microgram group, 96 in 100-microgram group and remained steady for the rest of the 5 month period. This study showed that 100 micrograms is a safe dose as well as effective at raising calcidiol.

Gene variants affect calcidiol level in response to supplementation
Nimitphong H, Saetung S, Chanprasertyotin S, Chailurkit LO, Ongphiphadhanakul B. Changes in circulating 25-hydroxyvitamin D according to vitamin D-binding protein genotypes after vitamin D_3 or D_2 supplementation. Nutr J. 2013 Apr;12:39.

Many trials use 10 or 20 micrograms per day
Bischoff-Ferrari HA, Shao A, Dawson-Hughes B, Hathcock J, Giovannucci E, Willett WC. Benefit-risk assessment of vitamin D supplementation. Osteoporos Int. 2010 Jul;21(7):1121–32.

Calcidiol levels in relation to vitamin D in the diet
Lym YL, Joh HK Serum 25-hydroxyvitamin D_3 is related to fish intake and exercise in Korean adult men. Asia Pac J Clin Nutr. 2009;18(3):372–6.

Dunnigan MG, Henderson JB, Hole DJ, Barbara Mawer E, Berry JL. Meat consumption reduces the risk of nutritional rickets and osteomalacia. Br J Nutr. 2005 Dec;94(6):983–91.

Outila TA, Mattila PH, Piironen VI, Lamberg-Allardt CJ. Bioavailability of vitamin D from wild edible mushrooms (*Cantharellus tubaeformis*) as measured with a human bioassay. Am J Clin Nutr. 1999 Jan;69(1):95–8.

Nakamura K, Nashimoto M, Okuda Y, Ota T. Yamamoto M. Fish as a major source of vitamin D in the Japanese diet. Nutrition. 2002 May;18(5):415–6.

Nakamura K, Nashimoto M, Hori Y, Yamamoto M. Serum 25-hydroxyvitamin D concentrations and related dietary factors in peri- and postmenopausal Japanese women. Am J Clin Nutr. 2000 May;71(5):1161–5.

van der Meer IM, et al. Fatty fish and supplements are the greatest modifiable contributors to the serum 25-hydroxyvitamin D concentration in a multiethnic population. Clin Endocrinol (Oxf). 2008 Mar;68(3):466–72.

Vitamin D intakes based upon food composition data
Hill TR, O'Brien MM, Cashman KD, Flynn A, Kiely M. Vitamin D intakes in 18–64-y-old Irish adults. Eur J Clin Nutr. 2004 Nov;58(11):1509–17.

Vaquero MP, Sánchez-Muniz FJ, Carbajal A, García-Linares MC, García-Fernández MC, García-Arias MT. Mineral and vitamin status in elderly persons from Northwest Spain consuming an Atlantic variant of the Mediterranean diet. Ann Nutr Metab. 2004;48(3):125–33.

Nakamura K, Nashimoto M, Okuda Y, Ota T. Yamamoto M. Fish as a major source of vitamin D in the Japanese diet. Nutrition. 2002 May;18(5):415–6.

The National Diet and Nutrition Survey: adults aged 19 to 64 years. 2004 The Stationery Office.

Table 3.6 of this survey gives average daily intake of vitamins and minerals (from food sources, i.e. excluding dietary supplements) and average daily intakes as a percentage of the Reference Nutrient Intake (RNI) by sex and age of respondent.

Calvo MS, Whiting SJ, Barton CN. Vitamin D intake: A global perspective of current status. J Nutr. 2005 Feb;135(2):310–6.

Zittermann A. Vitamin D in preventive medicine: are we ignoring the evidence? Br J Nutr. 2003 May;89(5):552–72.

Räsänen M, et al. Intake of vitamin D by Finnish children aged 3 months to 3 years in relation to sociodemographic factors. Eur J Clin Nutr. 2006 Nov;60(11):1317–22.

Trends in vitamin D

Ginde AA, Liu MC, Camargo CA Jr. Demographic differences and trends of vitamin D insufficiency in the US population, 1988–2004. Arch Intern Med. 2009 Mar 23;169(6):626–32.

Calcidiol is seasonal

Hyppönen E, Power C. Hypovitaminosis D in British adults at age 45 y: nationwide cohort study of dietary and lifestyle predictors. Am J Clin Nutr. 2007 Mar;85(3):860–8.

Vitamin D is stored for later

Heaney RP, Horst RL, Cullen DM, Armas LA. Vitamin D_3 distribution and status in the body. J Am Coll Nutr. 2009 Jun;28(3):252–6.

Lawson DE, Paul AA, Black AE, Cole TJ, Mandal AR, Davie M. Relative contributions of diet and sunlight to vitamin D state in the elderly. Br Med J. 1979 Aug 4;2(6185):303–5.

Webb AR, Kift R, Durkin MT, O'Brien SJ, Vail A, Berry JL, Rhodes LE. The role of sunlight exposure in determining the vitamin D status of the UK white adult population. Br J Dermatol. 2010 Nov;163(5):1050–5.

Surveys of vitamin D status

Zittermann A. Vitamin D in preventive medicine: are we ignoring the evidence? Br J Nutr. 2003 May;89(5):552–72.

Looker AC, Dawson-Hughes B, Calvo MS, Gunter EW, Sahyoun NR. Serum 25-hydroxyvitamin D status of adolescents and adults in two seasonal subpopulations from NHANES III. Bone. 2002 May;30(5):771–7.

Yetley EA. Assessing the vitamin D status of the US population. Am J Clin Nutr. 2008 Aug;88(2):558S–64S.

Holick MF. Vitamin D: the underappreciated D-lightful hormone that is important for skeletal and cellular health. Curr Opin Endocrinol Diabetes. 2002 Feb;9(1):87–98.

Average calcidiol in UK
The National Diet and Nutrition Survey: adults aged 19 to 64 years. 2004 The Stationery Office (Section 4 Blood Analytes: Table 4.33).

Thousands of studies demonstrate a link between vitamin D deficiency and various diseases
Pludowski P, et al. Vitamin D effects on musculoskeletal health, immunity, autoimmunity, cardiovascular disease, cancer, fertility, pregnancy, dementia and mortality – a review of recent evidence. Autoimmun Rev. 2013 Aug;12(10):976–89.

Chapter 3 Atmospheric Obstruction

High pollution lowers calcidiol in children
Agarwal KS, Mughal MZ, Upadhyay P, Berry JL, Mawer EB, Puliyel JM. The impact of atmospheric pollution on vitamin D status of infants and toddlers in Delhi, India. Arch Dis Child. 2002 Aug;87(2):111–3.

Calcidiol levels were 31 nmol/l in Mori Gate compared to 68 nmol/l in Gurgaon.

Higher pollution, lower ultraviolet-B, lower calcidiol, higher weight
Hosseinpanah F, Pour SH, Heibatollahi M, Moghbel N, Asefzade S, Azizi F. The effects of air pollution on vitamin D status in healthy women: A cross sectional study. BMC Public Health. 2010 Aug 29;10:519.

Mean calcidiol was 32.5 nmol/l in Tehran compared to 45 in Ghazvin and mean body mass index was 28 in Tehran compared to 26 in Ghazvin.

Stratospheric ozone and UV estimates
United Nations Environment Programme, Environmental Effects Assessment Panel: Andrady AL, et al. Environmental effects of ozone depletion and its interactions with climate change: progress report 2011. Photochem Photobiol Sci. 2012 Jan;11(1):13–27.

See also previous reports from the United Nations Environmental Effects Assessment Panel.

Is ultraviolet increasing or decreasing?
Kazadzis S, Bais A, Arola A, Krotkov N, Kouremeti N, Meleti C. Ozone Monitoring Instrument spectral UV irradiance products: comparison with ground based measurements at an urban environment. Atmos Chem Phys. 2009 Jan;9:585–94.

Ialongo I, Casale GR, Siani AM. Comparison of total ozone and erythemal UV data from OMI with ground-based measurements at Rome station. Atmos Chem Phys. 2008 Jun;8:3283–9.

Seckmeyer G, et al. Variability of UV irradiance in Europe. Photochem Photobiol. 2008 Jan–Feb;84(1):172–9.

Kazantzidis A, et al. Comparison of satellite-derived UV irradiances with ground-based measurements at four European stations. J Geophys Res. 2006 Jul;111:D13207.

McKenzie RL, Seckmeyer G, Bais AF, Kerr JB, Madronich S. Satellite retrievals of erythemal UV dose compared with ground-based measurements at northern and southern midlatitudes. J Geophys Res. 2001 Oct;106:24051–62.

Aircraft measurements of ultraviolet
Webb AR, Stromberg IM, Li H, Bartlett LM. Airborne spectral measurements of surface reflectivity at ultraviolet and visible wavelengths. J Geophys Res. 2000 Feb;105(4):4945–8.

Palancar GG, Shetter RE, Hall SR, Toselli BM, Madronich S. Ultraviolet actinic flux in clear and cloudy atmospheres: model calculations and aircraft-based measurements. Atmos Chem Phys. 2011 Jun;11(11):5457–69.

Pollution blocks ultraviolet
Elminir HK. Sensitivity of ultraviolet solar radiation to anthropogenic air pollutants and weather conditions. Atmos Res. 2007 May;84(3):250–64.

Barnard WF, Saxena VK, Wenny BN, DeLuisi JJ. Daily surface UV exposure and its relationship to surface pollutant measurements. J Air Waste Manage Assoc. 2003 Feb;53(2):237–45.

Volcanoes
Houghton J. Global Warming: The Complete Briefing (Third Edition). 2004 Cambridge University Press.

Longo BM. The Kilauea Volcano adult health study. Nurs Res. 2009 Jan-Feb;58(1):23–31.

Binkley N, Novotny R, Krueger D, Kawahara T, Daida YG, Lensmeyer G, Hollis BW, Drezner MK. J Clin Endocrinol Metab. 2007 Jun;92(6):2130–5.

Grattan J, Rabartin R, Self S, Thordarson T. Pollution atmosphérique volcanique et mortalité en France de 1783–1784 (Volcanic air pollution and mortality in France 1783–1784). CR Geoscience. 2005;337:635–7.

Dimethyl sulphide
Lovelock JE, Maggs RJ, Rasmussen RA. Atmospheric dimethyl sulphide and the natural sulphur cycle. Nature. 1972 Jun;237:452–3.

Charlson RJ, Lovelock JE, Andreae MO, Warren SG. Oceanic phytoplankton, atmospheric sulphur, cloud albedo and climate. Nature. 1987;326:655–661.

Kniveton DR, Todd MC, Sciare J, Mihalopoulos N. The net effect of ultraviolet radiation on atmospheric dimethylsuphide over the Southern Indian Ocean. Phil Trans R Soc A. 2005;363:187–9.

Fires and dust in Australia
Kalashnikova OV, Mills FP, Eldering A, Anderson D. Application of satellite and ground-based data to investigate the UV radiative effects of Australian aerosols. Remote Sens Environ. 2006;107:65–80.

The Industrial Revolution
Fagan B. The Little Ice Age: How Climate Made History 1300–1850. 2000 Basic Books.

Kvalevåg MM, Myhre G, Lund Myhre CE. Extensive reduction of surface UV radiation since 1750 in world's populated regions. Atmos Chem Phys. 2009 Oct;9(20):7737–51.

Aircraft emissions
European Federation for Transport and Environment and Climate Action Network Europe. Clearing the Air: The Myth and Reality of Aviation and Climate Change 2006.

This document can be obtained from the website of Transport and Environment, a campaign group for greener transport based in Brussels. (The document can be found in the 2006 archive by selecting publications from the footer menu).

Aircraft emit black carbon
Hendricks J, Kärcher B, Döpelheuer, Feichter J, Lohmann U, Baumgardner D. Simulating the global atmospheric black carbon cycle: a revisit to the contribution of aircraft emissions. Atmos Chem Phys. 2004 Dec;4:2521–41.

Transport statistics
Department for Transport. Transport Statistics Great Britain (Thirty-fifth Edition). November 2009 The Stationery Office. (Table 9.1 Number of vehicles; Table 9.14 Number of cars per household; Table 9.16 Per cent adults with driving licence; Table 2.1 Number of take offs or landings; Table 2.1 Number of passengers.)

Aircraft emissions
Penner JE, Lister DH, Griggs DJ, Dokken DJ, McFarland M. (Eds). Intergovernmental Panel on Climate Change Special Report on Climate Change: Aviation and the Global Atmosphere. 1999 Cambridge University Press.

This report is available from the IPCC website: www.ipcc.ch and can be found under Assessment Reports in the Publications and Data menu.

Aviation-related ozone over the Pacific islands
Gilmore CK, Barrett SRH, Koo J, Wang Q. Temporal and spatial variability in the aviation NO*x*-related O_3 impact. Environ Res Lett. 2013 Sep;8(3):034027.

Nations with the highest prevalence of overweight
World Health Organization Global Infobase International Comparisons. Estimated Overweight and Obesity (BMI ≥ 25 kg/m^2) Prevalence, Males, Aged 15+, 2010. https://apps.who.int/infobase/

Chapter 4 The Sunlight Paradox

Skin types

The following is a list of skin types with their burning and tanning characteristics and the ancestry of people in whom each skin type is most frequently found:

Type 1: Always burns, never tans. Fair with red or blond hair and freckles. Northern European, Scandinavian and Celtic; also albinos.

Type 2: Easily burns, hardly tans. Northern European, Scandinavian and Celtic.

Type 3: Occasionally burns, gradually tans. Mediterranean and Middle Eastern.

Type 4: Rarely burns and always tans. East Asian, Indian, Pakistani.

Type 5: Seldom burns, always tans. Medium – to dark skin. African, South-east Asian, Indian, Pakistani.

Type 6: Never burns, tans darkly. Black and dark skin, black hair. African and some Asian, such as Tamils.

Sunburn can double your risk of skin cancer
This is said in many articles giving advice about sunlight protection. For one example, see the Preventing Skin Cancer page of the website of The Skin Cancer Foundation: http://skincancer.org/ (Accessed 26th March 2014.)

Statistics show that melanoma is increasing at an alarming rate
The website of the Cancer Research UK: www.cancerresearchuk.org has these statistics on its cancerstats page.

Extreme sun protection measures

In early 2014 the Skin Cancer Foundation were still recommending that sunscreen should be applied when indoors, on their website http://skincancer.org

For a while the website of the American Academy of Dermatologists recommended the use of sunscreen every day, even when indoors. This advice has now (early 2014) changed to 'every day if you will be outside'. Their position statement of November 2008 (amended 2009) stated that vitamin D should not be obtained from unprotected exposure to ultraviolet. Their website is: www.aad.org

Around the world one in every three cancers diagnosed is a skin cancer
The website of the World Health Organization: www.who.int

There are about 70,000 new cases of skin cancer diagnosed each year in the UK
Sharpe G. Skin cancer: prevalence, prevention and treatment. Clin Med. 2006 Jul-Aug;6(4):333–4.

Skin cancer facts
The website of the British Association of Dermatologists: www.bad.org.uk

Skin cancer types, incidence and risk factors
Zanetti R, et al. The multicentre south European study 'Helios'. I: Skin characteristics and sunburns in basal cell and squamous cell carcinomas of the skin. Br J Cancer. 1996 Jun;73(11):1440–6.

Pho LN, Leachman SA. Genetics of pigmentation and melanoma predisposition. G Ital Dermatol Venereol. 2010 Feb;145(1):37–45.

Rass K, Reichrath J. UV damage and DNA repair in malignant melanoma and nonmelanoma skin cancer. Adv Exp Med Biol. 2008;624:162–78.

In Queensland in the 1960s the incidence of melanoma was 16 per 100,000
Davis NC, McLeod GR, Beardmore GL, Little JH, Quinn RL, Holt J. Primary cutaneous melanoma: a report from the Queensland melanoma project. CA–Cancer J Clin. 1976 Mar-Apr;26(2):80–107.

The sun protection campaigns were modified to allow for vitamin D production
In December 2010 a consensus statement was issued by the British Association of Dermatologists, Cancer Research UK, Diabetes UK, the Multiple Sclerosis Society, the National Heart Forum, the National Osteoporosis Society and the Primary Care Dermatology Society. This statement recognises that sun exposure is the main source of vitamin D: Consensus vitamin D position statement 2010

December. A copy of the statement can be found on the websites of the respective organisations and at the NHS Livewell website under the title *How to get vitamin D from sunlight:* www.nhs.uk

Similarly, in May 2007 the Australian and New Zealand Bone and Mineral Society, the Australasian College of Dermatologists, The Cancer Council Australia, and Osteoporosis Australia issued a consensus statement recommending a few minutes of exposure to sunlight on the face, arms and hands on most days of the week, and longer for those in southern Australia.

Risks and benefits of sun exposure: position statement. 3 May 2007. From the website of the Australasian College of Dermatologists: www.dermcoll.edu.au

Worldwide incidence of melanoma (and other cancers)
Ferlay J, Shin HR, Bray F, Forman D, Mathers C, Parkin DM. Estimates of worldwide burden of cancer in 2008: GLOBOCAN 2008. Int J Cancer. 2010 Dec 15;127(12):2893–917.

Here is a list of the countries with the highest rates of melanoma in 2008 in people aged under 75 years. These were taken from a database on the website of the International Agency for Research on Cancer GLOBOCAN: http://globocan.iarc.fr

These countries have an age standardised rate (ASR) above 30:

Australia, New Zealand

The following countries have an ASR between 15 and 20:

Switzerland, Denmark, Norway, Netherlands, Sweden

These countries have an ASR between 10 and 15:

Slovenia, USA, Ireland, UK, Czech Republic, Germany, Iceland, Canada, Finland, Belgium, Israel.

It is rare in Africa (apart from South Africa where the ASR is 6.2) and Asia (ASR is less than 1)

Note: Explanation of age-standardised rate (ASR): the number of cases of cancer per 100,000 people is adjusted to take into account the age distribution in populations. This avoids misleading differences in the statistics between populations that are due to age – for example, a country might have a higher rate of cancer because it has a higher proportion of people aged over 60.

For comparison:

The ASR for breast cancer is 85 in Australia, and 76 in USA, and 101 in Denmark. The ASR for colorectal cancer is 25 in USA, 33 in Denmark and 32 in Australia.

The ASR for prostate cancer is 105 in Australia, 72 in Denmark, 84 in USA.

Denmark has a high rate of non-melanoma skin cancer
Birch-Johansen F, Jensen A, Mortensen L, Olesen AB, Kjær SK. Trends in the incidence of nonmelanoma skin cancer in Denmark 1978–2007: Rapid incidence increase among young Danish women. Int J Cancer. 2010 Nov 1;127(9):2190–8.

Between 1978 and 2007, the age adjusted basal cell carcinoma incidence increased from 27.1 to 96.6 cases per 100,000 persons for women and from 34.2 to 91.2 for men. The squamous cell carcinoma incidence increased from 4.6 to 12.0 cases per 100,000 for women and 9.7 to 19.1 for men.

Iceland has a relatively high rate of skin cancer
Héry C, Tryggvadóttir L, Sigurdsson T, Olafsdóttir E, Sigurgeirsson B, Jonasson JG, Olafsson JH, Boniol M, Byrnes GB, Doré JF, Autier P. A melanoma epidemic in Iceland: possible influence of sunbed use. Am J Epidemiol. 2010 Oct 1;172(7):762–7.

Vitamin D deficiency can occur in Australia and New Zealand
Working Group of the Australian and New Zealand Bone and Mineral Society; Endocrine Society of Australia; Osteoporosis Australia. Vitamin D and adult bone health in Australia and New Zealand: a position statement. Med J Aust. 2005 Mar 21;182(6):281–5.

Mithal A, et al. IOF Committee of Scientific Advisors (CSA) Nutrition Working Group. Global vitamin D status and determinants of hypovitaminosis D. Osteoporos Int. 2009 Nov;20(11):1807–20.

Sandhu SK, Lee P, Center JR, Eisman JA. Vitamin D status in Oceania. International Osteoporosis Foundation 2009. Retrieved from the website of the International Osteoporosis Foundation: www.iofbonehealth.org (Accessed 16th March 2014.)

Vitamin D deficiency in Australia
Kimlin M, Harrison S, Nowak M, Moore M, Brodie A, Lang C. Does a high UV environment ensure adequate vitamin D status? J Photochem Photobiol B. 2007 Dec 14;89(2–3):139–47.

Erbas B, Ebeling PR, Couch D, Wark JD. Suburban clustering of vitamin D deficiency in Melbourne, Australia. Asia Pac J Clin Nutr. 2008;17(1):63–7.

Teale GR, Cunningham CE. Vitamin D deficiency is common among pregnant women in rural Victoria. Aust N Z J Obstet Gynaecol. 2010 Jun;50(3):259–61.

Vitamin D deficiency in New Zealand

Bartley J. Prevalence of vitamin D deficiency among patients attending a multidisciplinary tertiary pain clinic. N Z Med J. 2008 Nov 28;121(1286):57–62.

Judkins A, Eagleton C. Vitamin D deficiency in pregnant New Zealand women. N Z Med J 2006 Sep 8;119(1241):U2144.

Skin cancer and vitamin D might not be mutually exclusive

Tang JY, et al. Osteoporotic Fractures in Men (MrOS) Study Group. Inverse association between serum 25(OH) vitamin D levels and non-melanoma skin cancer in elderly men. Cancer Causes Control. 2010 Mar;21(3):387–91.

This study found that men with the highest calcidiol were the least likely to have suffered from skin cancer.

Vinceti M, et al. Inverse association between dietary vitamin D and risk of cutaneous melanoma in a northern Italy population. Nutr Cancer. 2011 May;63(4):506–13.

This study found that people with the lowest intake of vitamin D from their diet had the highest risk of melanoma.

Newton-Bishop JA, et al. Serum 25-hydroxyvitamin D_3 levels are associated with Breslow thickness at presentation and survival from melanoma. J Clin Oncol. 2009 Nov 10;27(32):5439–44.

Nürnberg B, Gräber S, Gärtner B, Geisel J, Pföhler C, Schadendorf D, Tilgen W, Reichrath J. Reduced serum 25-hydroxyvitamin D levels in stage IV melanoma patients. Anticancer Res. 2009 Sep;29(9):3669–74.

The above two studies found that higher vitamin D levels are associated with better survival from melanoma

We should be careful about making assumptions that fair-skinned people are less likely to be vitamin D deficient

Glass D, Lens M, Swaminathan R, Spector TD, Bataille V. Pigmentation and vitamin D metabolism in Caucasians: low vitamin D serum levels in fair skin types in the UK. PLoS One. 2009 Aug 3;4(8):e6477.

Holidays abroad could be the main cause of the increase in melanoma

Agredano YZ, Chan JL, Kimball RC, Kimball AB. Accessibility to air travel correlates strongly with increasing melanoma incidence. Melanoma Res. 2006 Feb;16(1):77–81.

Patients with xeroderma pigmentosum and kidney transplant patients have low calcidiol
Reichrath J, Nürnberg B. Cutaneous vitamin D synthesis versus skin cancer development: The Janus faces of solar UV radiation. Dermatoendocrinol. 2009 Sep;1(5):253–61.

Sunburn is more likely to occur in people on holiday or on a day off from work and is less likely in people who spend a lot of time outdoors, such as gardeners and golfers
Thieden E, Philipsen PA, Sandby-Møller J, Wulf HC. Sunburn related to UV radiation exposure, age, sex, occupation, and sun bed use based on time-stamped personal dosimetry and sun behaviour diaries. Arch Dermatol. 2005 Apr;141(4):482–8.

Evidence that diet can affect the photosensitivity of the skin
Sies H, Stahl W. Carotenoids and UV protection. Photochem Photobiol Sci. 2004 Aug;3(8):749–52.

Rhodes LE, O'Farrell S, Jackson MJ, Friedmann PS. Dietary fish-oil supplementation in humans reduces UVB-erythemal sensitivity but increases epidermal lipid peroxidation. J Invest Dermatol. 1994 Aug;103(2):151–4.

Stahl W, Sies H, Carotenoids and flavonoids contribute to nutritional protection against skin damage from sunlight. Mol Biotechnol. 2007 Sep;37(1):26–30.

Jackson MJ, Jackson MJ, McArdle F, Storey A, Jones SA, McArdle A, Rhodes LE. Effects of micronutrient supplements on u.v.-induced skin damage. Proc Nutr Soc. 2002 May;61(2):187–9.

Other cancers are also increasing in incidence
Héry C, Ferlay J, Boniol M, Autier P. Changes in breast cancer incidence and mortality in middle-aged and elderly women in 28 countries with Caucasian majority populations. Ann Oncol. 2008 May;19(5):1009–18.

Review of the evidence for vitamin D in melanoma
Egan KM. Vitamin D and melanoma. Ann Epidemiol. 2009 Jul;19(7):455–61.

Tributes to Frank Garland
Reichrath J. Dermato-Endocrinology remembers Dr. Frank C. Garland: A great scientist who made major contributions to improve our understanding about the importance of vitamin D for human health! Dermatoendocrinol. 2010 Apr;2(2):43–5.

Grant WB, Gorham ED. Dr. Frank Caldwell Garland, June 20 1950 – August 17 2010. Dermatoendocrinol. 2010 Apr;2(2):46–9.

The first paper from the Garland brothers linking vitamin D deficiency to cancer
Garland CF, Garland FC. Do sunlight and vitamin D reduce the likelihood of colon cancer? Int J Epidemiol. 1980 Sep;9(3):227–31.

The Garland brothers question the role of sunscreens
Garland CF, Garland FC, Gorham ED. Rising trends in melanoma. An hypothesis concerning sunscreen effectiveness. Ann Epidemiol. 1993 Jan;3(1):103–10.

Raising calcidiol could prevent deaths from cancer
Giovannucci E, Liu Y, Rimm EB, Hollis BW, Fuchs CS, Stampfer MJ, Willett WC. Prospective study of predictors of vitamin D status and cancer incidence and mortality in men. J Natl Cancer Inst. 2006 Apr 5;98(7):451–9.

Sunlight was used as medicine at the beginning of the twentieth century
Hobday R. The Healing Sun. 1999 Findhorn Press.

The disease burden of ultraviolet exposure in the year 2000 compared to the disease burden if ultraviolet exposure was lowered
Lucas RM, McMichael AJ, Armstrong BK, Smith WT. Estimating the global disease burden due to ultraviolet radiation exposure. Int J Epidemiol. 2008 Jun;37(3):654–67.

Chapter 5 Fatstat Facts

Leptin
Zhang Y, Proenca R, Maffei M, Barone M, Leopold L, Friedman JM. Positional cloning of the mouse obese gene and its human homologue. Nature. 1994 Dec 1;372(6505):425–32.

Rosenbaum M, et al. Low-dose leptin reverses skeletal muscle, autonomic, and neuroendocrine adaptations to maintenance of reduced weight. J Clin Invest. 2005 Dec;115(12):3579–86.

Hamrick MW. Leptin, bone mass and the thrifty phenotype. J Bone Miner Res. 2004 Oct;19(10):1607–11.

Energy homeostasis
Korner J, Aronne LJ. The emerging science of body weight regulation and its impact on obesity treatment. J Clin Invest. 2003 Mar;111(5):565–70.

Schwartz MW, Niswender KD. Adiposity signaling and biological defense against weight gain: absence of protection or central hormone resistance? J Clin Endocrinol Metab. 2004 Dec;89(12):5889–97.

Wynne K, Stanley S, McGowan N, Bloom S. Appetite control. J Endocrinol. 2005 Feb;184(2):291–318.

Bradbury J. What makes mice fat? How the brain controls energy balance. PLoS Biol. 2005 Nov;3(12).

Marks DL, Cone RD. Central melanocortins and the regulation of weight during acute and chronic disease. Recent Prog Horm Res. 2001;56:359–75.

Zigman JM, et al. Mice lacking ghrelin receptors resist the development of diet-induced obesity. J Clin Invest. 2005 Dec;115(12):3564–72.

Schwartz GJ. Biology of eating behaviour in obesity. Obes Res. 2004 Nov;12 Suppl 2:102S–6S.

Cholecystokinin was one of the first signals discovered
Ivy AC, Goldberg E. A hormone mechanism gall-bladder contraction and evacuation Am J Physiol. 1928 Oct;86(3):599–613.

Antinutrient phytate
Bohn T, Davidsson L, Walczyk T, Hurrell RF. Fractional magnesium absorption is significantly lower in human subjects from a meal served with an oxalate-rich vegetable. Br J Nutr. 2004 Apr;91(4):601–6.

Urbano G, López-Jurado M, Aranda P, Vidal-Valverde C, Tenorio E, Porres J. The role of phytic acid in legumes: antinutrient or benefical function? J Physiol Biochem. 2000 Sep;56(3):283–94.

Sandberg AS. Bioavailability of minerals in legumes. Br J Nutr. 2002 Dec;88 Suppl 3:S281–5.

Calcium and fat absorption
Jacobsen R, Lorenzen JK, Toubro S, Krog-Mikkelsen I, Astrup A. Effect of short-term high dietary calcium intake on 24-h energy expenditure, fat oxidation, and fecal fat excretion. Int J Obes (Lond). 2005 Mar;29(3):292–301.

Melanocortins
Garcia-Borrón JC, Sánchez-Laorden BL, Jiménez-Cervantes C. Melanocortin-1 receptor structure and functional regulation. Pigment Cell Res. 2005 Dec;19(6):393–410.

Bariatric surgery
Morínigo R, Casamitjana R, Moizé V, Lacy AM, Delgado S, Gomis R, Vidal J. Short-term effects of gastric bypass surgery on circulating ghrelin levels. Obes Res. 2004 Jul;12(7):1108–16.

Minnesota experiment
Kalm LM, Semba RD. They starved so that others be better fed: remembering Ancel Keys and the Minnesota experiment. J Nutr. 2005 Jun;135(6):1347–52.

The Biosphere 2 experiment
Weyer C, Walford RL, Harper IT, Milner M, MacCallum T, Tataranni PA, Ravussin E. Energy metabolism after two years of energy restriction: the biosphere 2 experiment. Am J Clin Nutr. 2000 Oct;72(4);946–53.

Energy expenditure is reduced after weight loss
Doucet E, et al. Greater than predicted decrease in energy expenditure during exercise after body weight loss in obese men. Clin Sci (Lond). 2003 Jul;105(1):89–95.

Rosenbaum M, Hirsch J, Gallagher DA, Leibel RL. Long-term persistence of adaptive thermogenesis in subjects who have maintained a reduced body weight. Am J Clin Nutr. 2008 Oct:88(4):906–12.

Theory of a disorder of energy homeostasis as the cause of obesity
Schwartz MW, Niswender KD. Adiposity signalling and biological defense against weight gain: Absence of protection or central hormone resistance? J Clin Endocrinol Metab. 2004 Dec;89(12):5889–97.

The thrifty genotype hypothesis
Neel JV. Diabetes mellitus: a 'thrifty' genotype rendered detrimental by 'progress'? Am J Hum Genet. 1962 Dec;14:353–62.

The body weight set point
Kennedy GC. The role of depot fat in the hypothalamic control of food intake in the rat. Proc R Soc Lond B Biol Sci. 1953 Jan 15;140(901):578–96.

Weigle DS. Human obesity. Exploding the myths. West J Med. 1990 Oct;153(4):421–8.

Speakman JR, et al. Set points, settling points and some alternative models: theoretical options to understand how genes and environments combine to regulate body adiposity. Dis Model Mech. 2011 Nov;4(6):733–45.

Chapter 6 Ice Age Endurance

The heaviest person recorded
Glenday C. (Ed.) Guinness World Records. 2012 Guinness World Records Ltd.

Information about the world's heaviest man is on page 084.

Energy metabolism in cold
Westerterp-Plantenga MS, van Marken Lichtenbelt WD, Cilissen C, Top S. Energy metabolism in women during short exposure to the thermoneutral zone. Physiol Behav. 2002 Feb 75(1–2):227–35.

Survival in cold water
Keatinge WR, Coleshaw SR, Millard CE, Axelsson J. Exceptional case of survival in cold water. Br Med J (Clin Res Ed). 1986 Jan 18;292(6514):171–2.

Tall people earn more money than short people
Case A, Paxson C. Stature and status: height, ability, and labor market outcomes. J Polit Econ. 2008 116(3):499–532.

George Orwell's slogan
Orwell G. Animal Farm: A Fairy Story. 1945 Secker and Warburg.

Size and metabolism
Kanwisher J. Temperature regulation. In: Introduction to Comparative Physiology. Goldstein LA. (Ed.). 1977 Holt, Rinehart and Winston.

Cope's rule
Cope ED. The Origin of the Fittest. 1887 Appleton.

Bergmann's rule
Bergmann C. Über die Verhältnisse der Wärmeőkonomie der Thiere zu ihrer Grősse. Gőttinger Studien. 1847 pt. 1:595–708.

Meiri S, Dayan T. On the validity of Bergmann's rule. J Biogeogr. 2003 Mar;30(3):331–51.

Rodríguez M, Olalla-Tárraga MÁ, Hawkins BA. Bergmann's rule and the geography of mammal body size in the Western Hemisphere. Global Ecol Biogeogr. 2008;17:274–83.

Allen's rule
Allen JA. The influence of physical conditions in the genesis of species. Radical Rev. 1877;1:108–40.

Gloger's rule
Gloger CL. Das Abändern der Vögel durch Einfluss des Klimas. 1833.

Ostracodes
Hunt F, Roy K. Climate change, body size evolution, and Cope's Rule in deep-sea ostracodes. Proc Natl Acad Sci USA. 2006 Jan;103(5):1347–52.

How birds and animals cope with the cold
Marchand PJ. Life in the Cold: An Introduction to Winter Ecology (Third Edition). 1996 University Press of New England.

Willmer P, Stone G, Johnston I. Environmental Physiology of Animals (Second Edition). 2004 Wiley-Blackwell.

Millar JS, Hickling GJ. Fasting endurance and the evolution of mammalian body size. Funct Ecol. 1990 4:5–12.

Bare hands freeze in the Antarctic
Piantadosi CA. The Biology of Human Survival: Life and Death in Extreme Environments. 2003 Oxford University Press.

Naturally obese
Pond CM. The Fats of Life. 1998 Cambridge University Press.

Hypothermia
Piantadosi CA. The Biology of Human Survival: Life and Death in Extreme Environments. 2003 Oxford University Press.

Winter deaths
De Lorenzo F, Sharma V, Scully M, Kakkar VV. Cold adaptation and the seasonal distribution of acute myocardial infarction. Q J Med. 1999 Dec;92(12):747–51.

Cold as a risk factor
Mercer JB. Cold – an underrated risk factor for health. Environ Res. 2003 May;92(1):8–13.

The metabolic syndrome
Zimmet P, Magliano D, Matsuzawa Y, Alberti G, Shaw J. The metabolic syndrome: a global health problem and a new definition. J Atheroscler Thromb. 2005;12(6):295–300.

Dandona P, Aljada A, Chaudhuri A, Mohanty P, Garg R. Metabolic syndrome: a comprehensive perspective based on interactions between obesity, diabetes and inflammation. Circulation. 2005 Mar 22;111(11):1448–54.

Thermogenesis
Silva JE. Thermogenic mechanisms and their hormonal regulation. Physiol Rev. 2006 Apr;86(2):435–64.

Internal temperature is maintained even when skin temperature drops
Haman F, Péronnet F, Kenny GP, Massicotte D, Lavoie C, Scott C, Weber JM. Effect of cold exposure on fuel utilization in humans: plasma glucose, muscle glycogen and lipids. J Appl Physiol 2002 Jul;93(1):77–84.

An explanation of the surface area to volume ratio

A cube of 1 cm × 1 cm × 1 cm has a surface area of 6 cm^2 and a volume of 1 cm^3, so the surface area to volume ratio is 6:1.

A cube of ten times bigger, 10 cm × 10 cm × 10 cm, would have a surface area of 600 cm^2 and a volume of 1,000 cm^3, so the surface area to volume ratio is 600:1,000, or 0.6:1.

So if you compare the large cube to the small cube:

The sides of the cube have increased by 10 times (from 1 cm to 10 cm)

The surface area has increased by 100 times (from 6 cm^2 to 600 cm^2)

The volume has increased by 1000 times (from 1 cm^3 to 1000 cm^3)

The surface area to volume ratio has *reduced* by 10 times (from 6 to 0.6).

As the cube gets bigger, the surface area doesn't increase as much as the volume. So, in relation to the volume, the surface area goes down. Thus, the bigger the cube, the lower the surface area to volume ratio.

The effect of body size on surface area to volume ratio

So much for a cube, but how much does a change in human body size affect surface area to volume ratio?

An adult man of height 1.75 m and 70 kg in weight has a body mass index (BMI) of 23 and a surface area/volume of 29.

If he gains 30 kg and his BMI becomes 33, his surface area/volume falls to 24. Gaining 30 kg can reduce the surface area to volume ratio by almost a quarter.

The Icelandic fisherman had a height of 1.93 cm, weight 125 kg and BMI of 34 with a surface area/volume of just 23.

A baby of 50 cm length and weight 3.4 kg has a surface area/volume of 72.

A 6-year-old child of 115 cm height and weighing 20 kg has a surface area/volume of 44.

These examples are shown in the following table:

	Height	Weight	BMI	Surface area/volume
Man	1.75 m	70 kg	23	29
Woman	1.62 m	60 kg	23	30
Obese man	1.75 m	100 kg	33	24
Obese woman	1.62 m	85 kg	32	26
Baby	50 cm	3.4 kg		72
6 year old child	115 cm	20 kg		44
Icelandic fisherman	1.93 m	125 kg	34	23

Note that when a body gets bigger, while both its volume and its surface area get bigger, the surface area doesn't go up as much as the volume, so the surface area to volume ratio is smaller. The lower this number, the easier it is to stay warm in the cold.

How to calculate human surface area to volume ratio

This example is for a man of 1.75 metres tall who weighs 70 kg and has a BMI of 23.

First, calculate the surface area:

Convert height to centimetres,

1.75 m × 100 = 175 cm

Multiply height by weight,

175 cm × 70 kg = 12,250

Divide by 3,600,

12250/3600 = 3.40

Find the square root,

$\sqrt{3.40} = 1.84$

Surface area is 1.84 m^2.

Next, calculate the volume:

Multiply weight by 0.9,

70 kg × 0.9 = 63 litres

Convert volume into cubic metres,

63 litres/1,000 = 0.063 m^3

Volume is 0.063 m^3.

The surface area is 1.84 m^2 and the volume is 0.063 m^3.

Now, calculate the surface area to volume ratio:

Divide the surface area by the volume

1.84/0.063 = 29 square metres per cubic metre

Surface area to volume ratio is 29:1

(Or surface area/volume is 29).

The Mosteller formula is used to calculate body surface area (BSA):

$$BSA\ (m^2) = ([\text{Height (cm)} \times \text{Weight (kg)}]/3600)^{1/2}$$

Volume in litres = weight in kg × 0.9.

The Mosteller formula: Mosteller RD. Simplified calculation of body surface area. N Engl J Med 1987 Oct 22;317(17) 1098 [letter].

Elert G. The Physics Factbook: An Encyclopedia of Scientific Essays website: www.hypertextbook.com/facts/ (Accessed 26th May 2014).

This website gives the Mosteller formula and other formulae for calculating body surface area on the page: 'Surface Area of Human Skin'. The website has a huge number of formulae for various measurements along with their primary sources.

The trunk is the main source of heat loss
Hayward MG, Keatinge WR. Roles of subcutaneous fat and thermoregulatory reflexes in determining ability to stabilize body temperature in water. J Physiol. 1981 Nov;320:229–51.

Metabolism in general
Newsholme EA, Leech AR. Biochemistry for the Medical Sciences. 1988 John Wiley & Sons.

Rate of energy production in humans
Goldstein L. (Ed.) Introduction to Comparative Physiology. 1977 Holt, Rinehart and Winston.

Brown fat
Blaza S. Brown adipose tissue in man: a review. J R Soc Med. 1983 Mar;76(3):213–6.

Nedergaard J, Bengtsson T, Cannon B. Unexpected evidence for active brown adipose tissue in adult humans. Am J Physiol Endocrinol Metab. 2007 Aug;293(2):E444–52.

Wijers SL, Schrauwen P, Saris WH, van Marken Lichtenbelt WD. Human skeletal muscle mitochondrial uncoupling is associated with cold induced adaptive thermogenesis. PLoS One. 2008 Mar 12;3(3):e1777.

Saito M, et al. High incidence of metabolically active brown adipose tissue in healthy adult humans: effects of cold exposure and adiposity. Diabetes. 2009 Jul;58(7):1526–31.

Uncoupling proteins
Argyropoulos G, Harper ME. Uncoupling proteins and thermoregulation. J Appl Physiol. 2002 May;92(5):2187–98.

Uncoupling proteins in overweight
Schrauwen P, Walder K, Ravussin E. Human uncoupling proteins and obesity. Obes Res. 1999 Jan;7(1):97–105.

Shivering vs. exercise
Tipton MJ, Franks GM, Meneilly GS, Mekjavic IB. Substrate utilization during exercise and shivering. Eur J Appl Physiol Occup Physiol. 1997;76(1):103–8.

Muscle fibre types

There are several differences between the two types of fibres, summarised below:

Red, type I fibres are also called slow-twitch fibres because the contractions are relatively slow. They are oxidative and vascularised, insulin sensitive and mitochondria-rich. They get their energy mainly from fat metabolism that provides a stable and long-lasting supply of ATP. They are resistant to fatigue, so they are better for endurance. These fibres are more abundant in large animals, because they need the strength to carry their weight. These are the powerful muscle fibres that support the cow standing all day long in the field.

White, type II fibres are also called fast-twitch fibres because they have a short contraction–relaxation cycle. They are insulin resistant. They are better for power and speed and are good for rapid responses like the escape response in fish or the rapid burst of flapping wings in a startled hen. They have lower levels of mitochondria than red fibres and rely on carbohydrate metabolism for their energy source. They are more susceptible to fatigue than red fibres.

Kriketos AD, Baur LA, O'Connor J, Carey D, King S, Caterson ID, Storlien LH. Muscle fibre type composition in infant and adult populations and relationships with obesity. Int J Obes Relat Metab Disord. 1997 Sep;21(9):796–801.

Houmard JA, O'Neill DS, Zheng D, Hickey MS, Dohm GL. Impact of hyperinsulinemia on myosin heavy chain gene regulation. J Appl Physiol. 1999 Jun;86(6):1828–32.

Wang YX, et al. Regulation of muscle fiber type and running endurance by PPARdelta. PLoS Biol. 2004 Oct;2(10):e294.

Shivering studies
Haman F, Legault SR, Weber JM. Fuel selection during intense shivering in humans: EMG pattern reflects carbohydrate oxidation. J Physiol. 2004 Apr 1;556(Pt 1):305–13.

Haman F, Legault SR, Rakobowchuk, Ducharme MB, Weber JM. Effects of carbohydrate availability on sustained shivering II. Relating muscle recruitment to fuel selection. J Appl Physiol. 2004 Jan;96(1):41–9.

Haman F, Peronnet F, Kenny GP, Doucet E, Massicotte D, Lavoie C, Weber JM. Effects of carbohydrate availability on sustained shivering I. Oxidation of plasma glucose, muscle glycogen, and proteins. J Appl Physiol. 2004 Jan;96(1):32–40.

Haman F. Shivering in the cold: from mechanisms of fuel selection to survival. J Appl Physiol. 2006 May;100(5):1702–8.

Shivering thermogenesis in birds
Dawson WR, Carey C, Hof TJV. Metabolic aspects of shivering thermogenesis in passerines during winter. Ornis Scand. 1992 Jul;23(3):381–7.

Low levels of red fibres (type I) have been found in overweight people, patients with insulin resistance and patients with high blood pressure
Hernelahti M, Tikkanen HO, Karjalainen J, Kujala UM. Muscle fiber-type distribution as a predictor of blood pressure: a 19-year follow-up study. Hypertension. 2005 May;45(5):1019–23.

Helge JW, Fraser AM, Kriketos AD, Jenkins AB, Calvert GD, Ayre KJ, Storlien LH. Interrelationships between muscle fibre type, substrate oxidation and body fat. Int J Obes Relat Metab Disord. 1999 Sep;23(9):986–91.

Wade AJ, Marbut MM, Round JM. Muscle fibre type and aetiology of obesity. Lancet. 1990 Apr 7;335(8693):805–8.

Tanner CJ, et al. Muscle fiber type is associated with obesity and weight loss. Am J Physiol Endocrinol Metab. 2002 Jun;282(6):E1191–6.

Gerrits MF, et al. Distinct skeletal muscle fiber characteristics and gene expression in diet-sensitive versus diet-resistant obesity. J Lipid Res. 2010 Aug;51(8):2394–404.

In this study, the subjects were those who lost the most and those who lost the least weight on an intensively supervised clinical weight loss programme (900-kcal diet). It was found that genes involved in oxidative phosphorylation and glucose and fatty acid metabolism were more active in those who lost the most weight. Also there was a higher proportion of type I fibres in those who lost the most weight. Altogether differences in muscle composition and metabolism were related to how much weight was lost.

Gene expression pattern supports glycolytic rather than oxidative metabolism in insulin resistance

Ptitsyn A, Hulver M, Cefalu W, York D, Smith SR. Unsupervised clustering of gene expression data points at hypoxia as possible trigger for metabolic syndrome. BMC Genomics. 2006 Dec 19;7:318.

Insulin resistance

Simoni RD, Hill RL, Vaughan M. The discovery of insulin: the work of Frederick Banting and Charles Best. J Biol Chem. 2002 Jun 277:e15.

Reaven GM. Banting lecture 1988. Role of insulin resistance in human disease. Diabetes. 1988 Dec;37(12):1595–607.

Insulin resistance and muscle fibres

Kern M, et al. Insulin responsiveness in skeletal muscle is determined by glucose transporter (Glut4) protein level. Biochem J. 1990 Sep 1;270(2):397–400.

Circulation – the countercurrent exchange

The superficial veins constrict and allow more blood to flow through the deeper veins that are close to the arteries. The venous blood is cooled by the loss of heat through the legs and feet. As it flows through the deep veins it is then warmed up by the arterial blood. By the time it has reached the trunk it has warmed up again to near core temperature. The arterial blood is losing heat as it travels down to the feet so that by the time it reaches the feet the temperature is lower and less heat is lost because the temperature difference is smaller. This is a countercurrent heat exchange and in whales' flippers, birds' legs and beavers' tails there are networks of arteries and veins called the *rete mirabile* (miraculous net) to facilitate it. In humans there is no *rete mirabile* because the temperature gradient from core to extremity is not as steep as that found in other animals. In other words, our circulation is the same kind of thing but milder, but perhaps it has the potential to be enhanced when we become cold-adapted.

Circulation and cold
Kellogg DL Jr. In vivo mechanisms of cutaneous vasodilation and vasoconstriction in humans during thermoregulatory challenges. J Appl Physiol. 2006 May;100(5):1709–18.

Shinozaki K, Ayajiki K, Kashiwagi A, Masada M, Okamura T. Malfunction of vascular control in lifestyle-related diseases: mechanisms underlying endothelial dysfunction in the insulin-resistant state. J Pharmacol Sci. 2004 Dec;96(4):401–5.

Demand for air conditioning
Battles SJ. Trends in residential air-conditioning usage from 1978 to 1997. US Energy Information Administration.

This is available from the EIA website: www.eia.doe.gov

Inuit had lower blood pressure and lipid levels in relation to their BMI
Young TK, Bjerregaard P, Dewailly E, Risica PM, Jørgensen ME, Ebbesson SE. Prevalence of obesity and its metabolic correlates among the circumpolar inuit in 3 countries. Am J Public Health. 2007 Apr;97(4):691–5.

It is still not clear whether it is abdominal fat or visceral fat that causes the metabolic syndrome
Kahn BB, Flier JS. Obesity and insulin resistance. J Clin Invest. 2000 Aug;106(4):473–81.

Chapter 7 An Evolutionary Exploration

Vitamin D in invertebrates
Zachariah TT, Mitchell MA. Vitamin D_3 in the hemolymph of goliath birdeater spiders (*Theraphosa blondi*). J Zoo Wildl Med. 2009 Jun;40(2):344–6.

Weiner S, Noff D, Meyer MS, Weisman Y, Edelstein S. Metabolism of cholecalciferol in land snails. Biochem J. 1979 Oct 15;184(1):157–61.

Vitamin D in plants
Boland R, Skliar M, Curino A, Milanesi L. Vitamin D compounds in plants. Plant Sci. 2003 Mar;164(3):357–69.

Prema TP, Raghuramulu N. Vitamin D_3 and its metabolites in the tomato plant. Phytochemistry. 1996 Jun;42(3):617–20.

Zavala JA, Botto JF, Impact of solar UV-B radiation on seedling emergence, chlorophyll fluorescence, and growth and yield of radish (*Raphanus sativus*). Funct Plant Biol. 2002 Jul;29(7) 797–804.

Vitamin D in fish
Copping AM. Origin of vitamin D in cod-liver oil: vitamin D content of zooplankton. Biochem J, 1934;28(4):1516–20.

Rao DS, Raghuramulu N. Food chain as origin of vitamin D in fish. Comp Biochem Phys A. 1996 May;114(1):15–19.

Rao DS, Raghuramulu N. Is vitamin D redundant in an aquatic habit? J Nutr Sci Vitaminol (Tokyo). 1999 Jan;45(1):1–8.

Callow RK, Fischmann CF. The occurrence of vitamin D in lampreys (Petromyzontidae) Biochem J. 1931;25(5):1464–9.

Vitamin D in reptiles
Karsten KB, Ferguson GW, Chen TC, Holick MF. Panther chameleons, *Furcifer pardalis*, behaviourally regulate optimal exposure to UV depending on dietary vitamin D_3 status. Physiol Biochem Zool. 2009 May-Jun;82(3):218–25.

Vitamin D in birds
Uva B, Mandich A, Vallarino M. The site of 7-dehydrocholesterol ultraviolet photolysis in domestic fowls. Acta Histochem. 1983;73(2):175–80.

Olea PP, Casas F, Redpath S, Viñuela J. Bottoms up: great bustards use the sun to maximise signal efficacy. Behav Ecol Sociobiol. 2010 May;64(6):927–37.

Reindeer and musk oxen eat lichens
Wang T, Bengtsson G, Kärnefelt I, Björn LO. Provitamins and vitamins D_2 and D_3 in Cladina spp. over a latitudinal gradient: possible correlation with UV levels. J Photochem Photobiol B. 2001 Sep 1;62(1–2):118–22.

The Damara mole rat is deficient in vitamin D
Skinner DC, Moodley G, Buffenstein R. Is vitamin D_3 essential for mineral metabolism in the Damara mole-rat (*Cryptomys damarensis*)? Gen Comp Endocrinol. 1991 Mar;81(3):500–5.

Vitamin D in the fruit bat
Cavaleros M, Buffenstein R, Ross FP, Pettifor JM. Vitamin D metabolism in a frugivorous nocturnal mammal, the Egyptian fruit bat (*Rousettus aegyptiacus*). Gen Comp Endocrinol. 2003 Aug;133(1):109–17.

Björn and Wang hypothesis that vitamin D is a sunlight detector
Björn LO, Wang T. Is provitamin D a UV-B receptor in plants? Plant Ecol. 2001 Jun;154(1–2):1–8.

Vitamin D in plankton
Holick MF. Vitamin D: A millennium perspective. J Cell Biochem. 2003 Feb 1;88(2) 296–307.

The spectrum of solar radiation in Archaean
Gaustad JE, Vogel SN. High energy solar radiation and the origin of life. Orig Life. 1982 Mar;12(1):3–8.

Bergmann's rule
Ashton KG, Feldman CR. Bergmann's rule in nonavian reptiles: turtles follow it, lizards and snakes reverse it. Evolution. 2003 May;57(5):1151–63.

Adams DC, Church JO. Amphibians do not follow Bergmann's rule. Evolution. 2008 Feb;62(2):413–20.

Ashton KG. Are ecological and evolutionary rules being dismissed prematurely? Divers Distrib. 2001 Nov;7(6):289–95.

Meiri S, Dayan T. On the validity of Bergmann's rule. J Biogeogr. 2003Mar;30(3):331–51.

Rodríguez MÁ, Olalla-Tárraga MÁ, Hawkins BA. Bergmann's rule and the geography of mammal body size in the Western Hemisphere. Global Ecol Biogeogr. 2008 Mar;17(2):274–83.

Reindeer in the winter
Marchand PJ. Life in the Cold: An Introduction to Winter Ecology. (Third Edition) 1996 University Press of New England.

The mass extinction that occurred at the K-T boundary
Keller G, Adatte T, Stinnesbeck W, Rebolledo-Vieyra M, Fucugauchi JU, Kramar U, Stüben D. Chicxulub impact predates the K-T boundary mass extinction. Proc Natl Acad Sci USA. 2004 Mar;101(11) 3753–8.

Schulte P, Speijer RP, Brinkhuis H, Kontny A, Claeys P, Galeotti S, Smit J. Comment on the paper 'Chicxulub impact predates K-T boundary: new evidence from Brazos, Texas' by Keller et al. (2007). Earth Planet Sci Lett. 2008 May;269(3–4):614–20.

Giant penguins
Clarke JA, et al. Paleogene equatorial penguins challenge the proposed relationship between biogeography, diversity, and Cenozoic climate change. Proc Natl Acad Sci USA. 2007 Jul 10;104(28):11545–50.

Evolution of vitamin D
Baker ME. Origin and diversification of steroids: co-evolution of enzymes and nuclear receptors. Mol Cell Endocrinol. 2011 Mar 1;334(1–2):14–20.

Calcitriol modulates the immune system
Rosenblatt J, et al. Immunomodulatory effects of vitamin D: implications for GVHD. Bone Marrow Transplant. 2010 Sep;45(9):1463–8.

Vitamin D in the skin
Lehmann B, Querings K, Reichrath J. Vitamin D and skin: new aspects for dermatology. Exp Dermatol. 2004;13 Suppl 4:11–5.

Reichrath J. Vitamin D and the skin: an ancient friend, revisited. Exp Dermatol. 2007 Jul;16(7):618–25.

De Haes P, et al. 1,23-Dihydroxyvitamin D3 and analogues protect primary human keratinocytes against UVB-induced DNA damage. J Photochem Photobiol B. 2005 Feb 1;78(2):141–8.

Thrifty genotype
Neel JV. Diabetes mellitus: a 'thrifty' genotype rendered detrimental by 'progress'? Am J Hum Genet. 1962 Dec;14:353–62.

Weiss KM, Ward RH. James V. Neel, M.D., Ph.D. (March 22, 1915–January 31, 2000): founder effect. Am J Hum Genet. 2000 Mar;66(3):755–60.

Diamond JM. The Third Chimpanzee: The Evolution and Future of the Human Animal. 1992 Harper Collins, reissued 2006. (Chapter 10 Agriculture's mixed blessings.)

Prentice AM. Early influences on human energy regulation: thrifty genotypes and thrifty phenotypes. Physiol Behav. 2005 Dec 15;86(5):640–5.

Speakman JR. Thrifty genes for obesity and the metabolic syndrome – time to call off the search? Diab Vasc Dis Res. 2006 May;3(1):7–11.

Human migration
Stringer C, McKie R. African Exodus: The Origins of Modern Humanity. 1996 Jonathan Cape.

Forster P. Ice ages and the mitochondrial DNA chronology of human dispersals: a review. Philos Trans R Soc Lond B Biol Sci. 2004 Feb 29;359(1442):255–64.

Stringer C. Homo Britannicus: The incredible story of human life in Britain. 2006 Allen Lane.

The Palaeolithic diet

O'Keefe JH Jr, Cordain L. Cardiovascular disease resulting from a diet and lifestyle at odds with our Paleolithic genome: how to become a 21st-century hunter-gatherer. Mayo Clin Proc. 2004 Jan;79(1):101–8.

Jönsson T, et al. Beneficial effects of a Paleolithic diet on cardiovascular risk factors in type 2 diabetes: a randomized cross-over pilot study. Cardiovasc Diabetol. 2009 Jul 16;8:35.

There have been small changes in our genome in the past few thousand years

Voight BF, Kudaravalli S, Wen X, Pritchard JK. A map of recent positive selection in the human genome. PLoS Biol. 2006 Mar;4(3):e72. Erratum in: PLoS Biol.2006 Apr;4(4):e154.

Lactase persistence

Bersaglieri T, et al. Genetic signatures of strong recent positive selection at the lactase gene. Am J Hum Genet. 2004 Jun;74(6):1111–20.

Lactose intolerance

Brostoff J, Gamlin L. The Complete Guide to Food Allergy and Intolerance. 1998 Bloomsbury Publishing plc.

The evolution of lactase persistence

Ingram CJ, Mulcare CA, Itan Y, Thomas MG, Swallow DM. Lactose digestion and the evolutionary genetics of lactase persistence. Hum Genet. 2009 Jan;124(6):579–91.

Burger J, Kirchner M, Bramanti B, Haak W, Thomas MG. Absence of the lactase-persistence-associated allele in early Neolithic Europeans. Proc Natl Acad Sci USA. 2007 Mar 6;104(10):3736–41.

Itan Y, Powell A, Beaumont MA, Burger J, Thomas MG. The origins of lactase persistence in Europe. PLoS Comput Biol. 2009 Aug;5(8):e1000491.

Flatz G, Rotthauwe HW. Lactose nutrition and natural selection. Lancet. 1973 Jul 14;2(7820):76–7.

Cook GC, al-Torki MT. High intestinal lactase concentrations in adult Arabs in Saudi Arabia. Br Med J. 1975 Jul 19;3(5976):135–6.

Hair

Schwartz GG, Rosenblum LA. Allometry of primate hair density and the evolution of human hairlessness. Am J Phys Anthropol. 1981 May;55(1):9–12.

Jablonski NG. The naked truth. Sci Am. 2010 Feb;302(2):42–9.

Wheeler PE. The evolution of bipedality and loss of functional body hair in hominids. J Hum Evol. 1984 Jan;13(1):91–98.

The Aquatic Ape hypothesis

Morgan E. The aquatic ape hypothesis: most credible theory of human evolution. 1999 Souvenir Press.

Pigmentation

Slominski A, Tobin DJ, Shibahara S, Wortsman J. Melanin pigmentation in mammalian skin and its hormonal regulation. Physiol Rev. 2004 Oct;84(4):1155–228.

Darwin C. The Descent of Man, and Selection in Relation to Sex. 2004 Penguin Classics (in Chapter 7 The formation of races).

Diamond JM. The Third Chimpanzee: The Evolution and Future of the Human Animal. 1992 Harper Collins, reissued 2006 (Chapter 6 Sexual selection and the origin of human races).

Jablonski NG, Chaplin G. The evolution of human skin coloration. J Hum Evol. 2000 Jul;39(1):57–106.

Yuen AW, Jablonski NG. Vitamin D: in the evolution of human skin colour. Med Hypotheses. 2010 Jan;74(1):39–44.

Willmer P, Stone G, Johnston I. Environmental Physiology of Animals (Second Edition). 2005 Blackwell Publishing Oxford.

Rees JL. The genetics of sun sensitivity in humans. Am J Hum Genet. 2004 Nov;75(5):739–51.

Hair loss in captivity

Novak MA, Meyer JS. Alopecia: possible causes and treatments, particularly in captive nonhuman primates. Comp Med. 2009 Feb;59(1):18–26.

Bernard Wood says we are 'reducing our ignorance'

Wood B. Human Evolution: A very short introduction. 2005 Oxford University Press.

Nutrient deficiencies were more common in the overweight that in those of normal weight

McCarron DA, Morris CD, Henry HJ, Stanton JL. Blood pressure and nutrient intake in the United States. Science. 1984 Jun 29;224(4656):1392–8.

Venus figurines
Mellars P. The upper palaeolithic revolution. Chapter 2 in The Oxford Illustrated History of Prehistoric Europe. Cunliffe B. (Ed.) 1994 Oxford University Press.

Link between modern urban-industrial living and overweight
World Health Organization. Obesity: Preventing and Managing the Global Epidemic. 2000 WHO Technical Report Series 894. 2000 World Health Organisation.

Urbanisation
United Nations. World Urbanization Prospects: The 2007 Revision. 2008 United Nations.

Chapter 8 Weightonomics

Overweight is sometimes healthier
Oreopoulos A, Padwal R, Kalantar-Zadeh K, Fonarow GC, Norris CM, McAlister FA. Body mass index and mortality in heart failure: a meta-analysis. Am Heart J. 2008 Jul;156(1):13–22.

Hirachan P, Thijssen S, Levin NW, Kotanko P. Body composition and outcomes in chronic hemodialysis patients. Contrib Nephrol. 2008;161:108–14.

De Laet C, et al. Body mass index as a predictor of fracture risk: a meta-analysis. Osteoporos Int. 2005 Nov;16(11):1330–8.

Weight loss can be healthier in the short term but not in the long term
Zheng H, Tumin D, Qian Z. Obesity and mortality risk: new findings from body mass index trajectories. Am J Epidemiol. 2013 Dec 1;178(11):1591–9.

In this study, Zheng et al. found that body mass index (BMI) trajectories were more predictive of mortality risk than static BMI status. In other words it is weight *change* (whether up or down) that is important to health.

Sørensen TI, Rissanen A, Korkeila M, Kaprio J. Intention to lose weight, weight changes, and 18-y mortality in overweight individuals without co-morbidities. PLoS Med. 2005 Jun;2(6):e171.

In this study, people who intended to lose weight in 1975 and succeeded were at higher risk of death over the next 18 years compared to both those who intended to lose weight but did not, and those who lost weight without intending to. Several studies have found similar results but the findings are controversial. The following two references are reviews with different viewpoints:

Sørensen TI. Weight loss causes increased mortality: pros. Obes Rev. 2003 Feb;4(1):3–7.

Yang D, Fontaine KR, Wang C, Allison DB. Weight loss causes increased mortality: cons. Obes Rev. 2003 Feb;4(1):9–16.

Bariatric surgery

Batsis JA, Romero-Corral A, Collazo-Clavell ML, Sarr MG, Somers VK, Lopez-Jimenez F. Effect of bariatric surgery on the metabolic syndrome: a population-based, long-term controlled study. Mayo Clin Proc. 2008 Aug;83(8):897–907.

De Prisco C, Levine SN. Metabolic bone disease after gastric bypass surgery for obesity. Am J Med Sci. 2005 Feb;329(2):57–61.

Differences between population groups

Razzouk L, Muntner P. Ethnic, gender, and age-related differences in patients with the metabolic syndrome. Curr Hypertens Rep. 2009 Apr;11(2):127–32.

Kaluski DN, Berry EM. Prevalence of obesity in Israel. Obes Rev. 2005 May;6(2):115–6.

Wang Y, Beydoun MA. The obesity epidemic in the United States – gender, age, socioeconomic, racial/ethnic, and geographic characteristics: a systematic review and meta-regression analysis. Epidemiol Rev. 2007;29:6–28.

Goulding A, Grant AM, Taylor RW, Williams SM, Parnell WR, Wilson N, Mann J. Ethnic differences in extreme obesity. J Pediatr. 2007 Nov;151(5):542–4.

El-Sayed AM, Scarborough P, Galea S. Ethnic inequalities in obesity among children and adults in the UK: a systematic review of the literature. Obes Rev. 2011 May;12(5):e516–34.

Australian Institute of Health and Welfare. Are all Australians gaining weight? Differentials in overweight and obesity among adults, 1989–90 to 2001. Bulletin Issue, 11 Dec 2003.

Population groups are subject to the same trend

Wang Y, Beydoun MA. The obesity epidemic in the United States – gender, age, socioeconomic, racial/ethnic, and geographic characteristics: a systematic review and meta-regression analysis. Epidemiol Rev. 2007;29:6–28.

BMI may overestimate the number who are overweight and obese

Charbonneau-Roberts G, Saudny-Unterberger H, Kuhnlein HV, Egeland GM. Body mass index may overestimate the prevalence of overweight and obesity among the Inuit. Int J Circumpolar Health. 2005 Apr;64(2):163–9.

South Asians develop metabolic abnormalities at a lower BMI than other groups
Enas EA, Mohan V, Deepa M, Farooq S, Pazhoor S, Chennikkara H. The metabolic syndrome and dyslipidemia among Asian Indians: a population with high rates of diabetes and premature coronary artery disease. J Cardiometab Syndr. 2007 Fall;2(4):267–75.

There is no genetic basis for ethnicity
Race, Ethnicity, and Genetics Working Group. The use of racial, ethnic, and ancestral categories in human genetics research. Am J Hum Genet. 2005 Oct;77(4):519–32.

Black African Americans have higher rates of high blood pressure than white Americans, black sub-Saharan Africans and Caribbeans
Cappuccio FP, et al. Body size and blood pressure: an analysis of Africans and the African diaspora. Epidemiology. 2008 Jan;19(1):38–46.

The vitamin D status of immigrants in Europe is lower than the indigenous population
van der Meer IM, Middelkoop BJ, Boeke AJ, Lips P. Prevalence of vitamin D deficiency among Turkish, Moroccan, Indian and sub-Sahara African populations in Europe and their countries of origin: an overview. Osteoporos Int. 2011 Apr;22(4):1009–21.

Black people drink less milk in adulthood than white people
National Dairy Council. Dairy foods' role in minority health. Dairy Council Digests 2004 Sept/Oct 75(5). Retrieved from the website of the US National Dairy Council: www.nationaldairycouncil.org

Veiled women tend to have lower calcidiol levels
Guzel R, Kozanoglu E, Guler-Uysal F, Soyupak S, Sarpel T. Vitamin D status and bone mineral density of veiled and unveiled Turkish women. J Womens Health Gend Based Med. 2001 Oct;10(8):765–70.

Overweight is associated with wealth on a country-by-country basis
Low S, Chin MC, Deurenberg-Yap M. Review on epidemic of obesity. Ann Acad Med Singapore. 2009 Jan;38(1):57–9.

In Africa, overweight is higher in the wealthiest but increased faster in the poor
Ziraba AK, Fotso JC, Ochako R. Overweight and obesity in urban Africa: A problem of the rich or the poor? BMC Public Health. 2009 Dec 15;9:465.

The poverty–obesity paradox
Hruschka DJ. Do economic constraints on food choice make people fat? A critical review of two hypotheses for the poverty-obesity paradox. Am J Hum Biol. 2012 May-Jun;24(3):277–85.

Differences between regions within countries
Pouliou T, Elliott SJ. An exploratory spatial analysis of overweight and obesity in Canada. Prev Med. 2009 Apr;48(4):362–7.

Großschädl F, Stronegger WJ. Regional trends in obesity and overweight among Austrian adults between 1973 and 2007. Wien Klin Wochenschr. 2012 Jun;124(11–12):363–9.

Wang Y, Beydoun MA. The obesity epidemic in the United States – gender, age, socioeconomic, racial/ethnic, and geographic characteristics: a systematic review and meta-regression analysis. Epidemiol Rev. 2007;29:6–28.

Welsh Health Survey 2011 and 2012 Local Authority/Local Health Board Results Statistical Bulletin SB 87/2013.

This is available from the website of the Welsh government: wales.gov.uk/statistics-and-research (under Health and Social Care, Welsh Health Survey 2012, select *Local authority and local health board results, 2011 and 2012* from the menu). Data are taken from Table 4: Adults who reported key health-related lifestyles (age-standardised), on page 8 of the bulletin.

The effect of neighbourhood status is greater than individual income or education
Krishnan S, Cozier YC, Rosenberg L, Palmer JR. Socioeconomic status and incidence of type 2 diabetes: results from the Black Women's Health study. Am J Epidemiol. 2010 Mar 1;171(5):564–70.

Ludwig J, et al. Neighborhoods, obesity and diabetes – a randomised social experiment. N Engl J Med. 2011 Oct 20;365(16):1509–19.

When household wealth or individual wealth is studied in detail in relation to overweight, the results become confusing and contradictory
El-Sayed AM, Scarborough P, Galea S. Unevenly distributed: a systematic review of the health literature about socioeconomic inequalities in adult obesity in the United Kingdom. BMC Public Health. 2012 Jan 9;12:18.

Being poor may be a consequence of overweight
Jolliffe D. Overweight and poor? On the relationship between income and the body mass index. Econ Hum Biol. 2011 Dec;9(4):342–55.

Differences between men and women
Kanter R. Caballero B. Global gender disparities in obesity: a review. Adv Nutr. 2012 Jul 1;3(4):491–8.

Obesity in different age groups
Craig R, Shelton N (Eds.) Health Survey for England 2007. Volume 1, Healthy Lifestyles: knowledge, attitudes and behaviour. The NHS Information Centre for Health and Social Care.

In Chapter 8 Children's BMI, overweight and obesity, by Shaun Scholes, Table 8.11: Trends in BMI, overweight and obesity prevalence among children aged 2–10, 1995–2007, by sex, on page 244 shows 14% of girls obese and 16% of boys obese in 2007.

In Chapter 3 Adult anthropometric measures, overweight and obesity, by Faiza Tabassum, Table 3.14: Trends in overweight and obesity prevalence, 1993 to 2007, by age and sex, on pages 65–6 shows the following obesity rates for 2007:

Men aged 45–54 years: 35%, aged 55–64 years: 31%, aged 65–74 years: 28%

Women aged 45–54 years: 30%, aged 55–64 years: 31%, aged 65–74 years: 32%.

Elephants in European zoos have shorter life spans
Clubb R, Rowcliffe M, Lee P, Mar KU, Moss C, Mason GJ. Compromised survivorship in zoo elephants. Science. 2008 Dec 12;322(5908):1649.

Reports of species loss suggest the possibility of a sixth mass extinction event
Barnosky AD, et al. Has the Earth's sixth mass extinction already arrived? Nature. 2011 Mar 3;471(7336):51–7.

Wake DB, Vredenburg VT. Colloquium paper: are we in the midst of the sixth mass extinction? A view from the world of amphibians. Proc Natl Acad Sci USA. 2008 Aug 12;105 Suppl 1:11466–73.

The decline in frogs may be caused by chytridiomycosis
Rachowicz LJ, Knapp RA, Morgan JA, Stice MJ, Vredenburg VT, Parker JM, Briggs CJ. Emerging infectious disease as a proximate cause of amphibian mass mortality. Ecology. 2006 Jul;87(7):1671–83.

More than a dozen factors may contribute to the decline in bee populations
United Nations Environment Programme. UNEP Emerging Issues: Global Honey Bee Colony Disorder and Other Threats to Insect Pollinators. 2010 United Nations Environment Programme.

Increased (but not lower) ultraviolet-B is one of the causes of species decline considered
Antwis RE, Browne RK. Ultraviolet radiation and vitamin D_3 in amphibian health, behaviour, diet and conservation. Comp Biochem Physiol A Mol Integr Physiol. 2009 Oct;154(2):184–90.

Overweight horses

World Horse Welfare. Horse owners fail to recognise dangers of obesity. News report 24/2/2010 on the website of the World Horse Welfare: www.worldhorsewelfare.org

Stephenson HM, Green MJ, Freeman SL. Prevalence of obesity in a population of horses in the UK. Vet Rec. 2011 Feb 5;168(5):131.

This study of 160 horses, by vets at the University of Nottingham, estimated at least one in five horses used for leisure in England are overweight or obese.

Otters have increased in size in the last quarter of the twentieth century

Yom-Tov Y, Heggberget TM, Wiig Ø, Yom-Tov S. Body size changes among otters, Lutra lutra, in Norway: the possible effects of food availability and global warming. Oecologia. 2006 Nov;150(1):155–60.

Yom-Tov Y, Roos A, Mortensen P, Wiig Ø, Yom-Tov S, Heggberget TM. Recent changes in body size of the Eurasian otter Lutra lutra in Sweden. Ambio. 2010 Nov;39(7):496–503.

The weight of many animals has increased

Klimentidis YC, et al. Canaries in the coal mine: a cross-species analysis of the plurality of obesity epidemics. Proc Biol Sci. 2011 Jun 7;278(1712):1626–32.

Chapter 9 The Reversal Strategy

'The only trouble was that scurvy is not a first symptom of a lack but a final collapse, a premortal syndrome and there is a very wide gap between scurvy and full health.'

Szent-Györgyi A. Foreword in Stone I. The Healing Factor: 'Vitamin C' Against Disease. 1972 Grosset & Dunlap.

Dietary fat

Dixon LB, Ernst ND. Choose a diet that is low in saturated fat and cholesterol and moderate in total fat: subtle changes to a familiar message. J Nutr. 2001 Feb;131(2S–1):510S–26S.

Flegal KM, Carroll MD, Kuczmarski RJ, Johnson CL. Overweight and obesity in the United States: prevalence and trends, 1960–1994. Int J Obes Relat Metab Disord. 1998 Jan;22(1):39–47.

David Weigle's presentation

Weigle DS. Human Obesity. Exploding the myths. West J Med. 1990 Oct;153(4):421–8.

The body weight set point

Keesey RE, Hirvonen MD. Body weight set points: determination and adjustment. J Nutr. 1997 Sep;127(9):1875S–83S.

Speakman JR, et al. Set points settling points and some alternative models: theoretical options to understand how genes and environments combine to regulate body adiposity. Dis Model Mech. 2011 Nov;4(6):733–45.

The findings of the EarlyBird project

Wilkin TJ, Mallam KM, Metcalf BS, Jeffery AN, Voss LD. Variation in physical activity lies with the child, not his environment: evidence for an 'activitystat' in young children (EarlyBird 16). Int J Obes (Lond). 2006 Jul;30(7):1050–5.

Metcalf BS, Hosking J, Jeffery AN, Voss LD, Henley W, Wilkin TJ. Fatness leads to activity, but inactivity does not lead to fatness: a longitudinal study in children (EarlyBird 45). Arch Dis Child. Oct;96(10):942–7.

Flagellants

Margotta M. History of Medicine. 1996 Octopus Publishing Group London.

Foresight study

The Foresight Programme. Tackling Obesities: Future choices – Summary of key messages 2007. Available from the UK Government Department for Business, Innovation & Skills website: www.bis.gov.uk

Benefit claims

Anyadike-Danes M, McVicar D. Has the boom in incapacity benefit claimant numbers passed its peak? Fiscal Studies 2008 Dec;29(4):415–547.

John Major quotation

HC Deb (Series 6) 15 June 1993 vol 226 cc729-34.

(Question 4)

Prevalence of longstanding illness

Rickards L, Fox K, Roberts C, Fletcher L, Goddard E. Living in Britain No.31: Results from the 2002 General Household Survey. 2004 The Stationery Office.

Data were taken from Chapter 7 *General health and use of health services: Chronic sickness* on page 86. This survey found other parameters of health indicating an increase in ill health such as per cent of respondents reporting having recently seen a GP.

Prescriptions
Hawe E, Cockcroft L. Office of Health Economics Guide to UK Health and Health Care Statistics (Second Edition) 2013 Office of Health Economics Research.

The data given are taken from Table 4.9: Number of NHS prescriptions (based on fees) dispensed by community pharmacists and appliance contractor, and per capita, UK, 1948–2012, on page 146.

Persistence of the inequalities in health and deprivation
Thomas B, Dorling D, Smith GD. Inequalities in premature mortality in Britain: observational study from 1921 to 2007. Br Med J. 2010 Jul 22;341:c3639.

Sunlight in building design
Hobday R. The Light Revolution: Health, Architecture and the Sun. 2006 Findhorn Press.

Fortification of food
Holick MF, Shao Q, Liu WW, Chen TC. The vitamin D content of fortified milk and infant formula. N Engl J Med. 1992 Apr 30;326(18):1178–81.

Sedrani SH. The vitamin D content of fortified milk produced locally. Proc Nutr Soc Aust 2004, 28. Asia Pac J Clin Nutr. 2004;13 Suppl:S165.

Calvo MS, Whiting SJ, Barton CN. Vitamin D fortification in the United States and Canada: current status and data needs. Am J Clin Nutr. 2004 Dec;80(6 Suppl):1710S–6S.

Darnton-Hill I, Darnton-Hill I, Nalubola R. Fortification strategies to meet micronutrient needs: successes and failures. Proc Nutr Soc. 2002 May;61(2):231–41.

Increasing vitamin D in food
Fleming RH. Nutritional factors affecting poultry bone health. Proc Nutr Soc. 2008 May;67(2):177–83.

Mattila P, Lehikoinen K, Kiiskinen T, Piironen V. Cholecalciferol and 25-hydroxycholecalciferol content of chicken egg yolk as affected by the cholecalciferol content of feed. J Agric Food Chem. 1999 Oct:47(10):4089–92.

Mattila P, Valaja J, Rossow L, Venäläinen E, Tupasela T. Effect of vitamin D_2- and D_3-enriched diets on egg vitamin D content, production, and bird condition during an entire production period. Poult Sci. 2004 Mar;83(3):433–40.

Koyyalamudi SR, Jeong SC, Song CH, Cho KY, Pang G. Vitamin D_2 formation and bioavailability from Agaricus bisporus button mushrooms treated with ultraviolet irradiation. J Agric Food Chem. 2009 Apr 22;57(8):3351–5.

Dietary fish
Welch AA, et al. Variability of fish consumption within the 10 European countries participating in the European Investigation into Cancer and Nutrition (EPIC) study. Public Health Nutr. 2002 Dec;5(6B):1273–85.

Can we get enough vitamin D from the sun?
Webb AR, Engelsen O. Ultraviolet exposure scenarios: risks of erythema from recommendations on cutaneous vitamin D synthesis. Adv Exp Med Biol. 2008;624:72–85.

On 22 February, I also encountered rays alongside violet in the colour spectrum of colours – outside it – by means of horn silver. They reduced even more strongly than violet light itself and the field of these rays is very wide. More to come soon.

Johann Wilhelm Ritter cited in:

Frercks J, Weber H, Wiesenfeldt G. Reception and discovery: the nature of Johann Wilhelm Ritter's invisible rays. Studies Hist Phil Sci. 2009 Jun;40(2):143–56.

It has been difficult though not impossible to conceive how two such apparently different agencies, light and vitamin, should have the same effect.

Steenbock H, Black A. Fat-soluble vitamins: XVII. The induction of growth–promoting and calcifying properties in a ration by exposure to ultra-violet light. J Biol Chem. 1924 Sep;61:405–22.

Chapter 10 Crisps

Question 6 How can losing weight result in higher vitamin D levels?
Tzotzas T, Papadopoulou FG, Tziomalos K, Karras S, Gastaris K, Perros P, Krassas GE. Rising serum 25-hydroxy-vitamin D levels after weight loss in obese women correlate with improvement in insulin resistance. J Clin Endocrinol Metab. 2010 Sep;95(9):4251–7.

Question 11 Why do the muscles of overweight people have more white fibres and fewer red fibres?
Helge JW, Fraser AM, Kriketos AD, Jenkins AB, Calvert GD, Ayre KJ, Storlien LH. Interrelationships between muscle fibre type, substrate oxidation and body fat. Int J Obes Relat Metab Disord. 1999 Sep;23(9):986–91.

Wade AJ, Marbut MM, Round JM. Muscle fibre type and aetiology of obesity. Lancet. 1990 Apr 7;335(8693):805–8.

Tanner CJ, et al. Muscle fiber type is associated with obesity and weight loss. Am J Physiol Endocrinol Metab. 2002 Jun;282(6):E1191–6.

Gerrits MF, et al. Distinct skeletal muscle fiber characteristics and gene expression in diet-sensitive versus diet-resistant obesity. J Lipid Res. 2010 Aug;51(8):2394–404.

Question 13 Why is overweight associated with changes in fats and glucose and with insulin resistance?

Stannard SR, Johnson NA. Insulin resistance and elevated triglyceride in muscle: more important for survival than 'thrifty' genes? J Physiol. 2004 Feb 1;554(Pt 3):595–607.

Moro C, Bajpeyi S, Smith SR. Determinants of intramyocellular triglyceride turnover: implications for insulin sensitivity. Am J Physiol Endocrinol Metab. 2008 Feb;294(2):E203–13.

Question 14 Why is overweight associated with high blood pressure?

Alpérovitch A, Lacombe JM, Hanon O, Dartigues JF, Ritchie K, Ducimetiére P, Tzourio C. Relationship between blood pressure and outdoor temperature in a large sample of elderly individuals: the Three-City study. Arch Intern Med. 2009 Jan 12;169(1):75–80.

Rostand SG. Ultraviolet light may contribute to geographic and racial blood pressure differences. Hypertension. 1997 Aug;30(2 Pt. 1):150–6.

Ullah MI, Uwaifo GI, Nicholas WC, Koch CA. Does vitamin D deficiency cause hypertension? Current evidence from clinical studies and potential mechanisms. Int J Endocrinol. 2010 (2010) Article ID:579640, 11 pages.

Question 19 Why do Inuit have lower blood pressure and lipid levels in relation to BMI or waist circumference than Canadian populations?

Young TK, Bjerregaard P, Dewailly E, Risica PM, Jørgensen ME, Ebbesson SE. Prevalence of obesity and its metabolic correlates among the circumpolar inuit in 3 countries. Am J Public Health. 2007 Apr;97(4):691–5.

Question 21 Why are we getting taller as well as fatter?

Epstein LH, McCurley J, Valoski A, Wing RR. Growth in obese children treated for obesity. Am J Dis Child. 1990 Dec;144(12):1360–4.

Heude B, Lafay L, Borys JM, Thibult N, Lommez A, Romon M, Ducimetiére P, Charles MA. Time trend in height, weight, and obesity prevalence in school children from Northern France, 1992–2000. Diabetes Metab. 2003 Jun;29(3):235–40.

Martinelli CE, et al. Obesity due to melanocortin 4 receptor (MC4R) deficiency is associated with increased linear growth and final height, fasting hyperinsulinemia, and incompletely suppressed growth hormone secretion. J Clin Endocrinol Metab. 2011 Jan;96(1)E181–8.

Question 22 Why do overweight children enter puberty earlier?
Aksglaede L, Juul A, Olsen LW, Sørensen TI. Age at puberty and the emerging obesity epidemic. PLoS One. 2009 Dec 24;4(12):e8450.

Question 26 Why are you more likely to be overweight if you live in the UK than in France?
Volatier JL, Verger P. Recent national French food and nutrient intake data. Br J Nutr. 1999 Apr;81 Suppl 2:S57–9.

Clower W. The Fat Fallacy: The French Diet Secrets to Permanent Weight Loss. 2003 Three Rivers Press.

Guiliano M. French Women Don't Get Fat: The Secret of Eating for Pleasure. 2006 Vintage.

Question 29 Why are you less likely to be overweight if you live in Japan?
Cockerham WC, Yamori Y. Okinawa: an exception to the social gradient of life expectancy in Japan. Asia Pac J Clin Nutr. 2001;10(2):154–8.

Nakamura K, Nashimoto M, Okuda Y, Ota T, Yamamoto M. Fish as a major source of vitamin D in the Japanese diet. Nutrition. 2002 May;18(5):415–6.

Bernstein AM, et al. First autopsy study of an Okinawan centenarian: absence of many age-related diseases. J Gerontol A Biol Sci Med Sci. 2004 Nov;59(11):1195–9.

Question 33 Why are you more likely to be overweight if you eat processed foods than a traditional diet?
Parry J. Pacific Islanders pay a heavy price for abandoning traditional diet. Bull World Health Org. 2010 Jul;88(7):481–560.

Question 34 Why are you more likely to be overweight if you are a king or queen?
Lipscomb S. 1536: The Year that Changed Henry VIII. 2009 Lion Hudson.

Question 35 Why are women sometimes more overweight than men?
Gannagé-Yared MH, Chemali R, Sfeir C, Maalouf G, Halaby G. Dietary calcium and vitamin D intake in an adult Middle Eastern population: food sources and relation to lifestyle and PTH. Int J Vitam Nutr Res. 2005 Jul;75(4):281–9.

Question 37 Why you are more likely to be overweight if you are an adult than if you are a child
Popkin BM, Conde W, Hou N, Monteiro C. Is there a lag globally in overweight trends for children compared with adults? Obesity. 2006 Oct;14:1846–53.

Question 47 Do trans fats cause overweight?
Kavanagh K, Jones KL, Sawyer J, Kelley K, Carr JJ, Wagner JD, Rudel LL. Trans fat diet induces abdominal obesity and changes in insulin sensitivity in monkeys. Obesity (Silver Spring). 2007 Jul;15(7):1675–84.

Mozaffarian D, Aro A, Willett WC. Health effects of trans-fatty acids: experimental and observational evidence. Eur J Clin Nutr. 2009 May;63 Suppl 2:S5–21.

Question 48 Do soft drinks containing high-fructose corn syrup cause overweight?
Forshee RA, et al. A critical examination of the evidence relating high fructose corn syrup and weight gain. Crit Rev Food Sci Nutr. 2007;47(6):561–82.

Question 56 How does vitamin D deficiency and overweight fit in with Barker's foetal origins hypothesis?
Barker DJ. The origins of the developmental origins theory. J Intern Med. 2007 May;261(5):412–7.

Question 63 Why have the studies failed to demonstrate a direct relationship between overweight and activity?
Wilkin TJ, Mallam KM, Metcalf BS, Jeffery AN, Voss LD. Variation in physical activity lies with the child, not his environment: evidence for an 'activitystat' in young children. Int J Obes (Lond). 2006 Jul;30(7):1050–5.

Question 75 Why do people who work in the Antarctic sometimes gain weight?
Vats P, Singh SN, Singh VK, Shyam R, Upadhyay TN, Singh SB, Banerjee PK. Appetite regulatory peptides in Indian Antarctic expeditioners. Nutr Neurosci. 2005 Aug;8(4):233–8.

Smith SM, Gardner KK, Locke J, Zwart SR. Vitamin D supplementation during Antarctic winter. Am J Clin Nutr. 2009 Apr;89(4):1092–8.

Wilson O. Changes in body-weight of men in the Antarctic. Br J Nutr. 1960;14:391–401.

Zérath E, Holy X, Gaud R, Schmitt D. Decreased serum levels of 1,25-(OH)2 vitamin D during 1 year of sunlight deprivation in the Antarctic. Eur J Appl Physiol Occup Physiol. 1999 Jan;79(2):141–7.

Question 76 Why do people who work on submarines sometimes gain weight?
Dlugos DJ, Perrotta PL, Horn WG. Effects of the submarine environment on renal-stone risk factors and vitamin D metabolism. Undersea Hyperb Med. 1995 Jun;22(2):145–52.

Duplessis CA, Harris EB, Watenpaugh DE, Horn WG. Vitamin D supplementation in underway submariners. Aviat Space Environ Med. 2005 Jun;76(6):569–75.

Luria T, et al. Effects of a prolonged submersion on bone strength and metabolism in young healthy submariners. Calcif Tissue Int. Jan;86(1):8–13.

Question 77 Why do some people gain weight when they give up smoking?
Supervía A, et al. Effect of smoking and smoking cessation on bone mass, bone remodeling, vitamin D, PTH and sex hormones. J Musculoskelet Neuronal Interact. 2006 Jul-Sep;6(3):234–41.

Brot C, Jorgensen NR, Sorensen OH. The influence of smoking on vitamin D status and calcium metabolism. Eur J Clin Nutr. 1999 Dec;53(12):920–6.

Sneve M, Jorde R. Cross-sectional study on the relationship between body mass index and smoking, and longitudinal changes in body mass index in relation to change in smoking status: the Tromso Study. Scand J Public Health. 2008 Jun;36(4):397–407.

Lycett D, Munafò M, Johnstone E, Murphy M, Aveyard P. Associations between weight change over 8 years and baseline body mass index in a cohort of continuing and quitting smokers. Addiction. 2011 Jan;106(1):188–96.

Grimnes G, et al. Effect of smoking on the serum levels of 25-hydroxyvitamin D depends on the assay employed. Eur J Endocrinol. 2010 Aug;163(2):339–48.

Question 83 Why don't low fat diets work very well?
Hession M, Rolland C, Kulkarni U, Wise A, Broom J. Systematic review of randomized controlled trials of low-carbohydrate vs. low-fat/low-calorie diets in the management of obesity and its comorbidities. Obes Rev. 2009 Jan; 10(1):36–50.

Question 86 Why do people lose weight at high altitudes?
Lippl FJ, Neubauer S, Schipfer S, Lichter N, Tufman A, Otto B, Fischer R. Hypobaric hypoxia causes body weight reduction in obese subjects. Obesity (Silver Spring). 2010 Apr;18(4):675–81.

Question 87 Why do some women gain weight after childbirth?
Narchi H, Kochiyil J, Zayed R, Abdulrazzak W, Agarwal M. Maternal vitamin D status throughout and after pregnancy. J Obstet Gynaecol. 2010 Feb;30(2):137–42.

Bastian LA, West NA, Corcoran C, Munger RG; Cache County Study on Memory Health and Aging. Number of children and the risk of obesity in older women. Prev Med. 2005 Jan;40(1):99–104.

Question 89 Why are you more likely to be overweight if you were born in the winter?
Phillips DI, Young JB. Birth weight, climate at birth and the risk of obesity in adult life. Int J Obes Relat Metab Disord. 2000 Mar;24(3):281–7.

Wattie N, Ardern CI, Baker J. Season of birth and prevalence of overweight and obesity in Canada. Early Hum Dev. 2008 Aug;84(8):539–47.

Question 90 Why is there no clear evidence regarding the effects of breastfeeding on overweight?
Li L, Parsons TJ, Power C. Breast feeding and obesity in childhood: cross sectional study. BMJ. 2003 Oct 18;327(7420):904–5.

Martin RM, Ben'Shlomo Y, Gunnell D, Elwood P, Yarnell JW, Davey Smith G. Breast feeding and cardiovascular disease risk factors, incidence, and mortality: the Caerphilly study. J Epidemiol Commun Health. 2005 Feb;59(2):121–9.

Question 91 Why are babies who gain weight rapidly in the first week of life more likely to become overweight adults?
Weiler H, Fitzpatrick-Wong S, Veitch R, Kovacs H, Schellenberg J, McCloy U, Yuen CK. Vitamin D deficiency and whole-body and femur bone mass relative to weight in healthy newborns. CMAJ. 2005 Mar 15;172(6):757–61.

Question 93 Why are you more likely to be overweight if your mother was older when you were born?
Blair NJ, et al. Risk factors for obesity in 7-year-old European children: the Auckland Birthweight Collaborative Study. Arch Dis Child. 2007 Oct;92(10):866–71.

Question 96 How can overweight be good for your health?
Wardlaw GM. Putting body weight and osteoporosis into perspective. Am J Clin Nutr. 1996 Mar;63(3 Suppl):433S–6S.

Flicker L, McCaul KA, Hankey GJ, Jamrozik K, Brown WJ, Byles JE, Almeida OP. Body mass index and survival in men and women aged 70 to 75. J Am Geriatr Soc. 2010 Feb;58(2):234–41.

Question 99 Why do some types of medication cause weight gain?
Holick MF. Stay tuned to PXR: an orphan actor that may not be D-structive only to bone. J Clin Invest. 2005 Jan;115(1):32–4.

Pascussi JM, et al. Possible involvement of pregnane X receptor-enhanced CYP24 expression in drug-induced osteomalacia. J Clin Invest. 2005 Jan;115(1):177–86.

Question 100 Why does psychiatric treatment often result in overweight?

Cardinal RN, Gregory CA. Osteomalacia and vitamin D deficiency in a psychiatric rehabilitation unit: case report and survey. BMC Res Notes. 2009 May 9;2:82.

Megna JL, Raj Kunwar A, Wade MJ. A retrospective study of weight changes and the contributing factors in short term adult psychiatric inpatients. Ann Clin Psychiatry. 2006 Jul-Sep;18(3):163–7.

Gentile S. Long-term treatment with atypical antipsychotics and the risk of weight gain: a literature analysis. Drug Saf. 2006;29(4):303–19.

Padmavati R, McCreadie RG, Tirupati S. Low prevalence of obesity and metabolic syndrome in never-treated chronic schizophrenia. Schizophr Res. 2010 Aug;121(1–3):199–202.

Vanina Y, Podolskaya A, Sedky K, Shahab H, Siddiqui A, Munshi F, Lippmann S. Body weight changes associated with psychopharmacology. Psychiatr Serv. 2002 Jul;53(7):842–7.

In Table 1, Vanina et al. list psychotropic drugs that cause weight gain (and those that don't) and how much weight is gained.

Drugs that cause large weight gain are: Chlorpromazine, Clozapine, Olanzapine, Valproate, Lithium, Amitriptyline, Imipramine, and Mirtazapine.

Drugs that cause moderate weight gain are: Thioridazine, Quetiapine, and Carbamazepine.

Megna JL, Raj Kunwar A, Wade MJ. A retrospective study of weight changes and the contributing factors in short term adult psychiatric inpatients. Ann Clin Psychiatry. 2006 Jul-Sep;18(3):163–7.

Humble MB, Gustafsson S, Bejerot S. Low serum levels of 25-hydroxyvitamin D (25-OHD) among psychiatric out-patients in Sweden: relations with season, age, ethnic origin and psychiatric diagnosis. J Steroid Biochem Mol Biol. 2010 Jul;121 (1–2):467–70.

Appendix

Vitamin D deficiency and overweight have things in common

van Schoor NM, Lips P. Worldwide vitamin D status. Best Pract Res Clin Endocrinol Metab. 2011 Aug;25(4): 671–80.

Wang Y, Beydoun MA. The obesity epidemic in the United States – gender, age, socioeconomic, racial/ethnic, and geographic characteristics: a systematic review and meta-regression analysis. Epidemiol Rev. 2007;29:6–28.

Measuring vitamin D in the blood

Haddad JG, Chyu KJ. Competitive protein-binding radioassay for 25-hydroxycholecalciferol. J Clin Endocrinol Metab. 1971 Dec;33(6):992–5.

Haddad JG Jr, Walgate J. Radioimmunoassay of the binding protein for vitamin D and its metabolites in human serum: concentrations in normal subjects and patients with disorders of mineral homeostasis. J Clin Invest. 1976 Nov;58(5):1217–22.

Patients who had undergone surgery for obesity had low vitamin D

Teitelbaum SL, Halverson JD, Bates M, Wise L, Haddad JG. Abnormalities of circulating 25-OH vitamin D after jejunal-ileal bypass for obesity: evidence of an adaptive response. Ann Intern Med. 1977 Mar;86(3):289–93.

Patients had low vitamin D before obesity surgery

Compston JE, Vedi S, Ledger JE, Webb A, Gazet JC, Pilkington TR. Vitamin D status and bone histomorphometry in gross obesity. Am J Clin Nutr. 1981 Nov;34(11):2359–63.

Vitamin D deficiency is common in patients with obesity

Bell NH, Epstein S, Greene A, Shary J, Oexmann MJ, Shaw S. Evidence for alteration of the vitamin D-endocrine system in obese subjects. J Clin Invest. 1985 Jul;76(1):370–3.

Liel Y, Ulmer E, Shary J, Hollis BW, Bell NH. Low circulating vitamin D in obesity. Calcif Tissue Int. 1988 Oct;43(4):199–201.

People who are overweight tend to have lower levels of vitamin D

Earthman CP, Beckman LM, Masodkar K, Sibley SD. The link between obesity and low circulating 25-hydroxyvitamin D concentrations: considerations and implications. Int J Obes (Lond). 2012 Mar;36(3):387–96.

Vitamin D levels are inversely related to fat mass

Cheng S, et al. Adiposity, cardiometabolic risk, and vitamin D status: the Framingham Heart Study. Diabetes. 2010 Jan;59(1):242–8.

Vitamin D genes influence weight

Ye WZ, Reis AF, Dubois-Laforgue D, Bellanné-Chantelot C, Timsit J, Velho G. Vitamin D receptor gene polymorphisms are associated with obesity in type 2 diabetic subjects with early age of onset. Eur J Endocrinol. 2001 Aug;145(2):181–6.

Vitamin D is active in fat cells
Ding C, Gao D, Wilding J, Trayhurn P, Bing C. Vitamin D signalling in adipose tissue. Br J Nutr. 2012 Dec 14;108(11):1915–23.

BMI genes affect vitamin D, but vitamin D genes did not affect BMI
Vimaleswaran KS, et al. Causal relationship between obesity and vitamin D status: bi-directional Mendelian randomization analysis of multiple cohorts. PLoS Med 2013;10(2).

Vitamin D levels are related to fatty tissue
Looker AC. Body fat and vitamin D status in black versus white women. J Clin Endocrinol Metab. 2005 Feb;90(2):635–40.

Arunabh S, Pollack S, Yeh J, Aloia JF. Body fat content and 25-hydroxyvitamin D levels in healthy women. J Clin Endocrinol Metab. 2003 Jan;88(1):157–61.

Parikh SJ, Edelman M, Uwaifo GI, Freedman RJ, Semega-Janneh M, Reynolds J, Yanovski JA. The relationship between obesity and serum 1,25-dihydroxyvitamin D concentrations in healthy adults. J Clin Endocrinol Metab. 2004 Mar;89(3):1196–9.

Fat affects the response to increased vitamin D
Need AG, Morris HA, Horowitz M, Nordin C. Effects of skin thickness, age, body fat, and sunlight on serum 25-hydroxyvitamin D. Am J Clin Nutr. 1993 Dec;58(6):882–5.

Wortsman J, Matsuoka LY, Chen TC, Lu Z, Holick MF. Decreased biovailability of vitamin D in obesity. Am J Clin Nutr. 2000 Sep;72(3):690–3.

Saliba W, Barnett-Griness O, Rennert G. The relationship between obesity and the increase in serum 25(OH)D levels in response to vitamin D supplementation. Osteoporos Int. 2013 Apr;24(4):1447–54.

Vitamin D increases after weight loss
Reinehr T, de Sousa G, Alexy U, Kersting M, Andler W. Vitamin D status and parathyroid hormone in obese children before and after weight loss. Eur J Endocrinol. 2007 Aug;157(2):225–32.

Mason C, et al. Effects of weight loss on serum vitamin D in postmenopausal women. Am J Clin Nutr. 2011 Jul;94(1):95–103.

People who have less vitamin D in their diet are more likely to be overweight
Kamycheva E, Joakimsen RM, Jorde R. Intakes of calcium and vitamin D predict body mass index in the population of Northern Norway. J Nutr. 2003 Jan;133(1):102–6.

Caron-Jobin M, Morisset AS, Tremblay A, Huot C, Légaré D, Tchernof A. Elevated serum 25(OH)D concentrations, vitamin D, and calcium intakes are associated with reduced adipocyte size in women. Obesity (Silver Spring). 2011 Jul;19(7):1335–41.

Tidwell DK, Valliant MW. Higher amounts of body fat are associated with inadequate intakes of calcium and vitamin D in African American women. Nutr Res. 2011 Jul;31(7):527–36.

The increase in vitamin D levels after weight loss is temporary
Lin E, et al. Contribution of adipose tissue to plasma 25-hydroxyvitamin D concentrations during weight loss following gastric bypass surgery. Obesity (Silver Spring). 2011 Mar;19(3):588–94.

The rise in vitamin D is not related to the amount of fat in all studies
Canto-Costa MH, Kunii I, Hauache OM. Body fat and cholecalciferol supplementation in elderly homebound individuals. Braz J Med Biol Res. 2006 Jan;39(1):91–8.

Gallagher JC, Yalamanchili V, Smith LM. The effect of vitamin D supplementation on serum 25OHD in thin and obese women. J Steroid Biochem Mol Biol. 2013 Jul;136:195–200.

Vitamin D status predicts fat mass and overweight
Gilbert-Diamond D, et al. Vitamin D deficiency and anthropometric indicators of adiposity in school-age children: a prospective study. Am J Clin Nutr. 2010 Dec;92(6):1446–51.

Mai X-M, Chen Y, Camargo CA Jr, Langhammer A. Cross-sectional and prospective cohort study of serum 25-hydroxyvitamin D level and obesity in adults. Am J Epidemiol. 2012 May 15;175(10):1029–36.

González-Molero I, et al. Vitamin D and incidence of diabetes: A prospective cohort study. Clin Nutr. 2012 Aug;31(4):571–3.

González-Molero I, et al. Hypovitaminosis D and incidence of obesity: a prospective study. Eur J Clin Nutr. 2013 Jun;67(6):680–2.

Crozier SR, Harvey NC, Inskip HM, Godfrey KM, Cooper C, Robinson SM; SWS Study Group. Maternal vitamin D status in pregnancy is associated with adiposity in the offspring: findings from the Southampton Women's Survey. Am J Clin Nutr. 2012. Jul;96(1):57-63.

Short–term supplementation of vitamin D has no effect on mortality
Zheng Y, Zhu J, Zhou M, Cui L, Yao W, Liu Y. Meta–analysis of long–term vitamin D supplementation on overall mortality. PLoS One. 2013 Dec 3;8(12):e82109.

Index

A
absence of protection model, 138
acid rain, 85
activitystat, 293
adenosine triphosphate (ATP), 158–159, 169
adipokines, 168
adipostat, 140–141 see also fatstat
adolescents, 58
Agarwal, Kishore, 79
age, 238–239
ageing, 111, 208, 239, 305 see also elderly
agriculture, 194, 198, 215, 216, 286
AgRP/NPY circuit, 133
air conditioning, 36, 171, 248, 278–279
aircraft, 92–99, 259, 280
algae, 182, 209, 240
Allen's rule, 147–148, 149, 158
altitude, 28–29, 281–282, 301, 307
American Academy of Dermatologists, 102
American Journal of Clinical Nutrition, 69
American paradox, 293
amphibians, 241
Ancient Human Occupation of Britain Project, 197
animals
 cold-adapted, 149–151
 detection of ultraviolet radiation, 240
 extinct, 186–187
 as food source see food
 land animals, 185–187
 latitude, 147, 157, 181, 186
 nocturnal, 181
 overweight, 4
 vitamin D, 178, 180–181, 182, 185–187
 welfare, 46
anorexia, 127–128, 135
Antarctic, 149–150, 186, 247, 297
antipsychotic drugs, 306
appetite, 126–130, 132, 295, 298–299, 300
aquatic ape hypothesis, 204
Arctic, 4, 148, 149–150, 157, 203, 207
arctic fox, 153, 154, 203, 207
arctic hare, 147–148
arcuate nucleus, 132
arid climate hypothesis, 202
art, 213
artificial lighting, 30, 31, 35, 37, 261
atherosclerosis, 249
Atkins diet, 300
atmosphere
 composition, 84–85, 92
 obstruction see emissions; fires; industrial revolution; pollution; sulphur dioxide; volcanoes
 ozone layer see ozone, layer
 pollution see pollution
 ultraviolet radiation see ultraviolet-B
ATP (adenosine triphosphate), 158–159, 169
Australia, 88, 103–104, 105, 106, 232, 288
Austria, 214, 236
aviation see aircraft

B
babies
 brown fat, 159
 hypercalcaemia, 322
 mother's weight gain, 301
 overweight, 301–302
 sunlight exposure, 59, 102
 surface area to volume ratio, 345
 thermoregulation, 157
 vitamin D recommended intakes, 58–60
 vitamin D supplements, 62, 260, 267
 vitamin D toxicity, 63, 322
 see also children; infants
bacteria, 24,
baldness, 208
bariatric surgery, 129, 132, 231, 276, 307–308
Barker, David, 291
Barnard, Bill, 85
Barnosky, Tony, 241
Barrett, Steven, 98
bats, 181
battery farming, 46–48
bears, 147, 149, 150, 181, 186
bees, 240, 241

Bergmann's rule, 147, 148, 149, 183–184, 185, 291–292
Binkley, Neil, 52–53
birds, 25, 46, 47–48, 148, 150, 163, 180–181, 182
Björn, Lars Olof, 181–182
Black, Archie, 271–272
black carbon, 28, 85, 90–91
black melanin, 34, 35, 148, 284
black-tailed Jackrabbit, 147–148
blood
  blood-brain barrier, 188
  circulation, 165–167, 350–351
  pressure, 16, 155–156, 166–167, 169, 170, 231, 277, 278
BMI (body mass index), 11–12, 158, 194–195, 308, 309, 313
body
  fat, 308
  hair, 203–205
  height, 145, 279
  shape, 250
  size, 143–151, 183–187, 291–292
  temperature, 124, 188 see also thermoregulation
  weight see weight
body mass index (BMI), 11–12, 158, 194–195, 308, 309, 313
Boers, 205, 206
bone diseases, 10, 53–54, 56, 62, 113, 231, 245–246 see also osteomalacia; osteoporosis; rickets
bone mineral density, 54, 231
brain, 132–135, 137, 140, 187, 188, 219, 294, 311 see also hypothalamus
breast cancer, 110–111
breast milk, 45, 59–60, 301–302
breathing, 124–125
broiler chickens see chicken
brown fat, 159–160, 223
buildings, 29–30, 35–37, 287
bulimia, 128, 135
butter, 39, 40, 42, 44, 288

C
Caesarean sections, 255
calcidiol
  bats, 181
  calcium, 53–54
  chicken, 265
  deficiency, 192, 230
  diabetes, 310
  diet, 70–72
  functions, 188–190
  healthy levels, 51–54
  hypercalcaemia, 66
  measurement, 26, 40, 51, 64, 74, 267, 307, 314
  medication, 268–269
  metabolism, 65, 314
  milk, 40, 264, 290
  plants, 178
  pollution, 79–80
  potency, 40
  pregnancy, 311
  seasonal levels, 68, 74–75, 76, 187
  smoking, 298
  submariners, 297–298
  sunlight exposure, 52–53, 107, 108, 111, 297–298
  supplements see supplements
  volcanoes, 53, 87
  weight, 200, 219, 220, 221–223, 230, 235, 304
  see also vitamin D, measurement
calciferol, 177, 188, 222–223, 314, 315
  see also cholecalciferol; ergocalciferol
calcitriol
  deficiency, 192, 303, 304
  functions, 177, 188–192, 309, 314–315
  gene regulator, 76
  plants, 178
  pregnancy, 60
  toxicity, 64, 65–66
calcium
  deficiency, 53–54, 76
  excess levels, 63, 66 see also hypercalcaemia
  fat absorption, 130
  healthy diets, 45
  milk, 289–290
  reference nutrient intake, 55
  regulation, 190–191
calorie intake, 292–293, 296
camouflage, 207
Canada, 171, 236, 284
cancer
  breast, 110–111
  skin, 15, 24, 33, 37, 88, 101–110, 111–112
  sunbeds, 262
  vitamin D deficiency, 111, 191, 257

carbon dioxide, 5, 22, 86, 89, 96, 281
carbon monoxide, 89, 94
cardiovascular disease, 16, 42, 45, 249, 278, 304
 see also coronary heart disease
cars, 36, 37 see also road transport
CFCs (chlorofluorocarbons), 81–82
Chaplin, George, 206
cheese, 38, 39, 40, 43, 44, 59, 281
Chen, Tai C., 49
chicken, 42, 45, 47–48, 161, 162, 265, 288
childbirth, 17, 238, 301
children
 diets, 41–42, 45
 famines, 195
 height, 279
 hypercalcaemia, 322
 milk consumption, 285
 overweight, 8, 213, 238–239, 285
 puberty, 279
 recommended intakes of vitamin D, 56, 57–59, 60
 skin cancer, 107
 sunlight exposure, 102
 surface area to volume ratio, 345
 thermoregulation, 157
chimpanzees, 203
chlorofluorocarbons (CFCs), 81–82
chlorophyll, 176, 177
chocolate, 296
cholecalciferol
 animals, 178, 180, 181, 182
 form of vitamin D, 314
 hypercalcaemia, 66
 livestock, 265
 metabolism of, 65
 milk, 39, 264, 290
 pharmaceuticals, 268–269
 plants, 178
 potency, 40
 smoking, 298
 storage, 304
 synthesis, 25, 32
 see also calciferol
cholecystokinin, 128–130, 219
cholesterol, 16, 20, 42, 164, 170, 249, 264, 308
chylomicrons, 65, 165, 323
cities, 216, 235, 237, 282
Clarke, Julia, 186
climate change, 4–5, 7, 15, 88–89, 94–95, 99, 197, 241, 247, 255 see also global warming
clothing
 babies, 59
 hunter-gatherers, 199–200, 240, 286
 Islamic, 234–235, 238, 260, 285
 thermoregulation, 151–152, 154, 157, 171, 224, 297
 ultraviolet-B, 31–32, 36, 100, 108, 210, 234–235, 247
 vitamin D, 21, 37, 75, 234–235, 280
clouds, 29, 83, 90
Clubb, Ros, 240
coal, 89
coati, 153, 223
cod liver oil, 56, 61, 63, 179, 213, 322
cold
 adaptation, 12, 16, 149–151, 154, 229–231, 248, 276–279, 311–312
 body size, 143–144, 147–151, 183–187
 health problems, 151–153
 overweight, 144–145, 151, 155–156, 167, 169–170, 172–174, 218, 276
 winter genotype, 195–196, 197
 see also winter metabolism; winter response
Colorado, 281–282
colour
 hair, 34, 205, 207–208
 perception, 22, 25
 skin, 34–35, 75, 106–107, 108, 205–210, 235, 282–284
Compston, Juliet, 308
concrete, 29, 287
conservatories, 261, 268
Cook, Gordon, 202
copepods, 179
Cope's rule, 146–147, 148
Cordain, Loren, 198
core temperature, 156
coronary heart disease, 42, 156, 291
 see also cardiovascular disease
countercurrent exchange, 350–351
CYP24A1 gene, 66

D
dairy farming, 201–202, 210
dairy products
 fat, 43, 61, 249, 260, 289–290
 hunter-gatherers, 199–200
 lactase persistence, 200–202
 overweight, 289–290
 vitamin A, 42

vitamin D, 40, 45, 210, 287, 290
see also butter; milk
Damara mole rat, 181
Darhad, 193, 199, 200, 286
Darwin, Charles, 6, 205, 270
deficiency diseases, 10–11, 61
deficiency, vitamin D
cancer, 111, 191, 257
causes, 258–259, 273–274, 279–280, 307
definition, 51–54, 73–74
diabetes, 307, 310
eradication, 258, 259–270, 275–276
ethnicity, 234–235, 260, 262
geographic factors, 280–283
health impacts, 76–77, 206–207, 229–230, 255, 257, 303–306, 307
healthy diets, 44
historical perspective, 212–217, 258–259
medication, 268–269
in other species, 240–241, 246
overweight, 5–6, 10, 13–15, 17, 76, 78, 211–212, 218–230, 232–239, 244–245, 258, 275, 279–280, 293, 307–311
pregnancy and childbirth, 238, 291, 301
prevalence, 76, 237–238, 239–240, 246, 307
prevention, 70, 243
research findings, 307–311
skin pigmentation, 209
sunlight exposure see sunlight, exposure
supplements see supplements
ultraviolet radiation see ultraviolet-B
see also calcidiol
7-dehydrocholesterol
birds, 180
fish, 48
melanin, 34
plants, 178
vitamin D, 20–21, 25, 32–33, 48, 176, 178, 180, 182
Denmark, 105
Department of Health, 39, 42, 60
The Descent of Man, 205
detoxification, 190,
diabetes
Arctic and Antarctic animals, 149–150
Earlybird Diabetes Study, 253
insulin, 165, 171 see also insulin resistance
metabolic syndrome, 278
overweight, 1, 4, 5, 16, 123, 236, 253
thrifty genotype hypothesis, 138–139, 192, 198
vitamin D deficiency, 307, 310
Diamond, Jared, 194, 203, 205
Dietary Guidelines for Americans, 42
dietary reference intake, 55, 69
dieting
dieting pills, 300
difficulties with, 8, 299–301
personal cameos of, 118–121
post-starvation obesity, 135–136, 295–296
see also overweight; starvation; weight
diets
children, 41–42, 45
Dietary Guidelines for Americans, 42
France, 281
healthy eating, 44, 294
historical trends, 41–42
Japan, 283
low fat, 42–45, 220, 226, 248–250, 292, 293, 300
meat and fish, 46–49
modern, 198–199, 200, 284
Palaeolithic, 198–200
vegetarian, 265
vitamin D, 45–46, 70–72, 210, 243, 258, 263, 279–280, 287–288
see also dairy products; food
dimethyl sulphide, 87
dinosaurs, 87, 146, 186
disability, 1, 2, 256, 296
discrimination, 3–4
diseases
bone see bone diseases
cancer see cancer
cardiovascular see cardiovascular disease; coronary heart disease
deficiency, 10–11, 61
diabetes see diabetes
heart see cardiovascular disease
infectious, 47–48, 76, 192, 195, 206–207, 230, 241, 304
prevalence, 255–257
respiratory, 84, 99
vitamin D deficiency, 76–77, 206–207, 296–297, 303–306, 307
DNA, 32–33, 34, 37, 109, 182, 191, 196–197
driving, 36, 37
drugs, 3, 268–269, 305–306
dust, 88

dyslipidaemia, 189, 278

E
Earlybird Diabetes Study, 253
economic development, 237, 286
eggs
diets, 38, 41, 42, 43–44
production, 47–48
vitamin D, 39, 71, 199, 263, 265, 287, 288, 300
Egypt, 85, 86
Egyptian fruit bat, 181
elderly
health inequalities, 256
hypothermia, 152
overweight, 304
supplements, 62, 69
vitamin D, 56, 57, 72, 260, 262, 305
electromagnetic radiation, 21–23,
electron transfer, 158, 159, 169
elephants, 113, 240
Elminir, Hamdy, 85, 86
Elsie Widdowson Laboratory, 41, 140
emissions
aircraft, 93–99, 259, 280
fossil fuel, 14, 247, 259, 275
road vehicle, 93–95
transport, 28, 85–86, 237, 247, 283, 284
see also greenhouse gases; Industrial Revolution; volcanoes
Emperor penguins, 149–150
energy balance, 2–3, 10, 170, 255
energy homeostasis, 123, 126–131, 132–141, 219, 294–295
Engelson, Ola, 266
enteque seco, 64
enzootic calcinosis, 64
epidermis, 33
epilepsy, 305
ergocalciferol
form of vitamin D, 314
living organisms, 178
measurement, 40
milk fortification, 264
pharmaceuticals, 268
production, 190
sunlight detection, 182
toxicity, 63, 322
see also calciferol
ergosterol, 178, 182, 190
ethnicity, 232–236, 260, 262, 266, 284
exercise, 10, 161, 162, 164, 170–171, 277–278, 293–294
Eyjafjallajökull, 92

F
factory farming, 46–48
Fagan, Brian, 90
Family Food Survey, 42
famines, 138–139, 173, 192–195
Farmelo, Graham, 23
farming
agriculture, 194, 198, 215, 216, 286
dairy see dairy products
fish, 49
intensive, 46–48
modern, 288
poultry, 46–48
Farzaneh, Farzin, 9
fast food, 293
fast-twitch fibres, 348–349
fat
absorption, 130, 300
body size, 144–145
brown fat, 159–160, 223
calcium, 130
dairy products, 43, 61, 249, 260, 289–290
in diets, 42–45, 292, 293, 300
as energy store, 143, 276, 277
fat gene, 123
fatstat see fatstat
health benefits, 248–250
membranes, 152
omega-3 fatty acids, 61
post-starvation obesity, 135–136, 295–296
saturated fats, 4, 42–44, 150, 281
in thermoregulation, 156–158
trans fats, 4, 288
unsaturated fats, 44, 288
vitamin D, 38, 42–45, 275, 300, 304, 308, 309–310
see also cold, adaptation
Fat Fresher Syndrome, 297
fatstat, 16, 140–141, 172, 188, 219–222, 252, 294–296, 298–301
Ferguson, Gary, 180
fictional figures, 213
Finland, 64, 72, 163
fires, 84, 88, 247

fish
  in diets, 48–49, 198–199, 206, 243, 265, 281, 283–284
  fish farming, 49
  fish oils, 61
  in oceans, 184–185
  vitamin D, 48–49, 71, 179–180, 182, 190, 210, 260
  white fibres in, 162
Flatz, Gebhard, 202
foetal origins hypothesis, 291
folate, 206
food
  energy-dense, 296, 297
  fast food, 293
  functions, 122
  healthy eating, 294
  national surveys, 292
  nutrient deficiencies, 212
  overweight epidemic, 4
  preferences, 59
  processing, 287–288
  production, 46–48
  vitamin D fortification, 263–264
  vitamin D sources, 38–49, 70–72, 263–265, 287–289
  see also dieting; diets
Foresight Programme, 255
fortification, 63, 263–264, 322
fossil fuels, 5, 7, 14, 89, 94–95, 247, 248, 259, 275
fracking, 7
France, 265, 281, 282
Franklin, Benjamin, 87
freshers, 297
Friedman, Jeffrey, 122–123
fruit juice drinks, 288–289
fungi, 178, 182
fur see hair
futile cycling, 159

G
gamma rays, 21–22
Garland, Cedric, 111
Garland, Frank, 111
gas, 89
gastric band surgery, 129
  see also bariatric surgery
gender, 238, 285
genes
  CYP24A1 gene, 66
  effect on weight loss, 350
  fat gene, 123
  gene regulation, 76, 189–190
  height, 145
  lactase persistence, 201
  MC1R gene, 207, 208
  overweight, 137, 198, 211
  thrifty gene, 138, 173, 192, 193, 195, 197, 291
  vitamin D, 308–309, 310
  Williams syndrome, 322
  winter gene, 173, 195, 197, 211
Germany, 72, 74
ghrelin, 129, 219
gigantism, 185
Ginde, Adit, 74
Giovannucci, Edward, 111
glass, 29, 30–31, 261, 268
global warming, 4–5, 84, 88–89, 99, 247, 248
  see also climate change
globesity, 215
Gloger's rule, 147, 148, 208
glucose
  fuel, 131, 164–165
  overweight, 277
  tolerance, 156
  winter metabolism, 170, 171, 224, 278
González-Molero, Inmaculada, 310
Great Britain, 93, 197
Great Depression, 254–255
greenhouse gases, 89, 92–93, 95, 100
  see also emissions
ground cover, 29, 35
gut-brain axis, 132

H
Haddad, John, 307
Hadzabe, 53, 54
hair
  colour, 34, 205, 207–208
  functions, 203–204
  human beings, 156–157
  mammals, 146
  vitamin D, 204 205, 207–208, 276
Haman, François, 162
Hardy, Alister, 204
hat, 31
Hawaii, 52–53, 86–87

The Healing Sun, 111
health, 5, 229–231, 251–252, 255–257, 303–306 see also diseases
healthy eating, 294
Heaney, Robert, 65, 67, 68–69, 73
heart disease see cardiovascular disease; coronary heart disease
heat production, 158–159
height, 145, 279
Henry VIII, 284
Herschel, William, 271
high blood pressure, 16, 155–156, 166–167, 169, 170, 231, 277, 278
high fructose corn syrup, 288
high performance liquid chromatography, 40
Hill, Tom, 40
historical figures, 213–214
Hobday, Richard, 111, 261
Holick, Michael, 49, 56, 65, 104, 239
holidays, 107–108
Hollis, Bruce, 52, 54, 60, 67, 68
homeostasis, 123–125, 188
see also energy homeostasis
hospitals, 62
Hosseinpanah, Farhad, 80
Hruschka, Daniel, 235
Human Obesity - Exploding the Myths, 250
hunger see appetite
hunter-gatherers, 193–195, 198–200, 240, 286, 307 see also pastoral societies
hydrogenation, 288
hypercalcaemia, 63–64, 66, 322
hypertension see high blood pressure
hyperthermia, 159, 160 see also thermoregulation
hypothalamus, 123, 124, 132, 188, 189, 218–219
hypothermia, 151–152, 154, 157
see also thermoregulation
Hyppönen, Elina, 60, 74

I
ice age endurance, 167-170
ice ages, 173, 196, 197, 214–215
Iceland, 92,
illness see diseases
immune system, 5, 48, 54, 76, 81, 191, 195, 230, 304, 314
India, 79, 201, 232
industrialisation, 212, 215–217
Industrial Revolution, 86, 88–91, 213, 216
infants
hypercalcaemia, 63–64, 322
infant mortality, 2, 255–256
recommended intakes of vitamin D, 56, 57–59, 60
see also babies; children
infectious diseases, 47–48, 76, 192, 195, 206–207, 230, 241, 304
infrared radiation, 22, 177, 271
injury, 222, 296–297 see also disability; diseases
insufficiency, vitamin D, 73
insulin resistance, 16, 164–165, 169–170, 171, 277, 278
intensive farming, 46–48
Intergovernmental Panel on Climate Change, 95
Inuit, 171, 206, 210, 233, 278, 284
Invalidity Benefit, 256
invertebrates, 177–178, 240, 246
Iran, 79–80
Irish potato famine, 195
iron, 45–46
irradiance, 314
Islam, 234–235, 238, 260, 285
island nations, 98–99
Israel, 196, 232

J
Jablonski, Nina, 206–207
Japan, 71, 283
jets, 96–97

K
Kalashnikova, Olga, 88
Keatinge, Bill, 144
Kennedy, Gordon, 140
keratin, 33, 34
kings, 284
Korea, 71
Koyyalamudi, Sundar, 265
Krishnan, Supriya, 236
Kvalevåg, Maria, 90–91
Kyoto Protocol, 95

L
lactase persistence, 200–202
Laki, 87
land animals, 185–187
latitude
animals, 147, 157, 181, 186

aviation, 97
clothing, 234–235, 285
milk, 202, 286
overweight, 234, 281–282
skin cancer, 105–106
skin pigmentation, 208, 209, 210
ultraviolet radiation, 21, 26–28, 35, 79–80, 91, 206, 266
vitamin D, 5, 16, 21, 52, 79–80, 106, 260
layer hens see chicken
leptin, 122–123, 134–135, 136–137, 139, 140, 172, 219, 295
leukaemia, 9
Liebler, Daniel, 34
life expectancy, 2, 174, 255–256, 283
lifestyle choices, 252–255
light, 22
lighting, artificial, 30, 31, 35, 37, 48, 261
The Light Revolution, 261
The Little Ice Age, 90
livestock, 46–49, 263, 264–265, 266, 288
London, 237
Lovelock, James, 270
low fat milk, 249, 260, 289–290
Lucas, Robyn, 113
Ludwig, Jens, 236
Luxwolda, Martine, 53

M
Maasai, 53, 54
Major, John, 256
mammals
aquatic ape hypothesis, 204
body size, 147
hair, 146
vitamin D, 180–181, 182
mass extinctions, 87, 241
Mattila, Pirjo, 265
MC1R gene, 207, 208
McCarron, David, 212
meals, 126
meat, 43–44, 46–49, 71
Medical Hypotheses, 9
medication, 3, 268–269, 305–306
MED (minimal erythemal dose), 267, 314
melanin, 34–35, 109, 148, 207–208, 234, 284
melanocortins, 133–134, 207, 208
melanoma, 102, 103, 105, 107–108
metabolic syndrome, 155–156, 158, 163–164, 170–172, 189, 276–278, 289
metabolism, 158–159, 289
methane, 89, 96
Mexico City, 85–86, 282
Middle East, 285
migration, 106–107, 196–198, 208, 210, 234–235, 237
milk
breast milk, 45, 59–60, 302
child consumption, 285
diets, 41–44
digestion, 200–202
ethnicity, 234
functions, 46
latitude, 202, 286
low fat, 249, 260, 289–290
overweight, 289–290
vitamin D, 39–40, 57, 202, 258, 263, 264, 289–290, 322
mineral dust, 88
minerals, 45–46
minimal erythemal dose (MED), 267, 314
Minnesota experiment, 134–135
Minnoch, Jon Brower, 143
Mississippi, 281–282
mitochondrial DNA, 196–197
Montreal Protocol, 81–82
Morgan, Elaine, 204
Moriyama, Naomi, 283
mortality, 2
mothers, 58–60, 221–222, 301–303
Mount Pinatubo, 86
muscle fibres, 161–164, 165, 170–171, 172, 276–277, 278, 348–349
mushrooms, 265, 266, 283
Myhre, Cathrine Lund, 90–91
Myhre, Gunnar, 90–91

N
National Diet and Nutrition Survey, 72, 76
National Health and Nutrition Examination Survey, 74
National Institute for Health and Clinical Excellence (NICE), 60
Nauru, 98
Neel, James, V., 138, 192, 193, 197–198
Netherlands, 71, 72, 105
neuropeptide Y, 129, 133, 219
New Zealand, 105, 106, 232
NICE (National Institute for Health and Clinical Excellence), 60

nitric oxide, 94, 95, 96
nitrogen dioxide, 28, 85, 89, 90–91, 94, 95, 96
nocturnal animals, 181
Norway, 27, 105, 241, 310
nutrient deficiencies, 212

O
obesity
bariatric surgery, 132, 231, 276, 307–308
childhood, 8, 239, 285
cold-adapted animals, 150
definition, 11–12, 313
epidemic, 1–6, 7–8, 12, 50, 243, 311
globesity, 215
hotspots, 236
maps, 292
paradox, 230
poverty paradox, 235
pets, 150–151, 241
post-starvation obesity, 135–136, 295–296
see also overweight
obesogenic environment, 138, 211–212, 215, 216, 292
oceans, 184–185
oil, 89
Okinawa, 283
old people see elderly
omega-3 fatty acids, 61
organic carbon, 90–91
The Origin of Species, 6, 270
osteomalacia, 54, 55–56, 76, 77, 113, 180
osteoporosis, 62, 113, 180, 231, 304
ostracodes, 148
otters, 241
outdoor environments, 37, 101, 215, 228–229, 238–239, 260–261, 268–269, 285, 287
see also sunlight, exposure
overheating, 151, 153
overweight
causes, 15, 258, 259, 273, 283, 292, 307 see also deficiency, vitamin D
cold adaptation, 144–145, 151, 155–156, 167–170, 172–174, 218, 276–278
definition, 11–12, 313
diabetes see diabetes, overweight
diets see diets
energy homeostasis, 136–141
environmental factors, 211–212, 250–252, 292
epidemic see obesity, epidemic
ethnicity, 232–235, 236, 284
gender, 238, 285
geographic distribution, 236, 237, 259, 280–283
health impacts, 170–172, 230–231, 257, 303–306
historical perspective, 212–217
lifestyle choices, 252–255
other species, 240, 241–242
personal stories, 224–229
pollution see pollution
prevalence, 307
psychological factors, 252
socio-economic factors, 233, 235–238, 286–287
vitamin D deficiency, 5–6, 10, 13–15, 17, 76, 78, 211–212, 218, 230, 237–238, 244–245, 258, 275, 279–280, 293, 307–311
see also weight
oxalates, 130
oxidative phosphorylation, 158, 159, 169
ozone
aircraft, 95–96, 98–99
Antarctic, 297
depletion, 15, 80–82, 83, 84, 89–91, 107, 246–247
fossil fuels, 94
layer, 22, 24, 80–82, 84, 88–89, 183, 247
Ozone Monitoring Instrument, 81
pollution, 282
short wavelength radiation, 22
Total Ozone Mapping Spectrophotometer, 81, 206
ultraviolet-B, 28
ultraviolet-C, 24
see also ultraviolet radiation

P
Pacific Islands, 98–99,
package holidays, 107–108
paintings, 90
Palaeolithic diets, 198–200
pancreatic polypeptide, 129
Papua, 199
Paracelsus, 67
parathyroid hormone, 54
Paris, 282
Parisi, Alfio, 265–266

particles, 28, 84–85, 89, 94, 96, 283
pastoral societies, 53, 307 see also
  hunter-gatherers
penguins, 149–150, 181, 186–187
peptide YY, 129–130, 219
pets, 150–151, 180, 241, 266
pharmaceuticals see medication
photoadaptation, 109–110, 191
photoreceptors, 25, 176
phytates, 130
phytosterols, 130
pigmentation, skin, 22–23, 34–35, 75, 106–107,
  108, 205–210, 235, 282–284
plankton, 48–49, 87, 179–180
plants, 178–179
plumage colour, 148
polar bears, 147, 149, 150, 181, 186
pollution
  atmosphere, 84
  Australia, 88
  calcidiol levels, 79–80
  coal, 89
  emissions see emissions
  health problems, 5
  Mexico City, 282–283
  ultraviolet-B, 14, 28, 79–80, 84–86, 88,
    91–92, 96, 280, 282
  see also Industrial Revolution; particles
POMC circuit, 133
post-starvation obesity, 135–136, 295–296
poultry farming, 46–48
poverty, 11, 13, 215, 235, 238, 246, 286–287
  see also wealth
Power, Chris, 74
precalciferol, 269
preening, 180
pregnancy
  calcidiol levels, 221
  cod liver oil, 61
  overweight, 238
  polar bears, 149, 150
  supplements, 73, 260
  vitamin D-binding protein, 65, 301
  vitamin D deficiency, 238, 301
  vitamin D recommended intake, 56, 57, 60
pregnane X receptor, 305
prehistoric figures, 214–215
prejudice, 3–4, 8
Prentice, Andrew, 194
prescriptions, 257
Prynne, Celia, 41
psychiatric treatment, 306
puberty, 279, 303
Puerto Rico, 52

Q
Queen Anne, 213
queens, 284
Queensland, 103

R
radio waves, 21–22
rainfall, 29
recommended dietary allowances, 55, 69
red fox, 153, 223
red melanin, 34, 148
red muscle fibres, 161–164, 165, 170–171, 224,
  276–277, 278, 348–349
red squirrel, 154
reference nutrient intake, 55, 60
Reichrath, Jörg, 108
reindeer, 149, 150, 181, 186
reptiles, 180, 182
respiratory diseases, 99
retinal, 176, 177
rickets, 10, 11, 54, 55–56, 63, 77, 179, 246
Ritter, Johann Wilhelm, 271
road transport, 93–94, 259
royalty, 284

S
SAD lamps, 31
salmon, 49, 288
sand, 28
sandstorms, 85, 86
saturated fats, 42–44, 150, 281, 288
scurvy, 11, 245
seals, 149, 153, 154
seasonal affective disorder (SAD) lamps, 31
seasons, 27, 39–40, 210–211, 248, 301–302
Second World War, 213
set point see fatstat
shell temperature, 156
shivering, 159, 161, 162–165, 169,
  223–224, 276–278
sickness benefits, 256
Sierra Nevada Yellow-legged Frog, 241
size, body, 143–151, 183–187, 291–292
skeletons, 177, 190

skin
cancer, 15, 24, 33, 35, 37, 88, 101–113
photoadaptation, 109–110, 191
pigmentation, 34–35, 75, 106–107, 108, 134, 205–210, 284
sensitivity, 108–110
tanning, 109–110, 111–112
thickness, 33–34
types, 334
slimming see dieting
slow-twitch fibres, 348–349
smoke, 88, 89
smoking, 298, 305
snow, 29, 35
socio-economic factors, 233, 236–238, 287
soft drinks, 288–289
Solanum glaucophyllum, 64
South Africa, 4, 105, 149, 206
Speakman, John, 194–195
squids, 185, 186
starvation, 134–135, 141, 165, 172–173, 195, 295–296, 300
statins, 269
Steenbock, Harry, 271–272
storm petrel, 150
stratosphere, 81, 84, 86
stratum corneum, 33
Stringer, Chris, 197
stroke, 156, 278, 303
students, 297
submariners, 297–298
sulphur dioxide, 28, 84–85, 86, 87, 89, 90–91, 282
Sun, 20–23, 26–27, 30, 31,183
see also sunlight
sunbathing, 32, 33, 101, 106, 111–112
sunbeds, 101, 262–263, 266, 268, 284
sunburn, 29, 35, 93, 102, 108, 109–110, 206, 334
sunlamps, 31, 262–263, 268
sunlight
babies, 59
building penetration, 261
calcidiol levels, 52–53, 107, 108, 111, 297–298
clothing, 285
deficiency, 35–36
detection, 182–183, 244, 276
exposure, 17, 36, 49, 62, 101–114, 258, 265–266, 276, 279
nocturnal animals, 181
ocean zones, 184
protection campaigns, 61, 103–105, 108, 110
skin colour, 205–207
vitamin D, 265–266, 276 see also vitamin D, sunlight detection; vitamin D, sunlight exposure
see also skin, cancer
sun protection factor, 32
sunscreens, 32, 37, 102, 106, 111, 258
supplements, 13, 54, 60–63, 67–70, 266–267, 275–276, 310–311
surface area to volume ratio, 16, 147, 157–158, 159, 185, 204–205, 278–279, 345–347
surgery, 3, 307–308
Suri, 199
Sweden, 105, 241
Szent-Györgyi, Albert, 245
Szombathy, Josef, 214

T

tanning, 109–110, 111–112
Tanzania, 53
Tasmania, 205–206
temperature, 90, 124, 156
thermoregulation, 152–154, 155–167, 169, 171, 173–174 see also blood, circulation; shivering; winter metabolism; winter response
The Third Chimpanzee, 203, 205
Thomas, Mark, 201
thrifty genotype hypothesis, 138–139, 173, 192–195, 197–198, 291
thyroid hormones, 160
TOMS (Total Ozone Mapping Spectrophotometer), 81, 206
toxicity
calcitriol, 64, 65–66
ergocalciferol, 63, 322
vitamin D, 51, 52, 54, 56, 63–67, 73, 263, 322
trans fats, 4, 288
transport, 28, 85–86, 89–91, 93–99, 216, 237, 247, 283–284
Trayner, Ian, 9
triglycerides, 164, 165, 170, 224, 277
tropics, 27–28, 37, 105–106, 168–169, 173, 181, 203, 210
troposphere, 28, 84, 90, 95
turkey, 40, 42, 44
Turnbull, David, 265–266

type 1 muscle fibres, 161, 162, 348–349
type 2 muscle fibres, 161–162, 348–349

U
UK (United Kingdom), 197, 232, 256–257, 281
ultraviolet-A, 23, 24–25, 177, 262
ultraviolet-B
aircraft, 92–93, 95–96
altitude, 28–29
animal vision, 240
artificial lighting, 31
atmosphere, 14
benefits, 246–247
body size, 183–187
clothing, 31–32, 36, 100, 108, 210, 234–235, 247
discovery, 271
dose monitors, 267–268
geographic factors, 280
glass penetration, 29, 30–31, 261, 268
ground surface and building cover, 29–30
Industrial Revolution, 88–91
latitude, 21, 26, 27–28, 35, 52, 79–80, 91, 206, 266, 284
measurement, 81, 82–84, 91–92, 313–314
minimal erythemal dose (MED), 267, 314
national, regional and local factors, 237–238
ocean zones, 184
ozone, 28, 80–82
pollution, 28, 79–80, 84–86, 88, 91–92, 96, 280, 283
skin, 15, 32–35, 206, 208–210
sunlight detection, 182–183
urban-industrial sunlight deficiency, 35–36
vitamin D, 20–21, 22–23, 25–28, 82, 92, 99–100, 176–177, 247–248
volcanoes, 53
weather, 29
ultraviolet-C, 23–24, 31, 89, 247
ultraviolet protection factor (UPF), 32
ultraviolet radiation see ultraviolet-A; ultraviolet-B; ultraviolet-C
ultraviolet vision, 25
ultraviolet winter, 27
uncoupling proteins, 160
United Kingdom, 197, 232, 256–257, 281
United States of America, 42, 97, 232, 233, 234, 236, 281–282, 293
university students, 297
unsaturated fats, 44, 288
UPF (ultraviolet protection factor), 32
urban-industrial environment, 215–217, 286–287
urban-industrial sunlight deficiency, 35–36
urbanisation, 212, 216, 237, 287
uropygial gland, 180
USA (United States of America), 42, 97, 232, 233, 234, 236, 281–282, 293
UV index, 88, 92, 314

V
vascular system, 165–167, 350
vasoconstriction, 166
vasodilation, 166
vegetarians, 265
veiling, 235, 260, 285
Venus figurines, 214
Vieth, Reinhold, 52, 67
visible spectrum, 22, 177
vitamin A, 10, 42, 61, 176, 290, 322
vitamin C, 10–11, 41, 61, 245
vitamin D
age, 239
body size, 183–188
bone diseases, 53–54, 56
clothing, 21, 31, 37, 75, 234–235, 280
cold adaptation see cold, adaptation
dairy products, 40, 45, 210, 287, 289–290
deficiency see deficiency, vitamin D
7-dehydrocholesterol, 20–21, 25, 32–33, 48, 176, 178, 180, 182
diets, 45–46, 70–72, 210, 243, 258, 263, 279–280, 287–290
discovery, 271
ethnicity, 266
evolution, 16–17, 176–177, 182–183
fat, 38, 42–45, 275, 300, 304, 308, 309–310
food sources, 38–49, 70–72, 287–290
forms, 26, 40, 177, 188–189, 191, 314–315
see also calcidiol; calciferol; calcitriol; cholecalciferol; ergocalciferol
fortification, 263–264, 322
functions, 178–179, 189–192
healthy levels, 51–61, 64, 274–275
measurement, 40, 51, 274, 275, 314 see also calcidiol, measurement
metabolism, 65–67
milk, 39–40, 57, 202, 258, 263, 264, 289–290, 322

vitamin D (*continued*)
overweight see overweight, vitamin D deficiency
poverty see deficiency, vitamin D
pregnancy, 56–57, 60, 65, 221, 238, 260, 291, 301, 311, 322
production, 20–21
recommended intakes, 14, 50, 54–58, 59–60, 63–64, 67, 68–69, 75, 260
skin pigmentation, 34–35, 206–207, 208–210
storage, 65, 75, 309–310
sunlight detection, 174, 181–183, 187–188, 244, 246
sunlight exposure, 17, 265–266, 276, 279
supplements, 13, 54, 60–63, 67–70, 73, 266–267, 275–276, 310–311
testing, 62–63
toxicity, 51, 52, 54, 56, 63–67, 73, 263, 322
ultraviolet-B, 20–23, 25–28, 82, 99–100, 176–177, 247–248
wealth and socioeconomic factors, 236–238
vitamin D-binding protein, 65, 69, 190, 301
vitamin E, 44, 290
vitamins
children's diets, 45
deficiency diseases, 10–11
low fat diets, 249–250
meat, 44
vitamin A, 10, 42, 61, 176, 290, 322
vitamin C, 10–11, 41, 61, 245
vitamin D see vitamin D
vitamin E, 44, 290
vog, 53, 86–87
volcanoes, 28, 53, 84, 86–87, 92–93, 186, 247

W
Wagner, Carol, 60, 68
waist to hip ratio, 158, 250
Wake, David, 241
Wales, 236
Wang, Ting, 182
wavelengths, 21–22, 23
waxyleaf nightshade, 64, 178
wealth, 1, 194, 235–238, 286–287
weather, 28, 29
Webb, Ann, 75, 266
weight
calcidiol, 200, 219, 220, 221–223, 230, 235, 304
control see energy homeostasis
gain, 2–6, 11, 136–140, 189, 218–219, 221–222, 239, 294–298, 305
health, 231
loss, 134–141, 160, 220–223, 231, 250–251, 269–270, 275–276, 299–301, 304–305
set point, 16, 140–141, 172, 188, 219–222, 252, 294–296, 298–301
see also dieting; energy homeostasis; overweight; winter metabolism
Westerterp-Plantenga, Margriet, 143
whales, 146
white muscle fibres, 161–164, 165, 170, 224, 276, 278, 348–349
Weigle, David, 250, 251
Wilkin, Terence, 293–294
Williams syndrome, 322
windows, 30–31, 35, 261, 268
winter genotype, 195–196, 197
winter metabolism, 155, 164, 165, 170–172, 223–224, 231, 278–279, 303
winter response, 155–156, 167–170, 187–188, 189, 208, 291
Wood, Bernard, 209
wounds, 24

X
X-rays, 22

Y
Yanomama, 192, 199